# New Approaches to River Management

D1476220

Edited by

A.J.M. Smits, P.H. Nienhuis and R.S.E.W. Leuven

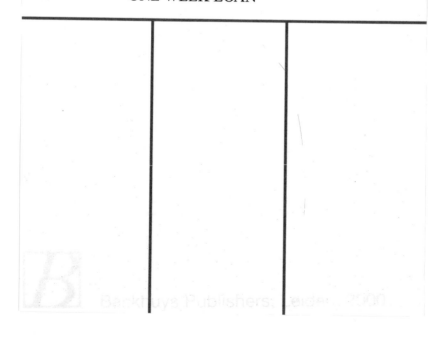

ISBN 90-5782-058-7

# CONTENTS

## Participation of new stakeholders in river basin management

## New methodologies and instruments in sustainable river basin management

**Discussion**

# PREFACE

From 28 September to 1 October, 1998, the Foundation for Extraordinary Chairs of Nature Conservation organised the international conference *New approaches to river management* in Nijmegen (The Netherlands). This book presents the actualised lectures. The papers includes the results of plenary discussions. In order to provide a well balanced picture of the state of the art in river management, the editors have sought to complement this by inviting a number of representative authors to publish their views for inclusion in the book. In addition, all papers have been peer reviewed by external referees. This procedure meant that it has taken us more time to get the book published, but we feel it has improved the quality of the papers and has hopefully increased the utility value of the book for our target group of scientists, river managers, policy makers, authorities and other stakeholders involved in integrated management of river basins.

The conference and the publication of this book were supported by: the Dutch Ministry of Agriculture, Nature Management and Fisheries, the Dutch Ministry of Transport, Public Works and Water Management, the Dutch Society for the Preservation of Nature, the World Wildlife Fund, the Ark Foundation, the Prince Bernhard Fund and the consultancy firms Grontmij and Arcadis Heidemij Advies.

We would like to thank A.E. Wolterbeek (Ministry of Transport, Public Works and Water Management, East-Netherlands Division, Arnhem, The Netherlands) and T. Verhey - van der Linden (Bureau Routine, Nijmegen, The Netherlands) for their help in organising the conference. We would also like to express our thanks to C.H.V. de Villeneuve (Ministry of Transport, Public Works and Water Management, The Hague, The Netherlands) for his advice on international water issues and to L.R.W. van der Horst and N. Janssen (Graphic Design Department, Faculty of Science, University of Nijmegen, The Netherlands) for preparing several illustrations.

Special thanks are due to the following referees of one or more chapters in this book: Prof. Dr W. de Groot (Faculty of Social Sciences, University of Nijmegen, The Netherlands), L.D. de Jong (World Wildlife Fund, Zeist, The Netherlands), Prof. Dr H.J. de Vriend (WL|Delft Hydraulics, Delft, The Netherlands), C. Drijver (World Wildlife Fund, Zeist, The Netherlands), Dr J. Fiszer (Institute of Water Engineering and Management, Cracow University of Technology, Poland), Prof. Dr C. Fremling (St. Mary's University of Minnesota, Winona, The United States of America), Prof. Dr G.E. Galloway (International Joint Commission of United States and Canada, Washington, The United States of America), R. Faber (Nijmegen, The Netherlands), Dr A.J. Hendriks (Institute for Inland Water Management and Waste Water Treatment – RIZA, Lelystad, The Netherlands), P. Huisman (Delft University of Technology, The Netherlands), C.E. Hunt (World Wildlife Fund, Washington, The United States of America), Dr R.H.G. Jongman (Department of Physical Planning and Rural Development, Wageningen University & Research Centre, The Netherlands), L. Knippenberg (Department of Social Environmental Science,

University of Nijmegen, The Netherlands), Dr A.A. Koelmans (Department of Aquatic Ecology and Water Management, Wageningen University & Research Center, The Netherlands), L. Kooistra (Department of Environmental Studies, University of Nijmegen, The Netherlands), Prof. Dr J. Leentvaar (Institute for Inland Water Management and Waste Water Treatment – RIZA, Lelystad, The Netherlands), H.J.R. Lenders (Department of Environmental Studies, University of Nijmegen, The Netherlands), Prof. Dr W. Majewski (Institute of Hydroengineering, Polish Academy of Sciences, Gdansk, Poland), Prof. Dr P. Meire (University of Antwerpen, Belgium), Prof. Dr T. Prus (International Centre of Ecology, Polish Academy of Sciences, Dziekanów Leśny k. Warszawy, Poland), Dr A.M.J. Ragas (Department of Environmental Studies, University of Nijmegen, The Netherlands), Dr B.L. Rhoads (Department of Geography, University of Illinois, Urbana, The United States of America), Prof. Dr H.H.G. Savenije (International Institute for Infrastructural, Hydraulic and Environmental Engineering, Delft, The Netherlands), Dr J.A.A.R. Schuurkes (Arcadis Heidemij Advies, Arnhem, The Netherlands), Dr R. Slootweg (Geoplan International Consultants, Amsterdam, The Netherlands), Dr R.E. Sparks (Water Resources Center, University of Illinois, Urbana, The United States of America), Prof. Dr I. Valiéla (Marine Biological Laboratory, Boston University, Woods Hole, The United States of America), Dr F.W.B. van den Brink (Province of Limburg, Maastricht, The Netherlands), Dr J. van der Straaten (Department of Leisure Studies, Tilburg University, The Netherlands), Prof. Dr G. van der Velde (Department of Aquatic Ecology, University of Nijmegen, The Netherlands), Dr B. van der Wateren - de Hoog (Department of Physical Geography, Utrecht University, The Netherlands), Prof. A. van Hall (Eemszijlvest Water Board, Appingedam, The Netherlands), Prof. Dr E.C. van Ierland (Department of Environmental Economics, Wageningen University & Research Centre, The Netherlands), Prof. Dr C.B. Vreugdenhil (Department Civil Engineering and Management - Water Resources Management, University of Twente, Enschede, The Netherlands) and Prof. Dr W. Wójcik (Department of Environmental Protection and Management Academy of Mining and Metallurgy, Cracow, Poland). Our thanks are extended to J.H.H.M. Klerkx (Vertaalbureau Bèta, Maastricht, The Netherlands) for linguistic revision of several manuscripts.

Last, but not least, we wish to thank R.M.M. Delmee and N.J. Ruitenbeek-Mohr (Department of Environmental Studies, University of Nijmegen, The Netherlands) for secretarial support.

*Nijmegen, February 18, 2000*

*A.J.M. Smits*
*P.H. Nienhuis*
*R.S.E.W. Leuven*

# NEW APPROACHES TO RIVER MANAGEMENT:
# INTEGRATION OF KNOWLEDGE AND IDEAS

C.W. Stortenbeker*
*Foundation for Extraordinary Chairs of Nature Conservation,*
*p.a. Noordereinde 60, NL-1243 JJ 's-Graveland, The Netherlands*

Since the time when the first astronauts had a look at it from the outside, Planet Earth has often been called the 'Blue Planet'. Water has a lot to do with this. There are three basic processes that have shaped our planet and sustain the natural functioning of the biosphere: the energy cycle, the hydrological cycle and the cycle of creation and remineralisation of organic matter. The energy cycle is, of course, the pre-condition for the other two, but the water cycle plays a vital role in the functioning of energy and organic matter cycles.

Chemically speaking, water is a unique substance. Within the periodic system, there is no other combination of elements conceivable with the same wide range of physical and chemical qualities which can sustain life as we know it. An essential characteristic is, of course, its liquid state within the average temperature range in the atmosphere, which means that water plays a vital role in sustaining our biosphere, both at the micro scale and at the macro level. Leonardo da Vinci called water 'the driver of nature'. It has shaped and is still shaping the face of Gaia, Mother Earth, by eroding mountains and transporting sediments and minerals. It leaves deposits in and along rivers and creates river deltas. In fact, the Netherlands consists entirely of sediments from the Rhine and Meuse rivers, supplemented by sandy deposits from the last ice age. Water bodies have a stabilising effect on regional and global climates and can act as important sinks.

At the micro scale, there is the basic role water plays in photosynthesis. It also provides building materials for the living cell: organisms largely consist of water. Water acts as a solvent and as a participant in innumerable chemical reactions. Thus, water is the most important renewable resource we have.

In this conference, it is the macro scale that interests us. In view of the many physical, chemical, biological and ecological functions of water, and the intensive use mankind makes of it, it is essential to realise that fresh water is relatively scarce, in terms of the percentage of the total amount of water on earth. More than 99% is salt water. The remainder is mostly ice in the form of glaciers and polar caps. A mere 0.002% is liquid fresh water, of which one quarter is ground water and another 14% is accumulated in aquifers.

---

* Prof. Dr C.W. Stortenbeker was chairperson of the Foundation for Extraordinary Chairs of Nature Conservation from 1993 to 1999. The present chairperson is Dr H.M. de Boois.

*New approaches to river management, pp. 1–2*
*edited by A.J.M. Smits, P.H. Nienhuis and R.S.E.W. Leuven*
*© 2000 Backhuys Publishers, Leiden, The Netherlands*

Considering the relative scarcity of fresh water on the one hand, and its irreplaceable role on the other, one might expect that mankind would be rather careful with it. Nothing could be further from the truth. We waste it, pollute it, deplete aquifers at high rate, while the demand for clean fresh water is huge. For example, the production of one kilogramme of grain requires some 200 litres of water, while a kilogramme of meat even requires 2000 litres of water.

Mankind suffers from many disasters; we can witness them on the TV news virtually every day. In September 1998 the hurricane George hit the Caribbean. The recent flooding of two thirds of Bangla Desh affected about 30 million people. Hurricanes are considered to be natural disasters, though some climatologists are of the opinion that climate change may well stimulate the occurrence and severity of so-called 'extreme events'. Some disasters certainly are a natural hazard, but others are not. It is particularly worrying that an increasing number of disasters have a strong man-made component, being at least partly due to environmental mismanagement. It is with rivers that these problems are particularly manifest.

However, it is beginning to dawn on mankind that sustainable use of this vital renewable resource of fresh water requires careful management. Gradually, it has also become clear that measures in one field alone will not help; the many components of a river system and the complexity of their interrelations demand not only a combined approach, but an integrated one. Rivers should be considered as physical, chemical, biological and ecological systems with many economic and social functions. This requires a truly integrated approach by environmentalists, economists, policy makers and planners. In this conference, we shall review the state of the art.

Broadly speaking, ecology has undergone a gradual scientific evolution from reductionist studies of organisms, via studies of populations and communities to a more holistic approach at the level of the ecosystem. The name of Eugene Odum should be gratefully mentioned here. The youngest branch of ecological science has even moved up one more integration level: landscape ecology. In the field of nature management and restoration ecology, researchers and managers think in terms of systems; they have little difficulty in seeing a river as an ecosystem, and in applying an integrated approach to its management.

Greater difficulties lie ahead for economists, policy makers and physical planners. They are also inclined to think in terms of systems, but in present-day Western Europe, we are experiencing how difficult it is to start thinking on a continental or global scale, rather than on a national scale, and to develop integrated approaches to entire river basins.

We know a lot about rivers and their management, but it is the integration of knowledge and ideas in many disciplines which poses the problem and which requires our attention this week. The conference programme guarantees an interesting week with useful discussions.

# THE VALUE OF SUSTAINABLE RIVER MANAGEMENT

His Royal Highness Prince Willem-Alexander of Orange

## 1. Importance of sustainable river management; global freshwater crisis

Some time ago, I had the honour of visiting Brazil. During my visit to the Parana river, the overwhelming beauty and power of this river struck me. Here, the almost unaffected river system presented itself in an enormous biodiversity. I was not only impressed by the rich variety of plant and animal species, but also by the large number of people that were directly or indirectly dependent on this river for their livelihood.

In general, river basins can be regarded as a vital source of life, not only in terms of biodiversity but also in an economic context. Agriculture, fisheries, industry, hydropower and navigation are connected with rivers and floodplains. Such user functions may very well conflict with others, such as the availability of clean drinking water and nature conservation. If we really want to preserve the benefits of our river basins for future generations, we should find a long-term balance between all user functions and the natural behaviour of stream corridors: a sustainable river management.

The importance of sustainable river management becomes clear when we focus on the global consumption of freshwater in the years to come. In the 20$^{th}$ century, the total consumption of freshwater has increased six and half times! If we assume that, for the next 25 years, no large changes will occur in the world population growth rate, the freshwater consumption will have increased by another 40%! You can imagine how huge the claim put on the freshwater supplies and the use of river basins will be!

## 2. Resilience of rivers

Unfortunately, nowadays, news reports on rivers tend to focus on disasters like pollution, floods and droughts, often accentuating the consequences of non-sustainable human development. In the past few weeks, our attention was drawn to the rivers in China and Bangladesh. We all witnessed turbulent masses of water breaking through dikes with devastating power, washing away settlements and villages. In the Netherlands, we also have some experience in this field. You may remember our floods in 1995, which caught the headlines of the international press because of the forced evacuation of some 250,000 people. And still we were very lucky, because our major dikes eventually held.

*New approaches to river management, pp. 3–6*
*edited by A.J.M. Smits, P.H. Nienhuis and R.S.E.W. Leuven*
*© 2000 Backhuys Publishers, Leiden, The Netherlands*

We learnt by trial and error that the resilience of our rivers needs attention. Rivers are like living creatures. They are dynamic and need space. It is in the nature of rivers that they refuse to stay straight. If you try to cage a river by building dikes too close to the main stream and by excessive normalisation and canalisation, it will struggle to break out like a wild beast. Eventually it will increase its pressure upon dikes, dams and artificial banks, look for their weak spots, and break through them. The usual response is of course to strengthen our dikes. But this will increase the water's pressure even further! It will get us into a spiral which will only make us more vulnerable. Therefore, we have opted for another approach: "giving rivers more space". During your stay in the Netherlands, you will have the occasion to hear more about this approach, and to see how it works out in practice.

## 3. Major activities affecting river basins

More specifically, we can distinguish four major activities in river basins that may have an impact on the hydrological regime and biodiversity: (1) land use reducing the "sponge effect"; (2) reclamation of floodplains; (3) hydropower dams; (4) normalisation and canalisation.

### 1. Land use reducing the "sponge effect"
Transforming woodland into highly productive agricultural land requires the removal of the original vegetation. However, this vegetation acts as a sponge, accumulating and slowly releasing valuable freshwater. When large areas are stripped of their vegetation, the buffer effect of the landscape is lost. The impact will be both a frequent occurrence of high water levels in the rivers and an increase in these levels, in times of heavy precipitation. Unbridled urbanisation may have a comparable impact.

### 2. The reclamation of floodplains
In many cases of land reclamation, dikes are built too close to the river. As a result, the water flow capacity of the river is severely reduced. This is likely to lead to high water levels even at moderate discharge levels. Sometimes, estuaries are closed by dams in order to minimise the risk of flooding. Unfortunately, these dams also disturb the sand and silt transport, resulting in extensive and expensive dredging programmes to allow navigation. Besides, the changing of an estuarine system into a riverine system causes the loss of specific habitats.

### 3. Hydropower dams
Hydropower dams are a relatively cheap and clean method of producing electricity. But when large parts of a dynamic river are turned into a lake, the water will become unsuitable for human consumption. Massive putrefying processes at the bottom of the lake are responsible for this effect. Moreover, we should not ignore the social misery that results from the forced removal of settlements required for the construction of such dams. Additionally, the river beyond the dam often becomes a minor stream, having lost most of its former habitats.

His Royal Highness Prince Willem-Alexander of Orange
(Photograph R. Hoff; © RVD, The Hague)

## *4. Normalisation and canalisation*
Many rivers are straightened and provided with dams and locks in order to improve navigation. The transport of both water and sediment is affected by such measures. In several cases, straightening a river has led to severe riverbed erosion. For instance, along the upper Rhine, the groundwater table dropped by several metres due to such measures. In addition, long series of dams and locks hinder fish migration.

The above-mentioned major activities are widely considered to be essential for the prosperity of growing nations, but at the same time, they may present a threat to the natural river systems. Therefore, we have to seek new approaches and techniques enabling us to achieve a better equilibrium between economy and ecology.

## 4. International co-operation

During the sixties, the rivers Rhine and Meuse, which you will visit in the next few days, were severely polluted. It is only through a joint effort of all countries in the Rhine river basin that the water quality has been considerably improved. Now we are working very hard to achieve the same for the Meuse river. However, sustainable river management cannot be limited to water quality improvement alone.

After feeling quite safe for several decades behind huge and tall dikes, the fact that we narrowly escaped major flood disasters in 1993 and 1995 opened the eyes of all countries in the Rhine and Meuse river basins. We all became aware that the classic approach to land use and water management had to be fundamentally changed. Once more, through a joint effort!

This symposium will show you how we agreed on bringing about a large number of improvements, based on an integrated approach of the complete river basin. We still have a long way to go and we face various challenges in implementing these improvements and in achieving sustainable management. This requires intense communication, mutual understanding and information exchange between nations sharing river basins such as those of the Rhine and the Meuse. International co-operation is a prerequisite for sustainable river basin management.

That is what this symposium is all about. All major activities I have just mentioned will be covered within the coming days. I hope our meeting will contribute to a better understanding between conservationists and river managers, consumers and users, and will stimulate international co-operation on sustainable river basin management.

I am aware of the large variety of cultural, economic and geographical aspects which influence the management of river basins. Indeed, there is no general formula for sustainable river management. Each river basin requires a tailor-made approach. To optimise the sustainable use of rivers, we must learn from each other's mistakes and successes. Therefore, international information exchange is a prerequisite. I hope that this symposium will contribute to that process.

I wish you all fruitful discussions and a pleasant and informative stay in the Netherlands!

# NEW APPROACHES TO RIVER MANAGEMENT: GENERAL INTRODUCTION

A.J.M. Smits[1,3], P.H. Nienhuis[2,3] & R.S.E.W. Leuven[2,3]
*[1] Department of Nature Management of Stream Corridors, Faculty of Science, University of Nijmegen, P.O. Box 9010, NL-6500 GL Nijmegen, The Netherlands; [2] Department of Environmental Studies, Faculty of Science, University of Nijmegen, P.O. Box 9010, NL-6500 GL Nijmegen, The Netherlands; [3] Member of the Netherlands Centre for River Studies (NCR), P.O. Box 177, NL-2600 MH Delft, The Netherlands*

## 1. Problem definition

In the present millennium, water issues will frequently appear on the international political agenda. Over the last decades, calamities of water shortage, flooding, habitat deterioration and pollution have occurred with alarming frequency. Many of these problems have their roots in the mismanagement of river basins, with the river management history of industrialised countries in particular comprising a long list of trial and error. In the 19th century, when science was making great progress, the idea arose that nature was pliable to the full extent of man's knowledge. It was also in that same age that far-reaching interventions were introduced in Western European and North-American river basins. River management in those days focused mainly on changing dynamic and unpredictable river systems into static and predictable systems. The aim was to adapt the natural system to user functions such as agriculture and navigation, and not *vice versa*. However, the long-term effects of such drastic interventions were underestimated or not known at all. At present, each new "water incident" increases our awareness that continuation of this classic approach to river management will eventually lead to a severe reduction of the water system's resilience. And loss of resilience means more problems of water shortage, flooding and loss of biodiversity over a relatively short timespan. It is now recognised that the abiotic and biotic complexity of natural water systems is only partly understood. Therefore, it is wise to search for ways to allow socio-economic development without drastic interventions in natural water systems, *i.e.*, sustainable river basin management. There is, however, no agreed definition of sustainable river basin management. What is considered to be sustainable depends on one's perspective. A broad spectrum of overlapping positions, from very "weak" to very "strong" sustainability can be distinguished (Wójcik *et al.* 1997). Sustainable development is a process of change in which the exploitation of resources, the allocation of investments, the orientation of technological developments and institutional arrangements must be in harmony and accommodate the present, as well as the future,

*New approaches to river management, pp. 7–14*
*edited by A.J.M. Smits, P.H. Nienhuis and R.S.E.W. Leuven*
© 2000 Backhuys Publishers, Leiden, The Netherlands

human needs (Leuven *et al.* 1997). This process has socio-economic as well as eco-logical dimensions, which in practice are closely related. From an ecological point of view, sustainable development means that natural resources should be used with-out degrading their quality or reducing their quantity. This also means that the car-rying capacity of an ecosystem like a river basin must not be exceeded (Aarts & Nienhuis 1999, Lorenz 1999). As Stortenbeker (2000) has pointed out in his open-ing address, river basins are an essential part of the earth's freshwater cycle and as such transcend national borders. Thus, ignorance and neglect of sustainable river basin management in one country will sooner or later have its impact on neigh-bouring countries. His Royal Highness Prince Willem-Alexander of Orange (2000) has underlined the importance of international efforts to search for ways that lead to sustainable river basin management. Mutual understanding and respect between nations are indispensable for this process.

## 2. Who organised the conference?

In the Netherlands a number of Extraordinary University Chairs for nature conser-vation are affiliated to the Foundation for Extraordinary University Chairs of Nature Management. Triggered by the recent flooding events in many river basins, the idea arose to co-ordinate the knowledge and experience of river managers, sci-entists, non governmental organisations (NGOs) and river authorities responsible for various river basins in a conference. The Foundation commissioned the Extraordinary University Chair of Nature Conservation of Stream Corridors (University of Nijmegen) to organise a conference entitled *New approaches to river management* from September 28 - October 1, 1998.

The participants to the conference originated from 11 countries (Argentina, Brazil, Cambodia, Canada, Germany, Hungary, the Netherlands, Poland, Thailand, the United States of America and Vietnam). In all of these countries, sustainable river basin management is an important societal issue. During the conference, a number of presentations reported on experiences with, and new approaches to, river basin management for the Mississippi (The United States of America), the Pantanal (Brazil), the Rhine and Meuse (Western Europe), the Danube, Elbe, Odra and Vistula (Central Europe) and the Mekong (Asia). The selection of participants and plenary lectures reflects the scientific contacts at that time and was not based on political or socio-economic arguments.

## 3. Goals of the conference

The conference had three goals:
1.  Exchange of knowledge and experience related to new concepts in water and river basin management between nations that share river basins.
2.  Network building between the various organisations, authorities, centres of expertise and NGOs involved in water and river basin management.
3.  A programme of activities to continue further research and dissemination of knowledge related to sustainable water and river basin management.

Despite the fact that the initiators of the conference were scientists, the tone of the presentations was not exclusively scientific. The prime objective of this conference was to integrate knowledge derived from the three goals mentioned above. The idea was not to reject or confirm hypotheses, but to elucidate and discuss new approaches as a basis for future research programmes.

Conferences that focus on water and river management frequently take a sectoral approach, focusing on technical or ecological aspects. In practice, however, it appears that the actual management policy is the result of a multi-sectoral iterative process in which an increasing number of stakeholders participate. Therefore, we choose to invite a balanced number of scientists, NGO representatives, policymakers, river managers and authorities. Since the conference, intensive communication and knowledge exchange has evolved between the various countries and stakeholder groups. Furthermore, this conference has led directly to a substantial involvement of the University of Nijmegen, and in particular the chair of Nature Conservation of Stream Corridors, in a number of activities:

– Organisation of a Water Seminar on the occasion of the Dutch state visit to China in April 1999.
– A declaration of intent by the Mekong River Commission and WWF Brazil to organise similar events in the Mekong river basin and the Pantanal wetlands, respectively.
– International co-operation between some Rhine river states on the research project entitled Cyclic Rejuvenation of Floodplains, which is financed by the European Union (Smits & Duel 1999).
– Expansion of scientific co-operation with several research institutes in Poland.

## 4. Conference book

Prior to, during and following the fruitful discussions at the conference, it was repeatedly emphasised by various participants that the results of the conference should be published. Why a book? Despite the enormous progress made by the internet and electronic publishing in recent years, many people from various countries still rely on books for their information. Moreover, even in countries where information technology is well implemented, there are still many situations where a hard copy is more useful than an electronic version. In January 1999, the Foundation for Extraordinary University Chairs of Nature Management approved the plan to publish the proceedings of the *New approaches to river management* conference in a book with the same title. From that time onwards, various authors and reviewers have been involved in preparing the proceedings of the conference.

Several books on river basin management have recently been published, discussing *e.g.*, physical processes and human impacts of floods (Smith & Ward 1998), flood response and crisis management (Rosenthal & 't Hart 1998), rehabilitation of rivers (De Waal *et al.* 1998) and new concepts for sustainable management of river basins (Nienhuis *et al.* 1998). In our opinion the present book nevertheless fills an open niche: it contributes to the dissemination of world-wide experience with comprehensive river catchment management planning and focuses on new approaches to promote sustainable management of river basins. The target groups are water authorities, policymakers, NGOs, scientists, students and all those who are involved in water and river basin management. The book intends to increase public awareness of the necessity of sustainable river basin management. Moreover, we hope that the experiences, innovative viewpoints and ideas presented may stimulate creativity and support activities for the further development of sustainable river basin management. Therefore, the present book must not be considered as a final product, but as an integral part of a number of activities which have resulted from the conference.

## 5. Contents

With comprehensive issues such as sustainable water and river management, it is almost impossible to avoid some overlap between the various contributions. However, we think we have succeeded in arranging the presentations in three sections: (1) Developments in integrated river basin management: applications and lessons learnt; (2) Participation of new stakeholders in river basin management; and (3) New methodologies and instruments in sustainable river basin management.

### 5.1 Developments in integrated river basin management: applications and lessons learnt

The first chapter focuses on the wide range of experiences and lessons learnt in river basin management. Rivers in Western Europe and the United Stated of America have had a particularly long history of technical interventions, many of which had a major impact on the natural processes. Havinga & Smits (2000) and Galloway (2000) describe the reasons and drives which underlie these interventions for the rivers Rhine and Mississippi, respectively. These interventions reduced the physical space allocated to the rivers concerned and reduced their hydromorphological dynamics. At present, technological developments and improved understanding of riverine processes have led to a new approach in the management of the Rhine and Mississippi. Both Havinga & Smits (2000) and Galloway (2000) advocate a flexible river management.

In contrast to the rivers Rhine and Mississippi, there are still many more or less natural rivers which have as yet not been subjected to drastic interventions. In general, the countries that use and manage these river basins have an economy in transition and are confronted with the increasing pressure of various user functions on the physical space and natural resources of these rivers. It is important that these countries do their best to avoid making the same mistakes as those which have already gone through this economic development before and are now facing expensive restoration programmes to regain sustainability. In this context, Nienhuis *et al.* (2000), Quang (2000) and Da Silva (2000) focus on developments in river and wetland management in Central Europe, Asia and South America, respectively. They describe the specific institutional aspects, socio-economic conditions, threats and opportunities that evolve from the planned interventions and possible alternatives. Schouten *et al.* (2000) describe how the costs of river management have increased dramatically due to historical pollution of floodplain sediments along the river Meuse and how a new policy of dynamic soil management was developed.

## 5.2 Participation of new stakeholders in river basin management

When it comes to public participation in river basin management, great progress has been made. Hunt (2000a) uses examples of river management practices in the United States of America to illustrate the growing role of public stakeholders in the decision-making process on water and river management. The increasing influence of these public stakeholders, and the awareness that many processes of wetland and river ecosystems are not fully understood, are important for present day water and river management, and there is no longer a place for rigid visions that remain unaltered for decades. Modern water and river management is based on flexible strategies, in which the response of the river system to small-scale interventions is carefully monitored and evaluated before up-scaling or additional interventions are introduced, *i.e.*, the aim is adaptive river basin management.

In adaptive management, experimenting with river management measures on a relatively small and reversible scale is essential. Only when an intervention or a user function of the water system appears to be sustainable can further up-scaling be considered. Timely involvement of public stakeholders in this process is important to provide social support for the management strategy concerned (Van Wetten 2000).

The accessibility of fast changing hydrological and technological information is another important issue in the public participation in water and river management. This is a problem especially in countries with a poorly developed infrastructure. However, large groups of people in remote areas have now also access to important data and expertise that can be used in achieving sustainable water and river management (Matthews & Horner 2000).

Economic arguments play an important role in justifying interventions in water and river systems. Bouma & Saeijs (2000) introduce a new concept for an ecocentric cost-benefit analysis, while Corporaal (2000) focuses on the impact of unbalanced land management on the water system's resilience. This type of land management is often stimulated by financial incentives that promote mismanagement. Corporaal (2000) presents an innovative concept in which society pays farmers for applying hydrologically and ecologically sound land and water management.

## 5.3 New methodologies and instruments in sustainable river basin management

The natural hydromorphological dynamics of rivers form the basis of differentiated riverine landscapes, generating a well-developed biodiversity. The construction of large dams constitutes a major threat, with irreversible effects on natural river systems. Goodland (2000) stresses the importance of a well considered and multi-sectoral decision process before the construction of large dams is initiated. In addition, Hunt (2000b) illustrates that there are often many alternatives to sustainable economic development in a river basin without the construction of large dams.

Within one country, it is relatively easy to achieve consensus on water and river management, but when various countries share one river basin, this becomes considerably more difficult. Leentvaar & Glas (2000) demonstrate for the Danube that a sound environmental study of the impacts of drastic interventions are indispensable for river basin management involving more countries sharing the same river basin.

In classic water and river management, most interventions are civil engineering answers to social questions. In general, the scientific attention and available means have been focused on adapting the natural water system to various user functions such as navigation and agriculture. Smits et al. (2000) emphasise that the modern river manager has to adopt a more pro-active attitude and must take the initiative to adapt the various user functions to the natural water system. This vision is illustrated with various concrete examples. In addition, Smits et al. (2000) also advocate the development of management instruments enabling the river manager to restore the hydromorphological dynamics which are a prerequisite of the ecological rehabilitation of rivers. Opportunities to restore the natural dynamics of river systems are being extensively studied in the United States of America. Sparks et al. (2000) describe a methodology for reintroducing hydrodynamics, providing new opportunities for the restoration of riverine biota.

Apart from the loss of natural hydromorphological dynamics, increasing water pollution has contributed also to the deterioration of river systems. Since the end of World War II in particular, the water quality of the rivers Meuse and Rhine has deteriorated as a result of unbridled emissions of pollutants. During a recovery period lasting many years, it became evident that only transnational agreements can limit the emissions of pollutants. Since the start of transnational co-operation in the Rhine and Meuse river basins, the water quality has improved considerably, although the polluted sediments deposited in the floodplains of these rivers in the past continue to present problems. Van Leussen et al. (2000) describe how the Netherlands deals with these polluted floodplains within the context of present-day river management and habitat restoration. Eijsackers & Doelman (2000) focus on the self-purifying capacity of polluted floodplains and the risks to riverine biota exposed to these pollutants.

Finally, the development from integrated approaches to sustainable river basin management and recommendations for river research are summarised and discussed by Leuven et al. (2000).

## 6. Final remarks

The editors are aware that there must be many other intriguing experiences and concepts related to modern water and river management that would fit in well with the contents of the book. For practical reasons, it has not been possible to include accounts from China, Africa and other regions that were unable to participate in this conference. However, we hope that the ideas and approaches described in the present book will provide sufficient inspiration for all those are involved in the search for sustainable water and river basin management.

# References

Aarts, B.G.W. & Nienhuis, P.H. 1999. Ecological sustainability and biodiversity. Int. J. Sustain. Dev. World Ecol. 6: 89-102.

Bouma, J.J. & Saeijs, H.L.F. 2000. Eco-centric cost-benefit analysis for hydraulic engineering in river basins. In: Smits, A.J.M., Nienhuis, P.H. & Leuven, R.S.E.W. (Eds.). New approaches to river management. Backhuys Publishers, Leiden. pp. 167-178.

Corporaal, A. 2000. "Fisquality", a proposal for a tax bonus to improve hydro-ecological resilience of river catchments. In: Smits, A.J.M., Nienhuis, P.H. & Leuven, R.S.E.W. (Eds.). New approaches to river management. Backhuys Publishers, Leiden. pp. 179-186.

Da Silva, C.J. 2000. Ecological basis for the management of the Pantanal – upper Paraguay basin. In: Smits, A.J.M., Nienhuis, P.H. & Leuven, R.S.E.W. (Eds.). New approaches to river management. Backhuys Publishers, Leiden. pp. 97-118.

De Waal, L.C., Large, A.R.G. & Wade, P.M. (Eds.). 1998. Rehabilitation of rivers: principles and implementation. J. Wiley & Sons, Chichester.

Eijsackers, H.J.P. & Doelman, P. 2000. Using natural cleaning processes in the river ecosystem: a new approach to environmental management. Does natural attenuation outbalance the risks of organic and inorganic contaminants in a river system? In: Smits, A.J.M., Nienhuis, P.H. & Leuven, R.S.E.W. (Eds.). New approaches to river management. Backhuys Publishers, Leiden. pp. 307-328.

Galloway, G.E. 2000. Three centuries of river management along the Mississippi river: Engineering and hydrological aspects. In: Smits, A.J.M., Nienhuis, P.H. & Leuven, R.S.E.W. (Eds.). New approaches to river management. Backhuys Publishers, Leiden. pp. 51-64.

Goodland, R.J.A. 2000. Is there future for big dams? In: Smits, A.J.M., Nienhuis, P.H. & Leuven, R.S.E.W. (Eds.). New approaches to river management. Backhuys Publishers, Leiden. pp. 187-207.

Havinga, H. & Smits, A.J.M. 2000. River management along the Rhine: a retrospective view. In: Smits, A.J.M., Nienhuis, P.H. & Leuven, R.S.E.W. (Eds.). New approaches to river management. Backhuys Publishers, Leiden. pp. 15-32.

His Royal Highness Prince Willem-Alexander of Orange. 2000 The value of sustainable river management. In: Smits, A.J.M., Nienhuis, P.H. & Leuven, R.S.E.W. (Eds.). New approaches to river management. Backhuys Publishers, Leiden. pp. 3-6.

Hunt, C.E. 2000a. New approaches to river management in the United States. In: Smits, A.J.M., Nienhuis, P.H. & Leuven, R.S.E.W. (Eds.). New approaches to river management. Backhuys Publishers, Leiden. pp. 119-139.

Hunt, C.E. 2000b. Following a diversified strategy to achieve the sustainable use of the Mekong river basin. In: Smits, A.J.M., Nienhuis, P.H. & Leuven, R.S.E.W. (Eds.). New approaches to river management. Backhuys Publishers, Leiden. pp. 209-223.

Leentvaar, J. & Glas, P.C.G. 2000. A policy analysis for the upper Danube river section in Hungary. In: Smits, A.J.M., Nienhuis, P.H. & Leuven, R.S.E.W. (Eds.). New approaches to river management. Backhuys Publishers, Leiden. pp. 249-266.

Leuven, R.S.E.W., Thörig, M.W.H., Nienhuis, P.H. & Van de Laar, B.J. 1997. Environmental utilisation space: a useful concept underpinning sustainable management of river catchments? In: Smith, P. & Tenner, A. (Eds.). Dimensions of sustainability. Nomos Verlagsgesellschaft, Baden-Baden. pp. 362-362.

Leuven, R.S.E.W., Smits, A.J.M. & Nienhuis, P.H. 2000. From integrated approaches to sustainable river basin management. In: Smits, A.J.M., Nienhuis, P.H. & Leuven, R.S.E.W. (Eds.). New approaches to river management. Backhuys Publishers, Leiden. pp. 329-347.

Lorenz, C.M. 1999. Indicators for sustainable river management. PhD thesis. Free University of Amsterdam, Amsterdam.

Matthews, G.J. & Horner, M. 2000. Bridging the communication gap in river management. In: Smits, A.J.M., Nienhuis, P.H. & Leuven, R.S.E.W. (Eds.). New approaches to river management. Backhuys Publishers, Leiden. pp. 155-165.

Nienhuis, P.H., Leuven, R.S.E.W. & Ragas, A.M.J. (Eds.). 1998. New concepts for sustainable management of river basins. Backhuys Publishers, Leiden.

Nienhuis, P.H., Chojnacki, J.C., Harms,, O., Majewski, W., Parzonka, W. & Prus, T. 2000. Elbe, Odra, and Vistula: reference rivers for the restoration of biodiversity and habitat quality. In: Smits, A.J.M., Nienhuis, P.H. & Leuven, R.S.E.W. (Eds.). New approaches to river management. Backhuys Publishers, Leiden. pp. 65-84.

Quang, N.N. 2000. Management of the Mekong river basin. In: Smits, A.J.M., Nienhuis, P.H. & Leuven, R.S.E.W. (Eds.). New approaches to river management. Backhuys Publishers, Leiden. pp. 85-96.

Rosenthal, U. & 't Hart, P. (Eds.). 1998. Flood response and crisis management in western Europe. A comparative analysis. Springer, Berlin.

Schouten, C.J.J., Rang, M.C., De Hamer, B.A. & Van Hout, H.R.A., 2000. Strongly polluted deposits in the Meuse river floodplain and their effect on river management. In: Smits, A.J.M., Nienhuis, P.H. & Leuven, R.S.E.W. (Eds.). New approaches to river management. Backhuys Publishers, Leiden. pp. 33-50.

Smith, K. & Ward, R. (Eds.). 1998. Floods: physical processes and human impacts. J. Wiley & Sons, Chichester.

Smits, A.J.M. & Duel, H. 1999. Cyclic rejuvenations of floodplains. Research proposal within the context of IRMA SPONGE Programme. University of Nijmegen, Nijmegen.

Smits, A.J.M., Havinga, H. & Marteijn, E.C.L. 2000. New concepts in river and water management in the Rhine river basin: How to live with the unexpected? In: Smits, A.J.M., Nienhuis, P.H. & Leuven, R.S.E.W. (Eds.). New approaches to river management. Backhuys Publishers, Leiden. pp. 267-286.

Sparks, R.E., Braden, J., Demissie, M., Mitral, P., Schneider, D., White, D. & Xia, R. 2000. Technical support of public decisions to restore floodplain ecosystems: a status report on the Illinois river project (USA). In: Smits, A.J.M., Nienhuis, P.H. & Leuven, R.S.E.W. (Eds.). New approaches to river management. Backhuys Publishers, Leiden. pp. 225-247.

Stortenbeker, C. 2000. New approaches to river management: integration of knowledge and ideas. In: Smits, A.J.M., Nienhuis, P.H. & Leuven, R.S.E.W. (Eds.). New approaches to river management. Backhuys Publishers, Leiden. pp. 1-2.

Van Leussen, W., Kater, G. & Van Meel, P. 2000. Multi-level approach to flood control in the Dutch part of the river Meuse. In: Smits, A.J.M., Nienhuis, P.H. & Leuven, R.S.E.W. (Eds.). New approaches to river management. Backhuys Publishers, Leiden. pp. 287-305.

Van Wetten, J.C.J. 2000. Partners in wetland conservation and development: strategic environmental analysis for the Ukrainian Danube delta. In: Smits, A.J.M., Nienhuis, P.H. & Leuven, R.S.E.W. (Eds.). New approaches to river management. Backhuys Publishers, Leiden. pp. 141-153.

Wójcik, W., Leuven, R.S.E.W. & Foxon, T. 1997. Challenges of sustainable water management of river catchments? In: Smith, P. & Tenner, A. (Eds.). Dimensions of sustainability. Nomos Verlagsgesellschaft, Baden-Baden. pp. 353-360.

# RIVER MANAGEMENT ALONG THE RHINE:
# A RETROSPECTIVE VIEW

H. Havinga[1,3] & A.J.M. Smits[2,3]
*1 Delft University of Technology, Faculty of Civil Engineering and Geoscience, Section Hydraulic and Offshore Engineering, River Morphology and Engineering Group, P.O. Box 5048, NL-2600 GA Delft, The Netherlands;*
*2 Department of Nature Management of Stream Corridors, Faculty of Science, University of Nijmegen, P.O. Box 9010, NL-6500 GL Nijmegen, The Netherlands;*
*3 Member of the Netherlands Centre for River Studies (NCR), P.O. Box 177, NL-2600 MH Delft, The Netherlands*

## Abstract

This paper presents a historical overview of the main interventions in the alluvial parts of the Rhine river, focusing on the developments in the Dutch Rhine delta and the German upper Rhine. It has become clear, by and by, that the virtues of the heavily regulated Rhine system are not without severe drawbacks. The river regulation measures that have been introduced, such as dikes, width reductions and bend cut-offs, have led to a river system, which has lost its hydrological resilience. Moreover, potential damage caused by future flooding is increasing and can only be prevented at great efforts and costs. Based on past experiences, the present day river management strives to be more in line with the river's natural behaviour. Therefore, the various Rhine states are looking for engineering solutions that can both maintain the original objectives and increase the hydrological resilience of the Rhine river basin. These solutions will have to be more flexible than traditional river management measures. Such aims seem achievable with the help of modern technology and an increasing knowledge of the system. This new form of river management should maximise the use of natural dynamics.

## 1. Introduction

About 5000 years ago, the first settlers in the "low lands" of the Rhine river delta, now better known as the Netherlands, found themselves in a poorly drained flat delta of floodplains intersected by creeks, tidal inlets and small and large rivers. Their dwelling places were the high ridges or hills along these water courses. Not the most comfortable of places as the Roman Plinius described, when he wrote: "There throws the Ocean itself, two times a day, daily and nightly, in a tremendous stream over a wide country, so one is doubting if the ground belongs to the land or to the sea. There is living a miserable people on the highest known level of the tide and at these they built their huts, living like sailors when the water covers their environment and like shipwrecked when the water has gone" (Huisman *et al.* 1999). This would seem like an unpleasant biotope for man to live in. People in these areas lived by hunting and fishing, although in Roman times, small dikes and flumes were built to create appropriate conditions for agriculture activities on a very local scale. The Romans undertook the first large-scale river interventions in the low countries. Generals Corbulo and Drusus connected the Rhine river with the Meuse and IJssel rivers (Huisman *et al.* 1999). Since then, many river management measures in the Rhine basin (Figure 1) have followed, resulting in a riverine landscape which is now completely different from the time when the Romans entered the Rhine basin.

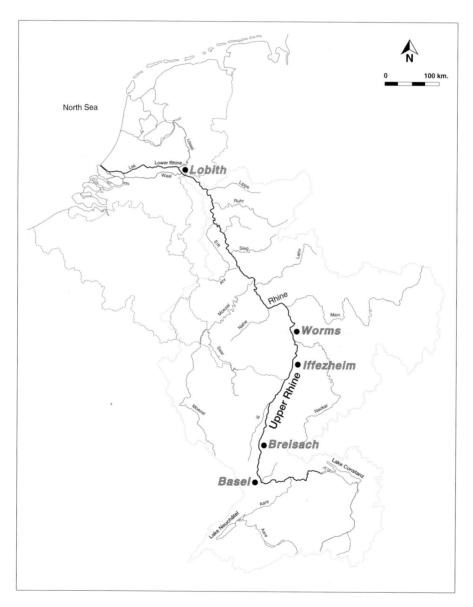

*Fig. 1.* The length of the Rhine river is 1,320 km and its basin area comprises 185,000 km².

This paper first reviews the main interventions that have modified the Rhine river and the response of the river system to these measures. This is followed by a discussion of the new approach to river management along the Rhine, that was triggered by the floods of 1993 and 1995, almost resulting in flooding disasters. This new approach is illustrated with some specific plans and projects for the Rhine tributaries in the Netherlands.

## 2. Early developments in the Rhine delta

The early developments in the Dutch delta are described in Huisman *et al.* (1999). Around the end of the first millennium, the population in Western Europe was expanding rapidly. To increase the rye and wheat production, the land was systematically cultivated and drained. In the marshy land consisting of peat and clay, which at that time lay 2 or 3 m above mean sea level, field drains and ditches were dug to lower the water table and allow agriculture. The drop in groundwater levels caused oxidation of the peat, which in turn lead to subsidence of the soil (Figure 2). After some time this subsidence forced the people to deepen drains and ditches again and dig canals to lower the water table further, in order to maintain agricultural productivity. The permanent need to lower water tables provoked an irreversible subsidence process.

Around the year 1100, the subsidence had resulted in large areas bordering the sea being flooded during high tide. In addition to the man-made subsidence, the natural

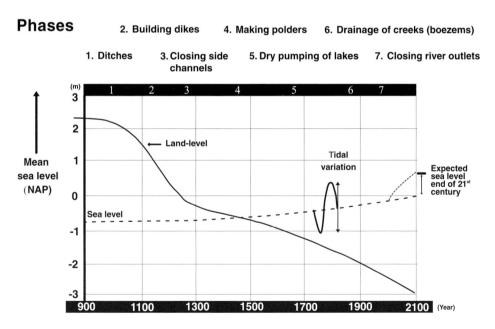

*Fig 2.* Land subsidence in the Rhine delta. The phases correspond to the engineering solutions that were applied to prevent the land from flooding (Source: Huisman 1999).

sea level rise also worsened the drainage problem. Both processes necessitated mitigating interventions, increasing in scale in the course of time. These measures such as digging ditches, constructing dikes and dams, creating polders with artificial drainage, reclaiming wetlands, draining by means of so-called "boezems" on a large scale and closing estuaries and inland seas, are illustrated in figure 2. Dikes were built to protect the land against flooding. To avoid high water levels inside the embanked areas, excess water was released through outlets at low tide. In the 13th century, local embankments along the rivers and streams were connected by dikes.

The considerable rate of subsidence and the sea level rise, however, could not be stopped. The surface behind the dikes and dams sank to below Mean Sea Level (MSL), making gravity discharge of the superfluous water from the embanked regions difficult and eventually impossible. Behind the dikes and closure dams the embankment of small areas was started. From these small inner embanked areas, better known as "polders", the excess water was artificially removed and conducted to the former tidal inlet or creek (step 4 in figure 2). It was then released from these water courses by sluices in the closure dam during low tide. The former inlets and creeks were and are still being used as water storage accommodations ("boezem") during high water levels. This stepwise drainage system is highly characteristic of the Netherlands.

## 3. Developments in the Dutch upper river reaches

Man has also been working in the more upstream reaches of the Rhine to improve living conditions. Also here, the first river regulation works consisted of local dikes for flood protection. Groynes and longitudinal dikes along the riverbed were built, to prevent erosion of the banks and to catch sediment to create farmland in the floodplain. Side channels were closed and river bends were cut off. These measures were intended to increase flow velocities in the main channel, thus preventing the formation of sandbanks. In winter periods, these shallows were prone to develop ice dams, which formed a serious threat to the dikes as the flowing water pushed them up (Figure 3). Later it was found that these measures were also beneficial for navigation, because they had deepened the main channel. In order to optimise the navigation channel so-called "width normalisations" were carried out around 1870 (Figure 4). Width normalisation means that the low water bed is limited to one main channel with a constant (normal) width. Groynes were constructed at regular intervals, which confined the low water bed into a narrower channel and kept the water flow away from the erodible bank. In the 19th and 20th centuries, after many uncoordinated regulations, two large scale width normalisations were carried out in the main Dutch Rhine branch.

It can be concluded that before these co-ordinated regulations, the irregular course of the low water bed and the unregulated human interventions in the floodplains considerably hampered the safe discharge of water and ice to the sea, resulting in dikes being breached and land being flooded.

*Fig. 3.* Flooding disaster along the Waal river in The Netherlands caused by ice dams (1799). To prevent the formation of ice dams many river management measures were introduced that would drastically change the original riverbed and its floodplains (Source: Driessen 1994).

## 4. Upper Rhine developments

Major interventions have been implemented not only in the downstream sections of the Rhine river and its tributaries, but also along the upper Rhine, as has been described in (Dister *et al.* 1990). Originally, the upper Rhine comprised two different morphological river. Between Basel (Switzerland) and Rastatt (Germany), the river was of the so-called "braided" type (Figure 5). This river section featured numerous channels, which shifted continuously. The section between Rastatt and Mainz (Germany) was of the so-called "meander" type. In the braided zone, the bed load transport and the erosive force of the Rhine were so enormous that it constantly created new channels, continually changing the floodplains. In contrast, the meander zone had a more or less uniform, meandering riverbed, with less dynamic fluvial hydromorphological processes.

Along the dynamic upper Rhine settlements located near the riverbed were never safe. Floods and a shifting riverbed formed a continuous threat. Moreover, the combination of poor hygienic conditions and an abundance of water pools and oxbow lakes led to waterborne diseases such as malaria and typhoid. To eliminate these plagues and to increase flood protection, the German hydraulic engineer Tulla developed improvement schemes (Mosonyi 1970). Navigation interests were only of secondary importance at that time. The implementation of Tulla's plans meant that numerous branches of the river in the braided zone were closed and meanders were straightened. These normalisation works were completed in 1878.

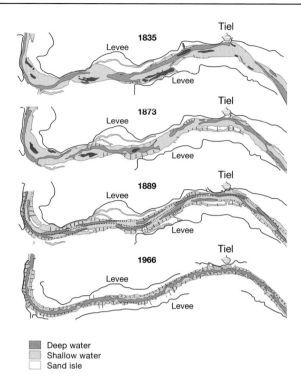

*Fig. 4.* In the 19th century, many river management measures were introduced along the Rhine tributaries in the Netherlands to prevent ice dam formation and to improve the fairway for shipping. The main developments that changed the middle section of the Waal river are depicted. A complex system of small dikes and groynes reduced the lateral interaction of the river with the floodplains and simplified this river. Sand banks and shoals disappeared leaving a fairway more suitable for shipping. The embanked floodplains are generally used as grassland for cattle (Source: Van der Ven 1993).

By the end of the 19th century, the result of this "upper Rhine correction" was an extensive system of flood protection along this section of the Rhine. However, straightening the Rhine induced a high stream velocity and thus severe erosion of the riverbed (Jansen 1979, IKSR 1993). The Rhine riverbed started to subside, causing water tables in the surrounding lands to fall. Former floodplain forests and crops started to suffer from severe water shortages. It should be noted, however, that in Tulla's original engineering's plans he intended to locate the dikes at a substantial distance from the main riverbed providing the Rhine with sufficient space. In periods of high water discharges, this was meant to relieve the eroding force on the main riverbed. However, contrary to Tulla's intentions, the dikes were constructed close to the main riverbed, in order to gain more land that would be suitable for urbanisation and farming. The resulting limited space for the river further increased the flow velocity of the river, especially during high water discharges.

With the appearance or steamships towards the end of the 19th century, navigation became more important. The continuous downstream movement of gravel and sand banks in the main riverbed was seen as a threat to navigation. In order to

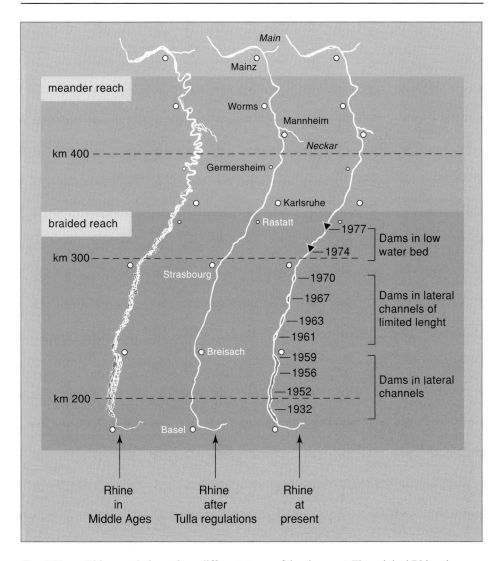

*Fig. 5.* Upper Rhine regulations: three different stages of development. The original Rhine river was a hydromorphological complex system with braided and meandering river sections (first stage). After the Tulla regulations a simplified low water bed remained (second stage). At present (third stage), the upper Rhine is provided with several hydroelectric dams constructed according to various strategies (Source: Dister 1985).

improve the navigational conditions, the so-called upper Rhine regulation was started at the beginning of the 20th century. A low water channel with a width of only 80 m was created by constructing groynes in the riverbed. This reduction of the width guaranteed sufficient navigable depth, but increased the bed erosion and a further lowering of the water table.

After World War I, the Treaty of Versailles (1919) granted the French Republic the sole utilisation of the hydropower potential of the upper Rhine. This stimulated

a new phase of hydraulic engineering. In 1928, the so-called "Moderne Ober-
rheinausbau" (modern upper Rhine extension) started with the construction of a lateral canal (Grand Canal d'Alsace, Figure 5). The lateral canal served not only as a
reservoir for hydroelectric power, but also as a navigation route. A residual flow of
between 20 $m^3$ $s^{-1}$ and 30 $m^3$ $s^{-1}$ was maintained in the original riverbed. Only when
the river had a discharge rate of more than 1,400 $m^3$ $s^{-1}$ (its mean discharge is
approx. 1,100 $m^3$ $s^{-1}$), the original channel received more than the residual water
discharge. The diversion of most of the river water into the lateral canal for use in
generating hydroelectric power, resulted in serious damage to wildlife areas and
crops.

During the construction of the canal, the problems caused by the falling water
tables became so serious, that the lateral canal from Basel to Strasbourg was not
completed as planned, but was only brought as far as Breisach (Germany). In order
to prevent further impacts on the water tables but retain the hydropower potential, a
new design was made for the river Breisach-Strasbourg section (German-France
border). The Germans called this plan the "Schlingenlösung". It comprises the construction of four by-pass canals each equipped with hydroelectric dams and navigation locks. The advantage of this solution was that the water flowed back into the
original riverbed after it had passed a hydroelectric dam, providing the original
riverbed with water. However, the construction of these dams had another underestimated impact. The sediment supplied by the river accumulated in front of the
dams, thus depriving the water that passed the dams via the hydroelectricity turbines of sediment. This was replenished by taking up sediment from the riverbed
downstream from the hydropower dams. As a consequence, severe degradation of
the riverbed occurred downstream of every dam. The solution to this problem was
sought in the construction of additional dams in the Rhine river itself, downstream
of the last constructed by-pass (so-called 'Vollausbau'). In total three of such dams
were built. Since the completion of the last dam (1977) at Iffezheim (Germany),
downstream erosion of the riverbed (yearly loss 170,000 $m^3$; Felkel 1987) has been
counterbalanced by gravel supplements to prevent further bed level degradation.
These supplements of gravel and sediment will have to be continued indefinitely.
Nowadays, bed-load supply is considered a better solution than continuing to construct dams further downstream.

## 5. Hydro-morphological impacts of river engineering measures along the Rhine

The various interventions along the Rhine have led to a considerable loss of flooding area. Figure 6 shows this reduction for the river section Basel-Breisach. The
reduced river width caused larger water depths with corresponding higher flow
velocities. As a result the river offered less resistance to the flow and flood waves
would travel faster and had higher peaks. Figure 7 shows the effects on the maximum flood discharges at Worms, caused by measures carried out in the Rhine basin
upstream of Worms, between 1882 and 1955. In the course of time, anticipating
increasing flood levels, dikes regularly had to be heightened in the entire Rhine
basin to maintain flood protection levels.

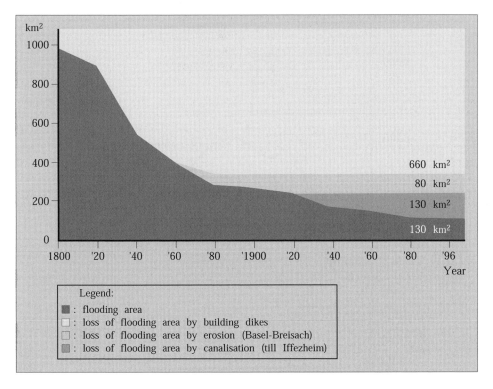

*Fig. 6.* Loss of flooding area along the upper Rhine (Basel-Mainz) in the course of time due to various interventions (Source: IKSR 1998).

Summarising the history of water and river management along the Rhine, it can be concluded that all the interventions were generally aimed at two goals:

1. making floodprone areas along the Rhine and its delta more suitable for urbanisation and agriculture;
2. improving the navigability of the Rhine and exploiting the hydroelectric potential of the upper reaches of the river.

However, these drastic interventions often caused unexpected or underestimated hydromorphological responses by the river system, which in turn necessitated new management measures to mitigate the system's response. Table 1 summarises some of the most important "intervention-response" relations in the Rhine basin.

These examples illustrate that almost every major intervention in the river system leads to responses by the river, often at a certain distance (distant response in place and in time). In the past, these responses were not always properly understood. The net effect of all these interventions (including those along smaller streams in the catchment area of the Rhine basin) has severely reduced the hydrological resilience of the Rhine basin. Moderate changes in rainfall intensity and frequency are very quickly reflected in extreme low or high water levels in the Rhine. Until some years ago it was thought that the construction of even higher dikes and

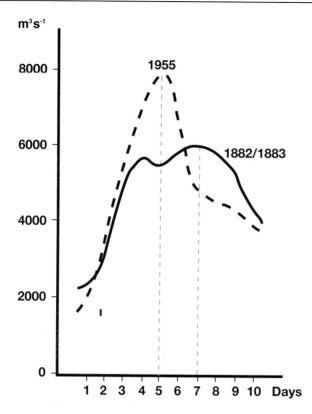

*Fig. 7.* The change of a flood wave caused by management interventions along the upper Rhine. The water discharge of the Rhine near Worms (Germany) during the period December 26, 1882 until January 4, 1883 is depicted. In addition the course of the water discharge for an identical volume of water was calculated for the geometric condition of the Rhine river in 1955. At that time far-reaching interventions had been introduced. Due to these interventions flood waves travel faster and have higher peaks (Source: IKSR 1993).

*Table 1.* Important hydromorphological "intervention-response" relations caused by water and river management interventions in the Rhine river basin.

| Intervention | Hydromorphological response | Mitigating measure |
|---|---|---|
| Drainage of peatland in the Rhine delta | Oxidation of peat leading to subsidence of the landside part of the dikes | Higher dikes and more powerful pumping stations in the polders |
| Regulation of river sections and constricting the floodplain by dike construction | Erosion of the riverbed and lowering of the water tables Increased peak levels | Higher dikes |
| Hydro-electric dams and navigation channels | Accumulation of sediment on the upstream side of the dam and increased riverbed erosion downstream of the dam | Sediment supply on the downstream side of the dam |

more powerful pumping stations would be the only management measure able to relieve the consequences of a reduced hydrological resilience.

With respect to the original goals of the Rhine river regulations, it is obvious that hydropower and navigation have profited enormously. Large parts of the riparian floodplains were separated from the river by dikes and transformed into relatively safe urban and highly productive agricultural areas. Because of these developments and because of its strategic location in Europe, the Rhine basin has developed into one of the most prosperous regions in the world. At the same time severe drawbacks have to be acknowledged, which are forcing us to reconsider the large-scale application of above described measures.

## 6. Modern river management along the Rhine: a new course

The high water discharges in the Rhine river in January 1995 constituted a turning point in the history of water and river management in the Rhine river basin. A general assembly of the Rhine states decided that further constriction of the floodplains of the Rhine had to be counteracted and that the river had to regain its hydrological resilience. This required a new approach to river basin management. In a so-called "Flood Action Plan" the Rhine states inventoried the management measures, which could enhance safety in a sustainable way (IKSR 1997). A number of measures were identified in order to regain the hydrological resilience of the Rhine river basin. Three important strategies that greatly differ from the traditional water and river management approach are:
1. The water storage capacity of urbanised and agricultural areas has to be increased to prevent the rapid run-off of rainwater (see also Smits *et al.* 2000).
2. Further reduction of space for the Rhine due to urbanisation has to be prevented. In the Netherlands a legislative policy named "Room for the River" was formulated. This policy is to prevent any building activities in the floodplain which are not of crucial importance to society (such as housing).
3. Available space for the Rhine riverbed and its tributaries has to be increased. This can be achieved by constructing retention-polders and by-passes or by removing obstacles from the riverbed.

Some recent studies have sought to find ways to increase the water storage and discharge capacity of the Dutch part of the Rhine basin.

*6.1 Increasing water discharge capacity on the river side of the dikes*

The goal of the "Room for the River" (RFR) project is to increase the safety level without further raising the dikes along the Rhine and its tributaries (Hendriksen 1999). General dike heightening would increase flood water levels and amplify the destructive power of a flood if a dike should be breached. Moreover, such dike elevation could be regarded as a continuation of the traditional river management approach. The RFR project is a study, which inventories the possibilities of lowering the level of the floodplains, which has risen due to increased sedimentation since the construction of the dikes. In addition, opportunities for removing some of

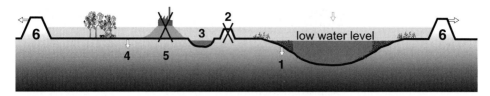

1  lowering of groyne
2  removing summer embankment
3  secondary channel

4  lowering of flood plain (excavation of clay/sand)
5  removing non-flooding areas
6  dike repositioning

*Fig. 8.* Possible flood level lowering measures between the dikes of the Rhine tributaries (Source: Silva & Kok 1996).

the hydraulic bottlenecks or reducing their hydraulic resistance are being studied. Figure 8 shows the measures being investigated within the context of the RFR project. This project intends to develop solutions that should be resilient and flexible. These intentions more or less rule out further dike heightening. The introduction of the flexibility criterion is a recognition of the fact that the extent and progress of future flood waves can not be accurately predicted.

### 6.2 Increasing water storage and water discharge capacity on the land side of the dikes

Measures should also be considered that could cope with larger water discharges than the flood discharge that the current flood protection measures were designed for (called the "design flood"). In the near future, climate change may lead to larger discharges. Since the above solutions in the RFR-project only provide for a limited amount of extra water to be discharged by the river, measures on the land side of the dikes should also be considered.

A preliminary analysis of the impact of high flood discharges has been carried out in a research and development project called "The Rhine in the long term perspective" (WL|Delft Hydraulics 1998). This project showed that a 25% higher design flood of the Rhine river could not be handled by the Dutch Rhine tributaries without dikes being raised by more than a metre. As an alternative to raising dikes, this project proposes to guide the surplus of water through one of the Rhine tributaries to the relatively large lake IJssel ("IJsselmeer"), which could serve as a temporary retention basin. In the near future, this lake could be equipped with huge pumps that could convey the surplus water into the North Sea, if the normal outlets (using gravity) prove to be insufficient. As a striking example of re-using traditional measures, a by-pass is proposed, which would only function during floods. Figure 9 shows how the section of the IJssel river downstream of the new confluence would be considerably widened. In this downstream section, the use of lands subject to occasional flooding will have to change. Nevertheless, there are possibilities for housing, recreation and habitat restoration. As a first step in this development, by-passes could be created around major cities to avoid catastrophic floods (WL|Delft Hydraulics 1999).

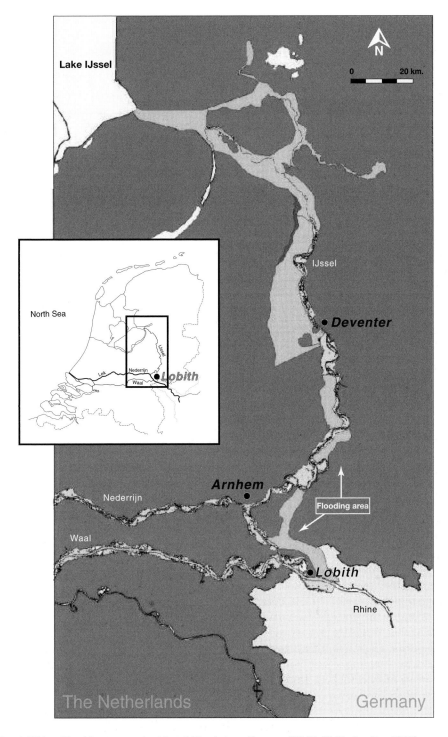

*Fig. 9.* Rhine-IJssel by-pass and widened IJssel river (Source: WL|Delft Hydraulics 1998).

Retention basins on the land side of the dike would also be very useful to reduce flood discharges downstream. They also have a limited capacity to lower water levels immediately upstream of the water intake. Figure 10 shows the "Rijnstrangen" area. Transformed into a retention polder, this area would perfectly fit a strategy of sustainable solutions to the flood protection problem. As it is situated in the upstream part of the Dutch Rhine branches, the damping effect of this retention polder on a potential flood wave would be tremendous (up to 0.3 m at peak water levels). Moreover, if this area is managed as a wetland, the ecological effects of occasional flooding would be negligible. The possible land side solutions for increasing the water storage and discharge capacity of the Rhine river and its tributaries underline the need for a pro-active attitude of the river manager in spatial planning.

## 7. Dynamic river management

How do the above management measures relate to the lessons learnt in the Rhine basin? Creating more room for the river by adding former floodplain areas to the river is one thing, but are the proposed measures in the riverbed itself (RFR project) not just repeating the drastic interventions of the past? Indeed, prudence is required. That is why we advocate a new approach to river management, also referred to as "Dynamic River Management" (DRM) to implement some of the measures that have been studied in the RFR project. DRM prefers management measures that are reversible and have no distant response. DRM recognises that the hydromorphological response of the river system to a management measure can only be partially predicted. Therefore, each measure has to be tested on a small scale. Only if the system's responses are positive, upscaling of the measure will be considered. Another important aspect of DRM is the involvement of the public stakeholders in the river basin. Based on experiences in the Rhine basin we have learnt that river management measures without public support are almost equivalent to mismanagement. For this reason, public participation is a prerequisite in the decision and implementation stages of the RFR project. From this point of view, DRM shows many similarities to Adaptive River Management (Hunt 2000).

Here, two examples of DRM measures are given that are currently realised along the Waal river. In order to increase the economic attractivity of shipping as the most environmentally sound method of transport, enlargement of the draught and a wider fairway in the Waal river would be required. In the traditional management approach, a smaller normal width by extending the present groynes would solve this problem. This measure permanently increases the flow velocity, causing a scouring of the riverbed that would lead to the desired fairway dimensions. DRM prefers locally effective and reversible measures. A pilot project is now investigating aspects of systematically dredging shoals and re-allocating the dredged material in troughs, as an alternative to extending groynes. Another example of DRM concerns the Waal river bends, where the fairway width is limited by the shallow inner bend, caused by the so-called "spiral flow". At present various forms of river bend improvement are being tested that have only locally and reversible effects. A most promising technique are the so-called "bottom vanes" which cause degradation of the inner bend (Figure 11).

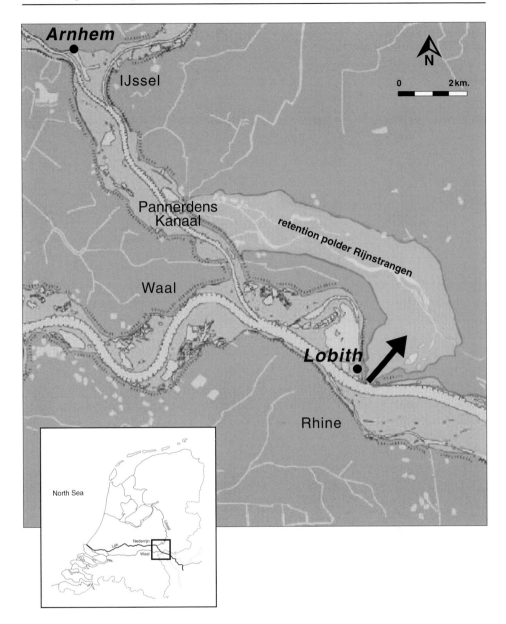

*Fig. 10.* Possible retention polder "Rijnstrangen" near Lobith (Source: WL|Delft Hydraulics 1998).

DRM means that measures will be applied that are able to cope with dynamic river reactions and that are flexible in view of future demands. Instead of large rigid constructions, small sized measures to correct river responses will be used. To restore riverine habitats, in the floodplains more vegetation will be allowed. In practice, the river will show more dynamic changes, in water levels as well as in bed geometry,

*Fig. 11.* Bottom vanes in outer river bend, forcing the inner bend to erode (↓) and the outer bend to aggradate (↑) by reducing the natural secondary flow in the bend. This solution may also reduce erosion of natural river banks (© C. Nuyten).

complicating river management. To be prepared to take action, information regarding these changes is essential. For this purpose an extensive monitoring and impact assessment programme (including forecasting) has to be available (a Dynamic River Management Monitoring System). It is laborious and expensive to monitor adequately any changes, which occur in the riverbed and its floodplains by conventional techniques (aerial photographs and field studies). In the future, therefore, faster and cheaper techniques will be needed to monitor the abundance and structure of vegetation in large parts of a river basin (*e.g.*, Smits *et al.* 2000). This type of river management demands detailed knowledge of physical phenomena and effects of hydromorphological changes on flora and fauna. For this purpose in the Netherlands research is carried out in the context of various pilot projects and related study programmes at the universities of Delft, Utrecht and Nijmegen (*e.g.*, Smits & Duel 1999).

## 8. Conclusions

On the one hand, the socio-economic development of the Rhine river basin has profited enormously from the Rhine regulation, because it afforded a high level of flood protection, an efficient navigation route, and high agricultural yields. On the other hand, the constructions which were used, fixing the river in a kind of harness, have led to large-scale river responses like tilting of the riverbed through upstream erosion, and deterioration of habitats in and along the Rhine river. A number of unfavourable effects ensued, such as greatly reduced biodiversity, disturbed hydrological systems and gradually increasing impacts of flooding. Retrospectively, it can be concluded that the long-term hydromorphological effects of the interventions in the Rhine basin were not foreseen or at least underestimated. This meant that for a long period there was no reason to change the traditional approach to water and river management in this river basin. The starting point of this traditional approach was that management measures tried to change an unpredictable and dynamic river system into a predictable and static system. Hydromorphological responses of the river system that were perceived as undesirable were counteracted with new measures. After a few centuries of such river management, we have ended up with a complicated and expensive river system, with a greatly reduced hydrological resilience. This situation can only be improved by allocating more space to the river. In addition, measures should be designed so as to take into account undesirable hydromorphological responses by the river system. Based on the experiences during the last centuries this requires flexible, reversible solutions that can be adapted if required and preferably have a local effect. A new type of river management is emerging from this approach. This dynamic river management gives more room to the original hydromorphodynamics of a living river and will only be successful if the river manager is still able to control the hydromorphological developments without eliminating the natural dynamic character of the river system. Less laborious and cheaper monitoring techniques will be needed for the evaluation of dynamic developments, that have to be known for impact containment and forecasting.

## References

Dister, E. 1985. Taschenpolder als Hochwasserschutzmanahme am Oberrhein. GR 37: 241-247 (in German).

Dister, E., Gomer, D., Obrdlik, P., Petermann, P. & Schneider, E. 1990. Water management and ecological perspectives of the Upper Rhine's floodplains. Regulated rivers: research and management 5: 1-15.

Driessen, A.M.A.J. 1994. Watersnood tussen Maas en Waal. Overstromingsrampen in het rivierengebied tussen 1780 en 1810. PhD Thesis. University of Amsterdam, Amsterdam. (in Dutch).

Felkel, E. 1987. Eight years of sediment supply in the Upper Rhine. Wasserwirtschaft 77/4: 181-185.

Hendriksen, E. 1999. Room for Rhine branches. State of affairs. Summary. Ministry of Transport, Public Works and Water Management, Division East, Arnhem.

Huisman, P., Cramer W., Van Ee, G., Hooghart, J.C., Salz, H. & Zuidema, F.C. 1999. Water in the Netherlands. Netherlands Hydrological Society, Delft.

Hunt, C.E. 2000. New approaches to river management in the United States. In: Smits, A.J.M., Nienhuis, P.H. & Leuven, R.S.E.W. (Eds.). New approaches to river management. Backhuys Publishers, Leiden. pp. 119-139.

IKSR. 1993. KHR-Arbeitsgruppe, Der Rhein unter der Einwirkung des Menschen – Ausbau, Schiffahrt, Wasserwirtschaft. Internationale Kommission für die Hydrologie des Rheingebietes. Änthropogene Enflüsse auf das Abflußregime. Internationale Kommission zum Schutze des Rheins (IKSR), Koblenz. (in German).

IKSR. 1997. Hochwasserschutz am Rhein. Bestandsaufname. Internationale Kommission zum Schutze des Rheins (IKSR), Koblenz. (in German).

IKSR. 1998. KÖ-Arbeitsgruppe, Bestandsaufname der ökologische wertvolle Gebiete am Rhein und erste Schritte auf dem Weg zum Biotopverbund. Internationale Kommission zum Schutze des Rheins (IKSR), Koblenz. (in German).

Jansen, P.Ph., Van Bendegom, L., Van den Berg, J., De Vries, M. & Zanen, A. 1979. Principles of river engineering. Pitman Publishing Ltd., London.

Mosonyi, E. 1970. Johann Gottfried Tulla. 10.3.1770-27.3.1828. Gesamtherstellung Badendruck Gmbh, Karlsruhe.

Silva, W. & Kok, M. 1996. Landscape planning river Rhine. Ministry of Transport, Public Works and Water Management, Institute for Inland Water Management and Waste Water Treatment, RIZA, Lelystad.

Smits, A.J.M. & Duel, H. 1999. Cyclic rejuvenations of floodplains. Research proposal within the context of IRMA SPONGE Programme. University of Nijmegen, Nijmegen.

Smits, A.J.M., Havinga, H., & Marteijn, E.C.L. 2000. New concept in river and water management in the Rhine River basin: how to live with the unexpected? In: Smits, A.J.M., Nienhuis, P.H. & Leuven, R.S.E.W. (Eds.). New Approaches to River Management. Backhuys Publishers, Leiden. pp. 267-286.

Van der Ven, G.P. (Ed.) 1993. Leefbaar Laagland. Geschiedenis van de waterbeheersing en lan-daanwining in Nederland. International Commission on irrigation and Drainage (ICID), Koninklijk Instituut van Ingenieurs (KIVI), Afdeling voor Waterbeheer. Utrecht. (in Dutch).

WL|Delft Hydraulics 1998. Rhine in the long term perspective. WL|Delft Hydraulics, Delft. (in Dutch).

WL|Delft Hydraulics 1999. Stedelijke knelpunten. Een verkenning van mogelijke oplossingen. RVR Rapport 99.11. WL|Delft Hydraulics, Delft. (in Dutch).

# STRONGLY POLLUTED DEPOSITS IN THE MEUSE RIVER FLOODPLAIN AND THEIR EFFECTS ON RIVER MANAGEMENT

Schouten, C.J.J., M.C. Rang, B.A. de Hamer & H.R.A. van Hout
*CSO Consultants for environmental management and survey, Regulierenring 20, NL-3981 LB Bunnik, The Netherlands*

## Abstract

Flood risk in the lower Meuse has increased as a result of changes in land and water management practices along with canalisation of the upper Meuse and its tributaries in Belgium and France. The dramatic floods of 1993 and 1995 prompted Dutch government to develop the Delta Plan for Large Rivers. Under this plan, the Dutch State Water Authority and the Province of Limburg launched the Maaswerken project in April 1997. The aims of the Maaswerken were to reduce flooding, to improve navigation and to create new riparian wetlands in the lower Meuse floodplain. Another important major goal of the Maaswerken project is the extraction of gravel and sand. The costs of the Maaswerken project, however, increased dramatically in areas where the floodplain sediments along the Meuse were highly polluted with heavy metals (*e.g.*, zinc, cadmium and lead) and organic contaminants (*e.g.*, PAHs and PCBs). The contaminated sediments represent a form of diffuse pollution and are redistributed during floods. A new policy of dynamic soil management was developed within the Maaswerken project in order to control costs while maintaining the original river management goals and reducing the risk to human health and the environment. In order to develop and apply dynamic soil management successfully, an accurate soil quality distribution map of the polluted sediments was generated.

## 1. Introduction

Flood risk in the Meuse valley has increased as a result of the increase in urban land use combined with the canalisation of the upper parts of the Meuse catchment in Belgium and France. Moreover, the effects of a global climate change on precipitation may result in a further increase of frequency and magnitude of floods. These developments have resulted in extensive measures to improve the safety of the low-lying plains and polders in the Netherlands (The Delta Plan for Large Rivers). The Dutch State Water Authority (Rijkswaterstaat) is involved in planning the combination of improvement of the navigational conditions of the Meuse river for shipping and increasing its capacity to carry floodwaters. Other planned large-scale works within the flood-prone areas are the extraction of gravel and sand along with the creation of new wetlands for nature development alongside the river, in combination with the improvement of its carrying capacity.

In order to prevent flooding, the Dutch government proposed the Delta Plan for Large Rivers. However, investigations during the last 15 years have revealed the pres-

*New approaches to river management, pp. 33–50*
*edited by A.J.M. Smits, P.H. Nienhuis and R.S.E.W. Leuven*
*© 2000 Backhuys Publishers, Leiden, The Netherlands*

ence of strongly polluted sediments throughout the Dutch floodplain of the Meuse river and its tributary, the Geul river. Most of the polluted sediments date back to the industrial revolution in the Meuse basin (early 19th century) and consist of the heavy metals (e.g., zinc, cadmium and lead) and of organic contaminants, *e.g.*, poly-aromatic hydrocarbons (PAHs) and polychlorinated biphenyls (PCBs). The Meuse and Geul rivers redistribute significant amounts of contaminated sediments during floods.

Within the Netherlands alone, strongly polluted sediments cover more than 100 km² of the floodplain. While some of this area is urbanised, most of it is used for agriculture and, hence, these polluted sediments represent a direct risk to human health. Under the strict Dutch Soil Laws, one has to completely remove all contaminated sediments if intervention values are exceeded. If they are impossible to clean, they have to be permanently stored in safe disposal sites. In the Meuse valley, this would mean removing top 0.5 m of large parts of the floodplain.

However, under stringent conditions based on local and regional knowledge and understanding of the soil pollution problems according to the Dutch Soil Laws, the soil may to be used as a building material. A very important condition is that these polluted materials are applied where they do not increase the pollution levels of the surrounding area. To be sure that this condition is met, one must firstly understand the mechanisms behind river sediment transport and then develop an accurate soil/sediment quality map showing the distribution of contamination. Based on such a soil quality map, the regional policy makers were able to develop a new policy of dynamic soil management for the Meuse river floodplain. This policy combines a risk-based remedial works approach combined with a relatively accurate soil quality map to target and remove contamination that represents the highest risk.

This paper reviews the research on soil pollution in the Meuse river floodplain and the development of soil quality maps along with how these results were used to design the dynamic soil management tool for this diffuse polluted area.

## 2. Hydrology of the Meuse river

The Meuse is a rain-fed river, flowing over 900 km from its source in the north-eastern part of France, through the Belgian Ardennes, through the Netherlands, and finally discharging into the North Sea (Figure 1). The Meuse river catchment covers 36,000 km² and is situated in France, Belgium, Germany and the Netherlands. From its source in France, at 400 m altitude, to Maastricht (The Netherlands), at 40 m altitude, the Meuse is an erosive river. This upstream section of the Meuse river has been canalised and contains numerous weirs. Between Maastricht and Maasbracht, the Meuse forms the natural border between Belgium and the Netherlands and is called the Grensmaas. The Grensmaas contains no weirs or dikes and has a unique, wild river character.

Downstream from Maasbracht, the flow rate of the Meuse decreases and the Meuse becomes a sedimentary river, known as the "Zandmaas". In the Zandmaas, suspended load is deposited in the river channel. The Zandmaas is often used for shipping and is also controlled with several weirs and canals. In the Province of Limburg, the Meuse river has no dikes and until 1996, floods in the floodplain were considered to be natural phenomena. The inhabitants were used to the recurrent floods and had adapted their houses and dwellings.

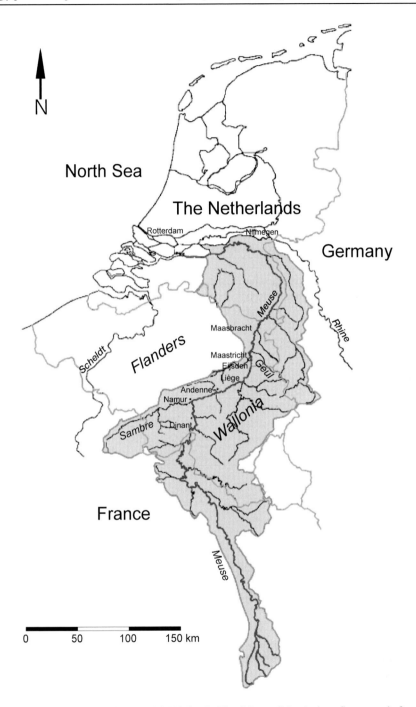

*Fig. 1.* The Meuse river catchment (36,000 km²). The Meuse (Maas) river flows north from its source in France (400 m altitude), through Belgium, Germany, and finally the Netherlands, where it discharges into the North Sea. The Dutch part of the river is divided into two flow regimes: the upper "Grensmaas" (erosive) and the lower "Zandmaas" (sedimentary).

The Meuse has an average flow of 245 m³s⁻¹ (RIWA 1976-1992). It is characterised by a very unstable discharge regime, due to the lengthy shape of the catchment, the steep gradient of its tributaries in the Ardennes, the relatively short storage of groundwater, and the annual variation in evaporation. Average annual discharges range between 74 m³s⁻¹ and 406 m³s⁻¹. Discharge peak values of the Meuse have increased with 10 to 12% during this century. Three reasons for this increase in discharge are:

1. Canalisation of (parts of) the river in France and Belgium as well as normalisation (construction of weirs) in Belgium (Micha & Borlee 1989) and the Netherlands (Ministerie van Verkeer en Waterstaat 1995).
2. Installation of road ditches, which have increased the drainage density in the upper catchment, thereby increasing the discharge values downstream.
3. New urbanisation in Dinant and Liege along with the modernisation of agricultural practices (*e.g.*, in the Dutch part of the Geul valley) has also lead to an increase in the discharge peak values.

For the Geul river, a tributary of the Meuse, Leenaers *et al.* (1988) concluded that moderate floods with a short recurrence time of more than 2 years increased in frequency between 40 and 50% during the last 30 years (Figure 2). The modernisation of agriculture especially has resulted in higher run-off from the slopes in the fertile loess areas of the region (Schouten *et al.* 1985, De Roo 1993).

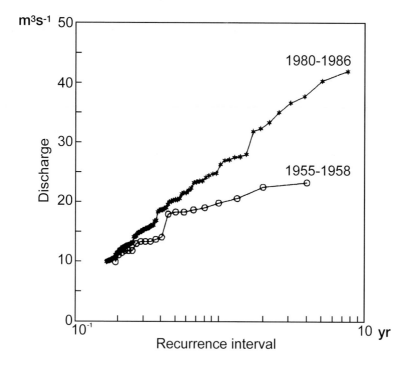

*Fig. 2.* Estimated recurrence interval between floods (years) versus discharge for the Geul river (m³s⁻¹) during two periods, 1955-58 and 1980-86 (Source: Leenaers 1989).

In addition to increasing discharge in the Geul river over the past 30 years, river discharges are expected to increase across Western Europe in the future as well. Global circulation models predict an increase in precipitation, concentrated during the winter period (the rainy season). Coupled with the predicted increase in urbanisation, a study by the "Ministerie van Verkeer en Waterstaat" and WL|Delft Hydraulics (1994) predicts an increase in the Meuse river discharge by 17%.

## 2. Sediment transport during floods

During floods, significant amounts of bed load and suspended load are transported and re-deposited (Figure 3). Due to the growing awareness of the role of suspended sediment in the transportation and deposition of contaminants, much research on floodplain sedimentation (rates) along the Meuse river has been carried out by Rang *et al.* (1985, 1986a,b) and Middelkoop (1997). Studies in the Meuse floodplains show total sediment accumulation increases with flood magnitude (Middelkoop 1997). During a high magnitude flood, deposition is in the order of 1.0 to 2.0 kg m$^{-2}$ for the Meuse river (*i.e.*, a 1 – 2 mm thick layer). The relationship between sediment accumulation and flood magnitude is non-linear and depends on floodplain morphology. For instance, local variations in floodplain elevation cause differences in inundation times. In depressions, sediment accumulation is higher than in other parts of the floodplains with observed sedimentation rates of several centimetres per year (Hoogerwerf & Van Hout 1994).

Fresh sediments in the Meuse river floodplains originate from three distinct sources (Leenaers *et al.* 1988):

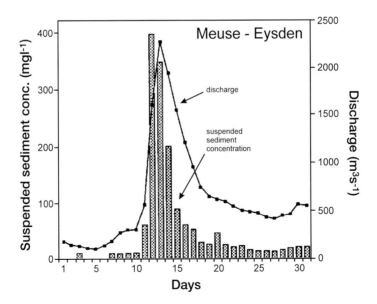

*Fig. 3.* Discharge and suspended sediment concentration of the river Meuse in January 1993 (Middelkoop 1997).

- Harbour mud (black anaerobic mud);
- Aerobic sands, silts and loamy clays derived from soil erosion in the loess covered hills far upstream of the sedimentation area;
- Local floodplain deposits eroded from nearby soils.

During the extended periods of low to average discharge (summer), black, organic-rich, anaerobic mud accumulates in deep parts of the river bed and in harbours with stagnant water. This mud will be flushed and deposited on the floodplains during the rising stage of major floods. The second type is a mixture of fine loamy (loess-type) sediments from upstream areas and gravel and sand derived from the main stream-channels. These sediments are derived from external sources and will accumulate depending on the local water velocity. The third and possibly the most important sources of the fresh floodplain deposits are from nearby bare cropland areas and local sources within the floodplain itself.

During surveys following floods it has been observed that most freshly eroded sediments are re-deposited in nearby areas of the same floodplain. These fresh sediment accumulations are characterised by a light brown colour indicating aerobic conditions.

Over large areas in the Meuse floodplain, locally re-suspended sediments are the main source of the flood deposits (Rang & Schouten 1988). After the 1993 flood, sediment and soil samples over 26 locations were analysed for heavy metals. According to a geo-statistical analysis correlating the concentrations of heavy metals with sample location, flood deposits show a higher correlation with nearby sediments, and not with flood deposits across the entire floodplain (Hoogerwerf & Van Hout 1994, 1995a). This means that the considerable variation of pollution over a certain area of floodplain, resulting from historic fluvial redeposition processes, is generally reflected in the amount of pollution present in fresh flood deposits. The overall variation in concentration of suspended matter from samples taken within the river is much smaller. It shows that the origin of most of the fresh sediment deposits is from a very local source and not the suspended matter from far upstream sources. This means that as long as the upper soil of the floodplain is strongly contaminated with heavy metals, the fresh flood deposits will be similarly polluted. Remediation of industrial sources of soil pollution in the floodplain will therefore be ineffective unless the upper 50 cm of the soil is completely cleaned.

## 3. Contamination in flood deposits of the Meuse river

Other sources of contaminated flood deposits include agricultural activities and the urban regions (no sewage treatment). Some of the original major industrial and coal-mining sources of contamination have disappeared for years now, but their pollutants are still moving through the river system. Floodplain and riverbank erosion during major floods release older layers of polluted deposits to be re-deposited elsewhere on the floodplain.

Since the Meuse river flows through the Ardennes, where these metals occur in the rocks, the sediments naturally contain heavy metals like zinc, cadmium and lead. Levels of these background concentrations are very low, causing no significant human- or eco-toxicological risks (Hakstege *et al*. 1993). Like many European rivers, the Meuse has been used as an open sewage system for the last centuries. With the rise of industry in the Liege area from 1820 onwards, the Meuse river became increasingly polluted and the aquatic ecosystem was virtually destroyed. Not only dissolved matters but also polluted sewage-sludge as well as solid wastes and colliery waste has been dumped in the river. Salomons *et al.* (1982) reports the concentrations of heavy metals which are transported by the rivers Rhine and Meuse to the Netherlands. They show for the Rhine river an increase of metal concentrations since 1900 with a peak around 1970. About two-thirds of the metal load accumulates in the freshwater basins and floodplains before the rivers discharges into the North Sea.

The enrichment of the sediments with heavy metals in the Meuse river reached its climax much earlier than in the Rhine (Rang *et al.* 1986b). From studies of sediment pollution in relation to soil development in the Dutch part of the Meuse valley, it can be concluded that sediment pollution, began more than 350 years ago. It reached its peak about 100 years ago in the late nineteenth century (Rang & Schouten 1989, Hakstege *et al.* 1993).

Besides heavy metals, flood deposits of the Meuse river contain organic contaminants such as mineral oil, PAHs, PCAs, PCBs and HCB (Busser *et al.* 1986, RIZA 1984, Hoogerwerf & Van Hout 1994). The contamination may form a direct threat to public health and to the ecosystem. Some of these contaminants originate from local sources, such as leaking oil tanks or the use of agricultural pesticides on agricultural land. PAHs and PCBs may be related to coal mining in the Meuse catchment. Other sources include agricultural activities and the urban regions with no sewage treatment facilities. Some of the original major industrial and coal mining sources of contamination have disappeared for years now, but their pollution is still moving through the river system. Floodplain and riverbank erosion during major floods released older layers of polluted deposits to be re-deposited elsewhere on the floodplain.

Sediment sampling surveys in Belgium two days after the flood of 1995 (Table 1) revealed that the fresh Meuse flood deposits upstream from Liege are much less polluted than downstream (Hoogerwerf & Van Hout 1995b). Figure 4 shows the sample locations and Table 1 shows concentrations of some contaminants of flood samples taken during 1995. Concentrations of zinc, lead, cadmium and PAHs increase downstream. Concentrations of zinc exceed the Dutch intervention level at the locations in the industrial area of Liege. PAH concentrations increase at Namur as a result of coal mining activities along the Sambre in the Charleroi area. Liege is the main source of heavy metal contamination in the Meuse river sediments.

The Geul river, is the main point source in the Netherlands of the Meuse river heavy metals. The Geul river is responsible for 9.7% of the lead-load in the Meuse river downstream of Maastricht, as well as 7.8% of the zinc-load and 4.7% of the cadmium-load (Leenaers 1989). Geul river sediment pollution originates from former ore mining activities in the Belgian part of the catchment. The heavy metals in Geul sediments are present mainly in the sand fraction as the contamination originates from mine tailings (Leenaers *et al.* 1988). There is a clear decrease in concentrations along the banks of the Geul river in the downstream direction. The bulk of the contaminated sediment has not yet reached the confluence of the Geul and the Meuse rivers, just downstream of Maastricht.

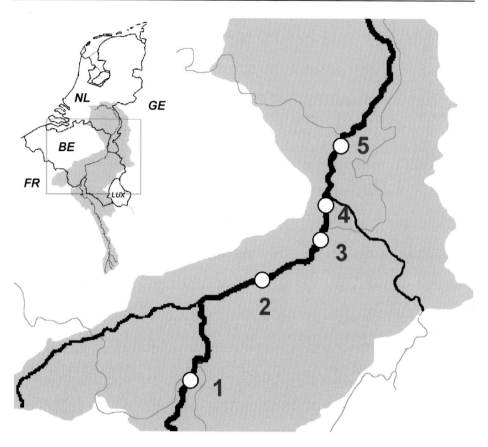

*Fig. 4.* Sampling locations of the 1995 flood in the Meuse catchment (see table 1). BE: Belgium; FR: France; GE: Germany; LUX: Luxemburg; NL: The Netherlands.

*Table 1.* Concentrations of zinc, cadmium, and lead (mg kg$^{-1}$) in flood deposits of the 1995 flood (for geographical location of sampling sites see figure 4).

| No. | Location | Zn | Cd | Pb |
|-----|----------|-----|-----|-----|
| 1 | Border with France | 311 | <0.23 | 50 |
| 2 | Andenne | 669 | <0.32 | 94 |
| 3 | Border with Netherlands | 3,092 | 8.7 | 444 |
| 4 | Maastricht | 1,039 | 10 | 200 |
| 5 | Maasbracht | 843 | 4.6 | 230 |

The heavy metals from the Meuse are mostly derived from liquid industrial wastes and the contamination concentrates in the clay fraction of the sediment. This results in a clear relationship in the Meuse sediments between the percentage soil fraction less than 2 μm and the concentration of heavy metals, but a rather weak relationship with distance to the source of the pollution, the industrial region of Liege.

## 3.1 Trends in sediment contamination

As a result of the introduction of strict environmental laws concerning the dumping of toxic substances into the rivers within Europe, water quality has generally improved in the Rhine river. The water quality of the Meuse, including the quality of suspended material, has also improved in recent years (Van Leusen *et al.* 1995). In particular, concentrations of zinc and cadmium during low and moderate flows have decreased considerably since 1980 (RIZA 1995).

In contrast to the Rhine river, the concentrations of organic toxic substances have not improved much in the Meuse. The old steel furnaces and heavy metal-producing industry in the Wallonia region, especially around Liege, have collapsed and the coal mining industry has ceased to exist. The sewage discharge to the Meuse from Wallonia is still largely untreated. There remain a few major sources of industrial heavy metal pollution, but very likely this is only minor in comparison to the magnitude of pollution released during the nineteenth century. Although, zinc and cadmium concentrations may have dropped slightly since 1984, different floodplain sediment studies conclude that no overall improvement of flood sediment quality took place during the last decade (Hoogerwerf & Van Hout 1995a).

Because of the differences in origin of the sediments discussed earlier in this paper, it is not possible to draw significant conclusions on the overall changes in sediment quality from samples taken in the floodplain. Also, highly contaminated sediments deposited in the floodplain affect the quality of floodplain sediments long-term (Rang & Schouten 1988). In fact, if the frequency of small floods increases, the quality of the transported sediments may even decrease as a result of stream-bank erosion of older, polluted deposits (Leenaers & Schouten 1989). Sediments deposited during normal flow at the weirs at Maastricht and Maasbracht are reasonable indicators of the quality of the freshly derived sediments from Belgium. When monitoring the quality of sediments over a period of time at these weirs, a much better indicator will be developed on the quality development of the recently supplied sediments from Belgium (Hoogerwerf & Van Hout 1995a).

## 3.2 Distribution of heavy metals in the Meuse river floodplain

Downstream from Liege, the first major opportunity for the river to deposit sediments is at Maastricht, where the Meuse floodplain is widening. During major floods, thick layers of strongly polluted sediments have locally been deposited in the floodplain behind the weir of Maastricht. This is the area on the map of figure 5. Onwards from Maasbracht, the quality of the sediments slightly improves and the area of strongly polluted soils (Hoogerwerf & Van Hout 1995a) is restricted to recent channel fills and borders alongside the Meuse.

As a result of the relatively recent increase of pollution during the last two centuries the concentrations of heavy metals decrease with depth in most soil types.

The highest concentrations are found in the top 20 cm of the soil. After being deposited during a flood, the fresh deposits are mixed with the topsoil in a matter

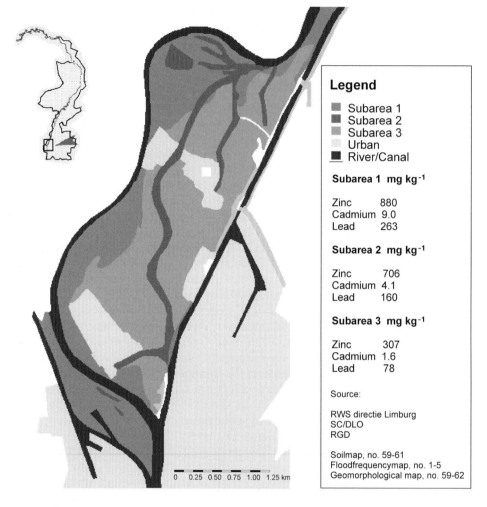

**Legend**

- Subarea 1
- Subarea 2
- Subarea 3
- Urban
- River/Canal

**Subarea 1  mg kg$^{-1}$**

Zinc        880
Cadmium  9.0
Lead        263

**Subarea 2  mg kg$^{-1}$**

Zinc        706
Cadmium  4.1
Lead        160

**Subarea 3  mg kg$^{-1}$**

Zinc        307
Cadmium  1.6
Lead        78

Source:

RWS directie Limburg
SC/DLO
RGD

Soilmap, no. 59-61
Floodfrequencymap, no. 1-5
Geomorphological map, no. 59-62

0    0.25  0.50  0.75  1.00  1.25 km

*Fig. 5.* Soil quality probability map of the Meuse floodplain downstream of the weir of Maastricht.

of weeks (Rang & Schouten 1987). This mixing occurs by ploughing and biological activity, which have caused a considerable increase in the heavy metal concentration of the topsoil over the years. At a depth of approximately 50 cm beneath surface level though, concentrations have decreased to 20 – 25% of the upper soil layer (Rang & Schouten 1989). In isolated meanders and other former stream channels that have been filled during the last centuries, the depth of strongly polluted soils may reach to up to four meters.

## 3.3 Geo-statistical relationships

At various field sites along the Meuse river in the Netherlands, a strong, positive relationship has been found between frequency of flooding, soil type and concentrations of heavy metals and PAHs. In areas with the highest flood frequencies, the highest concentrations of heavy metals were found (Rang *et al.* 1985, Crul & Heunks 1993, Hemel *et al.* 1996). The highest concentrations were found in floodplains with a flood frequency of once in every two years. A negative relationship has been found between local elevations and pollution; soils in lower gullies and old stream channels have higher metal concentrations than in surrounding higher areas (Rang *et al.* 1985, Crul & Heunks 1993). These lower gullies consist mainly of clays, which are known for their heavy metal binding capacity.

*3.4 Pollution prediction maps*

In 1994, the Dutch State Water Authority realised that they needed to have accurate soil pollution maps in order to estimate the problems and possible expenses related to the diffuse pollution in the floodplains. One of the conclusions from the studies on the occurrence of heavy metals in the river bed of the Meuse river during the winter was the possibility of producing soil quality probability maps with a high percentage explained variance. By dividing the floodplain into flood frequency classes, a probability map can be made in which the mean soil-quality per flood frequency class can be estimated with a reasonable accuracy and reliability (Figure 5). A geographic information system (GIS) survey was carried out in order to produce a probability map of polluted sediments (Hoogvliet & Rang 1999). Using the various statistical relationships in combination with geomorphologic and soil information, maps have been produced for the whole Dutch portion of the Meuse river floodplain with an accuracy of 80% and a reliability of 90% (Figure 5).

## 4. Measures to prevent future damage from flooding

*4.1 The floods of 1993 and 1995*

During the last decade, two major floods (1993 and 1995) occurred, causing an enormous economic loss. In contrast to the risks in the lower parts of the Netherlands, there was no serious threat of lives as people could be moved in time to higher ground. The total costs of the damage during the 1993 flood of the Meuse river was estimated to be about 250 million Dutch Guilder (125 million $US) (Ministerie van Verkeer en Waterstaat & WL|Delft Hydraulics 1994).

After the big flood of 1926, no real major events occurred for a long period. After 1950 the municipalities allowed widespread urban development and new industrial projects within the high flood-risk areas. Regional inhabitants had no distinct memory of the older floods, which as a matter of fact, rarely caused major damage because the older houses in the area were build to resist serious damage from flooding. Politicians and other decision-makers ignored the warnings of the State Water Authority officials. This was made easy, due to important financial interests of the municipalities and landowners and there was a shortage of houses after the war.

The next large flood in 1993 struck the Limburg region very hard. About 18,000 hectares of land was inundated creating problems for 13,000 people and 2,000 businesses. New urban areas with houses with modern facilities at the street level, expensive floor carpets, electrical appliances etc were inundated. The fast flowing muddy waters seriously damaged kitchens, carports etc. The same counted for several small businesses who faced bankruptcy after the damage and the lost days. The two floods prompted the Ministerie van Verkeer en Waterstaat (1995) to adjust recurrence times for the Meuse river discharge levels (Table 2). This adjustment made it clear that the expectancy of dramatic floods was considerably higher than thought, and that the risks of serious damage to property had even risen more as a result of building activities in the floodplain. Politically, the flood events of 1993 and 1995 resulted in strong public pressure to provide more protection for the inhabitants of threatened areas along the great rivers. The Dutch Parliament rapidly approved the Delta Plan for the Large Rivers. This cluster of plans included the building of embankments along the part of the Meuse river that was not protected by dikes, in combination with stream channel enlargement. The embankments were constructed with great speed during 1996 and have been finished. Keeping the main objectives of the flood protection scheme in mind, the authorities combined two large existing sub-projects concerning the Meuse river (Ministerie van Verkeer en Waterstaat 1997, Provincie Limburg 1998a,b, Van Leussen *et al.* 2000).

The first was the Grensmaas sub-project. In the section between Maastricht and Roosteren studies were carried out by the Province of Limburg to extract large quantities of gravel and to create a broader shallow river channel with marshes and large-scale nature development (Provincie Limburg 1998a,b).

The second sub-project is the Zandmaas/Maasroute project whose original aim was to improve the shipping route along the Meuse river over a length of 222 km. The important canals such as the Juliana Canal (parallel to the Grensmaas) and the Lateral Canal and Maas-Waal Canal were therefore included. The Zandmaas project was started under direction of the Dutch Ministry of Public Works. The main aim of the Zandmaas project is to enlarge the stream channel to protect the surroundings against floods. In this project, only limited nature development was planned.

Although objectives and responsible authorities were different in both sub-projects it was decided in 1995 to amalgamate them and still keep the objectives in tact. The advantage of this integration is that double work and double costs could be avoided while all expertise could be bundled. In addition to the original objectives, the sub-project also included the concepts of sustainable and balanced integration

*Table 2.* Recurrence times of serious decisive flood-peaks (in years) at Maastricht, the Netherlands (Ministerie van Verkeer en Waterstaat 1995). The peak discharge at a frequency of 1/1,250 years is the discharge that Dutch dikes north of Limburg must be able to handle. Since there are ample possibilities in the Limburg Meuse valley to flee to higher grounds, a peak discharge with a recurrence interval of 1/250 year is chosen as decisive in Limburg.

|  | Discharge peak December 1993 ($3,120$ m$^3$ s$^{-1}$) | Discharge peak January 1995 ($2,870$ m$^3$ s$^{-1}$) |
|---|---|---|
| **Before the 1993 flood** | ± 210 years | ± 100 years |
| **After the 1995 flood** | ± 125 years | ± 65 years |

of agriculture, recreation, nature, provision of drinking water, shipping and sand and gravel extraction for both sub-projects. As a result, employees from various services of the Department of Public Works (State Water Authority), the Province of Limburg, and the Ministry of Agriculture, Nature Conservation and Fisheries formed a new organisation called: The "Maaswerken".

### 4.2 The Maaswerken

The aims of the Maaswerken are to:
– Reduce the risk of major flooding in urban areas to 1/250 years;
– Improve navigation;
– Create natural riparian areas in the floodplains;
– Extract gravel and sand for use as construction materials elsewhere.

In order to reach these goals, the river channel will be broadened and deepened (Province of Limburg 1998a,b). Part of the floodplain will be lowered and new channels will be excavated (Figure 6). Older channels (meander branches) filled with recent sediments will be restored. This fits within the national and international policy of enlarging the carrying capacity of rivers and of ecological recovery. About 1,000 hectares of agricultural land will be transformed into new wetlands and other nature areas.

### 4.3 Problems for the Maaswerken resulting from soil pollution

Before the first systematic pollution mapping surveys between 1983 and 1989 by Utrecht University (Rang & Schouten 1989), there was little or no awareness of the scale of the problem of heavy metal pollution in the Meuse river floodplain. Nor was there any limitation on the application and the transport of soil materials from that area to other areas.

The strong Dutch soil protection laws developed during the eighties made it virtually impossible to carry out large-scale development and building activities in the floodplains without breaking the law. The sediments in large parts of the Meuse river floodplain exceed the intervention level of the Dutch soil qualification system, thus causing potential human and ecological risk (Leenaers 1989). Excessively high soil removal costs ranging between 60 and 150 Dutch guilder per ton at minor construction works were the result. For example, the large-scale diffuse pollution of the floodplains of the large Dutch rivers resulted in stagnation of the river widening and nature development projects. Also in the small towns and cities (partly) situated in the active floodplain construction works of roads, bridges or buildings became very difficult and costly because of the remedial costs of the polluted soil (removal and transport to disposal sites).

During the Maaswerken projects, large quantities of materials will have to be removed or relocated. The benefits from the sale of the gravel will reduce the costs of the Maaswerken significantly, but the seriously polluted floodplains are a threat to the projects' budget. Using soil quality probability maps, an estimate of the amount of polluted sediments to be removed as well as a cost calculation can be made.

## 4.4 Dynamic soil management in the Meuse valley

In order to prevent further serious stagnation and extreme increases in project expenses, the Dutch State Water Authority, in collaboration with the Province of Limburg, has formulated a new policy. In this policy rules and guidelines to work with polluted soils in the floodplain of the Meuse are presented (Rang 1998, Hakstege *et al.* 1998, Hoogvliet & Rang 1999). This policy is based on a risk assessment approach and a more flexible interpretation of the Dutch Soil Protection Law for diffuse river-bound regional pollution, characteristic of the floodplains and local point-source pollution (hot spots). Occasionally there are sediment hot spots with extremely high concentrations of the same pollutants, characteristic of the diffuse pollution. Since the floodplains of the large rivers are contaminated as a result of diffuse pollution, it is impossible to remove all polluted sediments in the floodplains. There are not enough locations for disposal due to public opposition against new disposal sites and the high costs involved (Hakstege *et al.* 1998). Therefore, the Dutch Government has decided that pollution levels in the floodplains must be reduced to the river-specific background levels instead of reduction to the national reference values. This approach is based on actual risks instead of potential risks. Various studies on the bio-availability of the heavy metals show that this risk is generally low in the lime and organic-rich clay soils of the floodplain (Leenaers *et al.* 1988).
Two principles form the base of the policy for the diffuse polluted soils:
–  An increase in risk levels as a result of the construction works must be prevented.
–  Risks to human health and the environment will be reduced as much as possible.

As long as polluted soils do not increase the overall risk, they may be re-used as much as possible within the floodplain area. This approach opens up the possibilities of re-using polluted sediments in local civil works where pollution already exists, reducing costs and risks at the same time. Removal or isolation of the strongly contaminated sediments should reduce the total emission of contaminants resulting from erosion and solution or dispersion after the work has been carried out. For example, the highly contaminated (loamy and clay-rich) sediments from the floodplains near Maastricht can be used as filling material in the local holes created by former and new gravel extractions (Figure 6), or for the construction of embankments and new dikes. The elongated gravel pits, filled with the contaminated clays, will act as barrier for groundwater discharging into the river and will result in a higher groundwater table. Raising the groundwater table will restore former riparian wetlands as natural areas along the Meuse.

Dynamic soil management has another benefit. The application of the highly polluted topsoil and channel fill, by using the material in clay pits outside the reach of the erosive force of floodwaters, will reduce the amount of polluted materials that are re-suspended during the major floods. As Wallonian industries inside the Meuse catchment reduce the total amount of waste they discharge in compliance with European Union rules, a gradual decrease in heavy metal pollution in the sediments derived from upstream areas is also expected to occur. This lowering of pollution levels of the fresh sediments will benefit the new riparian ecosystems of the Meuse valley. The quality of dredged mud in the harbours and waterways in the lower part of the Meuse catchment may show a similar improvement.

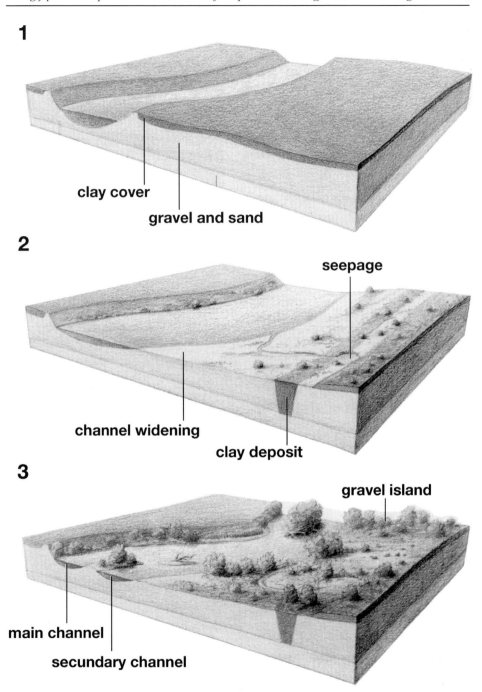

*Fig. 6.* Schematic presentation of flood defence measures and habitat creation along the Meuse river: 1) Present situation; 2) Channel widening and clay deposit; 3) Nature development, (Source: Provincie Limburg 1998a).

The lessons learned in dealing with the problems of diffuse polluted soils in the floodplain of the Meuse river are applicable in the river systems of the Rhine as well (Salomons *et al.* 1982).

## 5. Conclusions

Some of the major lessons with regards to the soil pollution learned during the Maaswerken project are:
- Standard soil regulations in the Netherlands should not be applied to river sediments because sediment contamination is too widespread and it remains in the river system for centuries. Because the laws require such extreme remedial goals, remedial work projects are often too cost prohibitive to be completed.
- To manage contaminated sediments, one must first understand the mechanisms behind river sediment transport and then develop an accurate soil/sediment quality map showing the distribution of contamination.
- Based on the distribution map of soil contamination, an appropriate and effective management policy can be developed. For the Maaswerken, policy makers developed dynamic soil management, a risk-based remedial approach combined with an accurate soil quality map to target and remove contamination that represents the highest risk and to control costs of cleaning up operations while maintaining the original soil pollution and river management goals..

## 6. Acknowledgements

The Maaswerken is acknowledged for the use of various materials and figures.

## References

Busser, F.J.M., Sinnige, Th.L. & Seinen, W. 1986. Inventariserend onderzoek naar het voorkomen van organische microverontreinigingen in grondmonsters uit de overstromingsvlakte van de Maas. Deelrapport 3. In: Seinen, W. & Schouten C.J. (Eds.) Inventariserend onderzoek "microverontreinigingen Maasoevers. Vakgroep Veterinaire Farmacologie, Farmacie en Toxicologie, Universiteit van Utrecht, Utrecht. (in Dutch).

Crul, R.A. & Heunks, E. 1993. Risico-evaluatie voor de volksgezondheid en het milieu ten aanzien van bodemverontreiniging met cadmium, zink en lood in de inundatievlakte van de Maas. Publication 95.018, Physical Geography Department, Utrecht University, Utrecht. (in Dutch).

De Roo, A.P.J. 1993. Modelling surface runoff and soil erosion in catchments using geographical information systems. Validity and applicability of the 'Answers' model in two catchments in the loess area of South Limburg (The Netherlands) and one in Devon (UK). Koninklijk Nederlands Aardrijkskundig Genootschap; Utrecht.

Hakstege, A.L., Kroonenberg, S.B. & Van Wijck, H. 1993. Geochemistry of Holocene clays of the Rhine and Meuse rivers in the central-eastern Netherlands. Geologie en Mijnbouw 71: 301-315.

Hakstege, A.L., Heynen, J.J.M., Eenhoorn, J.K. & Versteeg, H.P. 1998. Strategies for management of contaminated sediments within the Meuse river system. Water Sci. Tech. 37/6-7: 419-424.

Hemel, R.B.J., Leushuis, H. & De Ridder, J. 1996. Maasmetalen. Publication Physical Geography Department, University of Utrecht, Utrecht. (in Dutch).

Hoogerwerf, M.R. & Van Hout, H.R.A. 1994. Bemonstering van het hoogwaterslib van de Maas in het beheersgebied van Rijkswaterstaat Directie Limburg. CSO rapport 94.017 en 94.017a. CSO Adviesbureau voor Milieuonderzoek, Bunnik. (in Dutch).

Hoogerwerf, M.R. & Van Hout, H.R.A. 1995a. Bemonstering van het hoogwaterslib van de Maas in het beheersgebied van Rijkswaterstaat Directie Limburg. CSO rapport 95.092. CSO Adviesbureau voor Milieuonderzoek, Bunnik. (in Dutch).

Hoogerwerf, M.R. & Van Hout, H.R.A. 1995b. Bemonstering van het hoogwaterslib 1995 van de Maas in België. CSO rapport 95.256. CSO Adviesbureau voor Milieuonderzoek, Bunnik. (in Dutch).

Hoogvliet, M.C. & Rang, M.C. 1999. Bodemzoneringskaart Maasdal. CSO rapport 99.364. Onderzoeksrapportage van CSO Adviesbureau voor Milieuonderzoek in opdracht van de Provincie Limburg en de Rijkswaterstaat Directie Limburg, Bunnik. (in Dutch).

Leenaers H. 1989. The dispersal of metal mining wastes in the catchment of the river Geul (Belgium-The Netherlands) Netherlands. Geographical Studies, Koninklijk Nederlands Aardrijkskundig Genootschap, Utrecht.

Leenaers, H., Schouten, C.J. & Rang, M.C. 1988. Variability of the metal content of flood deposits. Environ. Geol. Water. Sci. 11/1: 95-106.

Leenaers, H. & Schouten, C.J. 1989. Soil erosion and floodplain soil pollution: Related problems in the geographical context of a river basin. In: Sediments and the environment. Proceedings of the 1989 Baltimore Symposium. IAHS Publication 184. International Association of Hydrological Sciences (IAHS), Washington.

Micha, J.C. & Borlee, M.C. 1989. Evidence for historical heavy metal pollution in floodplain soils in the Meuse. In: Petts, G.E., Moeller, H. & Roux, A.L. (Eds.) Historical change of large alluvial rivers: Western Europe. John Wiley and Sons, Chichester. pp. 269-296.

Middelkoop, H.1997. Embanked floodplains in the Netherlands. Geomorphological evolution over various time scales. Netherlands Geographical Studies, Koninklijk Nederlands Aardrijkskundig Genootschap, Utrecht.

Ministerie van Verkeer en Waterstaat & WL | Delft Hydraulics. 1994. Onderzoek watersnood Maas, hoofdrapport "De Maas Meester". Rapportage Commissie Boertien, Delft. (in Dutch).

Ministerie van Verkeer en Waterstaat. 1995. De Maas slaat weer toe. Verslag hoogwater Maas januari / februari 1995. Ministerie van Verkeer en Waterstaat, Directoraal-Generaal Rijkswaterstaat, Maastricht (in Dutch).

Ministerie van Verkeer en Waterstaat. 1997. Zandmaas/Maasroute. Ministerie van Verkeer en Waterstaat, Directoraal-Generaal Rijkswaterstaat, Maastricht. (in Dutch).

Provincie Limburg. 1998a. MER Grensmaas hoofdrapport A, hoofdlijnen. Provincie Limburg, Maastricht. (in Dutch).

Provincie Limburg 1998)b. Streekplanherziening Grensmaasgebied. Provincie Limburg, Maastricht. (in Dutch).

Rang, M.C., Schouten, C.J. & Kleijn, C.E. 1985. Bodemverontreiniging met zware metalen in een deel van het winterbed van de Maas. Geografisch Tijdschrift 5: 399-409. (in Dutch).

Rang, M.C., Kleijn, C.E. & Schouten, C.J. 1986a. Mapping of soil pollution by application of classical geomorphological and pedological field techniques. In: Gardiner, V. (Ed.) International geomorphology. Proceedings of the first international conference on Geomorphology, Manchester. John Wiley Press, Cambridge. pp. 1029-1044.

Rang, M.C., Kleijn, C.E. & Schouten, C.J. 1986b. Historical changes in the enrichment of fluvial deposits with heavy metals. In: Lerner, D. (Ed.). Monitoring to detect changes in water quality series. IAHS publication 157, Proceedings of the 1986 Budapest conference IAHS. International Association of Hydrological Sciences (IAHS), Washington. pp. 47-59.

Rang, M.C. & Schouten, C.J. 1988. Major obstacles to water quality management. Part 2: Hydroinertia. Verhandlungen Internat. Verein. Limnol 23: 1482-1487.

Rang, M.C. & Schouten, C.J. 1989. Evidence for historical heavy metal pollution in floodplain soils in the Meuse. In: Petts, G.E., Moeller, H. & Roux, A.L. (Eds.) Historical change of large alluvial rivers: Western Europe. John Wiley and Sons, Chichester. pp. 127-143.

Rang, M.C. 1998. Bouwstenen voor de operationalisering van aktief bodembeheer in het Maasdal. CSO rapport RS014.97. CSO Adviesbureau voor Milieuonderzoek, Bunnik. (in Dutch).

RIWA 1976-1992. Rapportages over de samenstelling van het Maaswater 1976 – 1998. Vereniging van Rivierwaterbedrijven, Amsterdam. (in Dutch).

RIZA 1984. Onderzoek naar de kwaliteit van het slib van de uiterwaarden van de Maas. Institute for Inland Water Management and Waste Water Treatment – RIZA, Rijkswaterstaat, Lelystad. (in Dutch).

RIZA 1995. Resultaten van het waterkwaliteitsonderzoek in de Maas in Nederland 1974 – 1993. Nota 95.018, Institute for Inland Water Management and Waste Water Treatment – RIZA, Rijkswaterstaat, Lelystad. (in Dutch).

Salomons, W., Van Driel, W., Kerdijk, H. & Boxma, R. 1982. Help! Holland is plated by the Rhine. In: Perry, R. (Ed.). Effects of waste disposal on groundwater. Proceedings of a symposium held during the first Scientific General Assembly of the IAHS in Exeter. IAHS Publication139. International Association of Hydrological Sciences (IAHS), Washington. pp. 255-269.

Schouten, C.J. M.C. Rang & P.M.J. Huigen. 1985. Erosie en wateroverlast in Zuid-Limburg. In: Landschap - Tijdschrift voor Landschapsecologie en Milieukunde 2/2: 118-132 (in Dutch).

Van Leusen, S.M., Albering, H.J. & Kleinjans, J.C.S. 1995. The environmental quality of the river Meuse. Department of Health Risk Analysis and Toxicology, University of Limburg, Maastricht.

Van Leussen, W., Kater, G. & Van Meel, P. .2000. Multi-level approach to master the floods in the Dutch part of the River Meuse. In: Smits, A.J.M., Nienhuis, P.H. & Leuven, R.S.E.W. (Eds.). New Approaches to River Management. Backhuys Publishers, Leiden. pp. 287-305.

# THREE CENTURIES OF RIVER MANAGEMENT ALONG THE MISSISSIPPI RIVER: ENGINEERING AND HYDROLOGICAL ASPECTS

G.E. Galloway Jr.
*International Joint Commission (United States and Canada), 1250 23rd St. NW, Washington DC 20440, The United States of America*

## Abstract

The Mississippi river basin drains 41% of the contiguous United States of America and is 65% larger than that of China's Yangtze and nearly three times that of India's Ganges. Its projected flood discharge of 85,000 $m^3s^{-1}$ creates enormous challenges for those who live along its floodplain; its average discharge of 15,000 $m^3s^{-1}$, provides similar challenges for those who use the river for navigation and seek to protect its natural resources. For nearly 300 years, these individuals have attempted to control some aspects of the river's character and attempted to live with others. Over the years, the balance between control and adaptation to the river has shifted. Today, those who deal with the river reap the benefits of years of earlier efforts and look out on problems created with these same efforts. Many lessons have been learned and adjustments are now being applied in the management of the river system. Advanced, work-with-nature, river engineering techniques, non-structural approaches to flood damage reduction, environmental enhancement and impact mitigation, increased public involvement, and comprehensive planning have become routine. In the aggregate, these adjustments point toward a sustainable future for the Mississippi.

## 1. Introduction

*"The military engineers of the Commission have taken upon their shoulders the job of making the Mississippi over again a job transcended in size by only the original job of creating it. ... One who knows the Mississippi will promptly aver – not aloud, but to himself – that ten thousand River Commissions, with the minds of the world at their back, cannot tame that lawless stream, cannot curb it or confine it..."* (Mark Twain 1883).

The Mississippi river is the largest, longest, and most important river in North America. The flows of the Mississippi as well as the management of these flows are vital to commerce and life along the river. For nearly three centuries, military and civilian engineers, planners and scientists have worked with and against this mighty river. They have seen successes and witnessed failures and learned from both. The challenge remains.

This paper outlines the myriad efforts that have been made to control the Mississippi and the adjustments that have been accomplished to accommodate

*New approaches to river management, pp. 51–64*
*edited by A.J.M. Smits, P.H. Nienhuis and R.S.E.W. Leuven*
*© 2000 Backhuys Publishers, Leiden, The Netherlands*

Twain's (1883) warnings about the difficulty of taming the mighty river. Management of the river was and will remain a necessary component of human occupance of the Mississippi valley and the use of the river's resources. Experience has revealed that many problems in dealing with the river could have been avoided, had those who were dealing with the river only had the benefits of today's knowledge. This newfound knowledge, however, will permit more sustainable management of the river, and rivers like it, in the years to come.

## 2. The Mississippi river basin – land and people

From its headwaters in upper Minnesota at lake Itasca, the Mississippi runs 3,700 km to its mouth in the Gulf of Mexico, some 145 km below New Orleans, Louisiana. The Mississippi river drainage basin is the fourth largest in the world, over 3,60,000 km², and includes 41% (portions of 31 states) of the contiguous United States of America (USA) and parts of two Canadian provinces (Figure 1). The Mississippi basin stretches from the Rocky Mountains in the West to the Appalachian Mountains in the East. Tributaries of the Mississippi include the second and third largest rivers in the USA, the Ohio and Missouri, as well as numerous smaller, yet still imposing rivers (Table 1). The Missouri river stretches from near St. Louis Missouri, to the Northwest into the Rocky Mountains. The Ohio flows from the Northeast, joining with the Mississippi near the town of Cairo at the southern tip of the state of Illinois.

The upper Mississippi river begins near the Canadian border and flows South to its confluence with the Ohio. The river is frequently divided into three segments: the

*Fig. 1.* Mississippi river basin.

*Table 1.* Mississippi basin catchment areas.

| Catchment | River length (km) | Mean flow (m³s⁻¹) | Catchment area (km²) |
|---|---|---|---|
| Upper Mississippi | 3,093 | | 390,000 |
| Missouri | 4,090 | 2,300 | 1,371,000 |
| Ohio | 2,100 | 7,870 | 419,000 |
| Lower Mississippi | 1,580 | 16,510 | 269,000 |
| Arkansas | 2,350 | 2,067 | 608,000 |

headwaters, from the origin at lake Itasca to St. Paul, Minnesota, 805 km; the upper Mississippi from St Paul to the mouth of the Missouri, just north of St. Louis, 1,874 km; and the middle Mississippi, from the Missouri to the Ohio, 314 km.

Just north of the junction of the Ohio and the Mississippi, the alluvial valley of the Mississippi river begins. This valley of 90,650 km², falls from an elevation of 91.5 m above Mean Surface Level (MSL) at Cairo to sea level at the Gulf of Mexico some 1,580 river km distant. Between Cairo and Vicksburg, it is joined by the Arkansas river. The valley varies in width from 32 km to 129 km across with an average width of 73 km. At Vicksburg, Mississippi, 874 km to the south of Cairo, the mean annual flow is nominally 16,510 m³s⁻¹, however; a flood flow of 64,500 m³s⁻¹ has been recorded. At a distance of 485 km above the Mississippi's mouth at the Gulf of Mexico, the Mississippi flows are shared with its principal distributary, the Atchafalaya river. This division results in the Atchafalaya receiving, on an average, approximately 30 percent of the flow at that latitude while the remaining 70 percent is carried by the main Mississippi channel.

The Mississippi and its tributaries have played a major role in the USA history. Their existence was critical to the growth of the Mid-west region and eventual movement to the Far West. It also fostered the development of major cities and a transportation network linking the region to the rest of the world. The floodplains of these rivers provide some of the most productive farmland in the country. They offer diverse recreational opportunities and contain important ecological systems. The earliest inhabitants of the Mississippi valley were native American indians, who roamed through its vast lands giving due acknowledgement to its power. Large mounds of earth, piled high by the Indians, dot the valley floor having served as ceremonial grounds and high water shelter from annual floods. European settlement, which began in earnest in the 18th century, used the Mississippi as the principal artery from the North (English and French), the South (Spanish and French) and the East by way of the Ohio river (English, German). The later expansion into the western lands of North America followed the courses of the Missouri, Arkansas, and Red rivers from their confluences with the Mississippi (Harrison 1961).

## 3. Initial intervention

Settlers along the banks of the Mississippi and within its valley quickly recognised the difficult nature of the river. It continually hampered river traffic with its snags, migrating river channels, and moving sandbars. In some years, drought reduced its flows and beached fast moving river traffic. High waters inundated the rich farm-lands and villages, and resulted in repeated loss of life and significant property damage. In an attempt to mitigate the flood damages, 18th century inhabitants began constructing earthen levees to control the floodwaters. By the middle of the 19th century, many of these individual levees had joined to form a flood protection line that attempted to contain the river over considerable distances. Unfortunately, major high-water events often pushed these ill-designed, flimsy structures aside with cat-astrophic effects. In addition to the sudden failures by these levee systems, the river simultaneously continued its natural process of meandering and changing its course within the floodplain. In 1824, the federal government appropriated funds for con-duct of river surveys. These initial efforts were followed by hydraulic studies, clear-ance of snags, and limited channel stabilisation through the use of dikes to focus river currents, but both travelling on the river and living in its floodplain remained hazardous (Elliot 1932).

Major floods occurred in the middle of the 19th century and brought cries for more federal action (Fox 1914). Swampland legislation in 1849 and 1850 gave state governments the authority to sell federal bottomlands and to use the money for draining swamps and providing flood protection. The federal government was also requested to conduct further studies of what might be done to alleviate the flood problems. Two studies were initiated in the 1850's when Ellet, Humphreys and Abbot began detailed investigations of the river system. Ellet (1927) reported that floods would continue to occur and placed his focus on the construction of reser-voirs to retain floodwaters where they fell. Humpreys & Abbot (1861) acknowl-edged the role of reservoirs and use of distributary channels to reduce flows but strongly recommended that federal efforts be placed on construction of appropri-ately sized levees to protect the inundated areas and to guide the Mississippi chan-nel. Even with this recommendation, local governments and individual landowners were seemingly powerless to prevent the destructive flooding that continued to occur. At the same time increased traffic on the river was placing pressure on the government to provide a reliable channel for navigation. In 1879 the Congress established the Mississippi River Commission (MRC) to review and assess condi-tions on the river and devise a programme to bring the river under control. The Commission's membership would include 3 military officers from the Army Corps of Engineers (one of whom would be President of the Commission), three civilians from the region, and a representative of the US coastal survey organisation. The MRC was chartered to improve navigation conditions and prevent floods on the Mississippi. The Commission set in motion long-term plans to harness the river. To improve navigation, the construction of additional dikes began as well as a pro-gramme of protecting highly erodible stretches of river bank with willow mattress facings. The MRC also provided engineering assistance to local agencies in con-struction and maintenance of levees and closed crevasses caused by major floods; however, its mandate was clearly 'navigation first.' By the dawn of the 20th centu-ry, communities and organisations along the lower Mississippi had linked their levee systems to provide an almost continuous line of flood barriers along both sides of the river from New Orleans to Cairo, Illinois. On the middle Mississippi and the lower segments of the upper river, levee construction was spotty and far less co-ordinated. While the line of levees below Cairo visibly existed, it was not strong at all points and between 1900 and 1927, failed several times with devastating results (Harrison 1961).

A catastrophic flood in 1927 engulfed both the lower Ohio and lower Mississippi river valleys, and focused federal attention once again on the lower Mississippi (Barry 1997). This single event resulted in flooding of over 67,340 km$^2$ of land, displaced more than 600,000 people from their homes, and cost over 200 lives. As a result, Congress assigned the MRC full responsibility for flood control in the lower Mississippi valley. This action provided the MRC authority and funding to carry out much needed flood damage reduction efforts in the lower valley.

## 4. Federal control and assistance

*Flood control*

Faced with the challenge of shackling the Mississippi, in 1928 the US Army Corps of Engineers (USACE) and the MRC began implementing a multi-faceted programme for flood control and navigation management of the lower Mississippi. Floodways and distributaries would provide relief for stressed channel sections. Cut-offs of tortuous river bends would speed flows toward the river's mouth to reduce flood stages. Levees would be strengthened and raised (essentially at federal expense) to serve as the principal protection against flooding. Banks would be protected from erosion by articulated concrete revetment (which had gone into use a decade earlier) and the river's channel would be stabilised through use of rock dikes to reduce channel width and block secondary channels. Lastly, until the channel improvement programme could result in a self-maintaining navigation channel, the river would be dredged (Ferguson 1940).

Following major floods throughout the USA in 1936, the Congress authorised a major flood control programme throughout the USA. In the Mississippi basin, primarily in the upper Mississippi, Ohio, and Missouri river basins, over 250 multi- and single-purpose dams were constructed by the USACE and other Federal agencies such as the Tennessee Valley Authority (TVA). These were not only to provide protection to those immediately downstream of the structures but also reduce the flows that would reach the lower valley (Holmes 1979, US Floodplain Management Review Committee 1994).

Four floodways were constructed to relieve flooding pressure on critical reaches of the river near Cairo, Illinois and above New Orleans Louisiana (Table 2). Without flow diversions, the bypassed river sections could not then and can not now safely contain the design flood flows. Construction of the New Madrid floodway with a present flow capacity of 15,580 m$^3$s$^{-1}$ across the south-east corner of Missouri mitigates the impact of Ohio river floodwaters entering the Mississippi and the possible backup of water into southern Illinois and western Kentucky. Another floodway, Bonnet Carre, built 40.2 km above New Orleans passes exceptionally high waters from the Mississippi eastward into lake Pontchartrain and thence to the Gulf of Mexico. The Bonnet Carre relieved flooding pressure on New Orleans by handling up to 7080 m$^3$s$^{-1}$ of floodwater flow. The remaining floodways, at Morganza, 17,000 m$^3$s$^{-1}$, and Old river, 17,560 m$^3$s$^{-1}$, relieves flooding pressures on both Baton Rouge and New Orleans by diverting flood waters westward into the Atchafalaya river (Ferguson 1940, USACE 1972, 1973, 1986, 1998).

While the lower valley was increasing its protection from flooding, progress in the upper basin was spotty. Levees and urban floodwalls were constructed by the federal government at several locations (under the 1936 flood control programme) but at varying levels of protection with the level tied to the conditions present at the sites at the time of construction. Some locally constructed public levees were incorporated into a federal programme that would provide federal reconstruction if the levees were damaged by a flood event. Participation in this latter programme required that the owning activities build and maintain the levees to federal standards. Flood control planning in the upper Mississippi basin lacked the comprehensive planning that was present in the lower valley and, as a result, many urban and agricultural areas remained at risk. Federal levees or federal support of public levees was limited to about 25% (3,200 km) of the levees that were built. Non-federal standards were mixed and levee heights reflected generally the capability of the builders to pay for the structures (USACE 1995, US Floodplain Management Review Committee 1994).

*Navigation and channel stabilisation*

While the efforts of the MRC added strength to flood control, the MRC was also tying this effort to the navigation programme. The authorised project included a 2.7 m channel from Cairo to Baton Rouge and a deeper channel (now 13.8 m) from there to the Gulf. Dikes, combined with revetment, were used to direct the river's flow in an attempt to force it to maintain its alignment and its channel depth. Where these approaches did not produce the needed results, dredges were employed to deepen the channel. The Mississippi flowed free of locks or dams though the lower valley.

Navigation continued to be important to and to have strong support in the upper Mississippi basin. Throughout the latter part of the 19th century and into the 1920's the river channel was maintained at various depths from the mouth of the Ohio to St. Paul. Rapids were overcome by blasting channels and construction of an occasional lock. Wing dams and dikes were used to direct the flow through one channel.

However, these techniques did not provide what was wanted by river interests and, in 1929, the Congress authorised the construction of a system of locks and dams that would provide a 2.7 m channel from the mouth of the Missouri to St Paul. Between 1930 and 1950, USACE constructed 29 locks and dams. In the middle

*Table 2.* Mississippi river floodways.

| Floodway | Capacity ($m^3s^{-1}$) |
|---|---|
| New Madrid | 15,580 |
| Old river | 17,650 |
| Morganza | 17,000 |
| Bonnet Carre | 7,080 |

Mississippi, the channel, with assistance from dikes and revetment, continued to flow free and to provide a 2.7 m depth (Tweet 1984, US National Park Service 1992, Strauser 1986).

## 5. Assessment of results

*Flood control*

Today, along the banks of the lower Mississippi we find the richest agricultural lands in the USA along with major factories and renewing urban communities. Behind the vast levee system, approximately 10 million people in the seven states of the lower valley live a life relatively free from the concerns of a major flood by the Mississippi. As a result of the levee system, $226 billion in flood damages have been prevented at a cost of $9.6 billion in construction and maintenance.

Over the period 1928-1999, there have been 12 major flood events on the lower Mississippi and all were passed without major incident. The need for a strong levee system is clear to those who live behind its protection. In response to this security, considerable development has taken place in the Mississippi basin since the 1927 flood. Forests have been cleared, fields plowed, and cities built and populated. The volume of run-off from within the lower valley and from the basin as a whole has increased enormously. Analysis of major high-water events between 1928 and 1990 has seen predicted flood flows and resultant flood stages grow steadily higher. The combined effects of increases in run-off, cut-offs, channel stabilisation, and reduction of flood areas by levee construction have forced the raising of the levee system on several occasions.

Since 1928, the USACE, in partnership with local agencies, has worked to bring all levees to the cross section required to carry the design flood. Today the MRC has responsibility for 2,596 km of levees along the Mississippi and Atchafalaya rivers. Of these, 2,146 km are complete to the section and grade required to pass the design flood. Construction of revetment and dikes to stabilise the channel continues. By 1998, the MRC had employed 1,658 km of revetment out of the total of 1,750 km authorised, and 479 km of dikes of the 545 km authorised (USACE 1998, Robinson 1998).

The situation in the upper Mississippi is not quite as sound. A major test of the flood control capability occurred in 1993 when rain over a several month period inundated millions of hectares, forced thousands from their homes for up to three months and throughout the Missouri and upper Mississippi basins caused $16 billion in damages. For the most part, federal levees and floodwalls performed well but the non-federal counterparts did not. The absence of both links among the different levee systems and a single agency to direct the flood control activity led to many individuals and communities being under-protected or unprotected. Essential facilities such as water and sewerage plants and hospitals were inundated or cut off and brought the effected communities to their knees. As a result of this disaster, the President of the USA directed a study of the reasons for the flooding. The results of this study have led to several efforts to develop a comprehensive approach to upper Mississippi flood damage reduction (US Floodplain Management Review Committee 1994, Bhowmik 1993).

*Navigation*

Each year over 130 billion ton-miles of cargo pass up and down the lower Mississippi. This cargo is predominately bulk and consists primarily of coal, grains, and other large items. The largest single cargoes travel from the coal and agricultural fields of the central USA to the ports of Baton Rouge and New Orleans for export overseas. Mississippi system traffic handles 42% of the agricultural products exported from the USA. Inland ports have developed in conjunction with each of the major cities, and single purpose terminals for the loading of grain and other commodities exist all along the river system. The Mississippi river navigation project provides a minimum channel depth of 2.7 m and a minimum channel width of 91.4 m between Cairo, Illinois and Baton Rouge, Louisiana. From Baton Rouge to the Gulf of Mexico, the navigable, channel is 13.8 m deep by 152.4 m wide allowing both Baton Rouge and New Orleans to serve as major termini for international waterborne commerce. This favourable location has resulted in New Orleans becoming the leading USA port and Baton Rouge the fourth largest (USACE 1998, Robinson 1998).

The lock and dam system on the upper Mississippi has been in place for over 60 years and the traffic on the river continues to increase. Millions of tons of cargo flow through the system. The ageing locks and dams continue to move vessels, although delays are frequent at some locks because of mechanical problems and the small size of the locks (184 m long). At one location on the southern end of the system, the Corps of Engineers has constructed two new locks (370 m, 184 m) to replace one of the 1930's structures. Studies are currently underway to assess the need for further replacements in the system.

*Environment*

The navigation and flood control work on the Mississippi has not taken place without degradation of the natural environment (Galloway & Manous 1994). By 1970, the Mississippi was clearly a river restrained from its natural wandering across the valley floor. It was a river that had, in times of high water, spilled over its banks to spread sediment and create fertile fields and swamps. It was this rich wetland habitat that once nurtured fish and wildlife that was no longer receiving the frequent flows to nourish its ecosystem. Ninety-three percent of the lower valley's floodplain sat behind levees and essentially its entire river channel had been restrained from movement. Agriculture had replaced bottomland forests and both fish and wildlife were under stress. At the lower end of the Mississippi river, the delta no longer received the deposition of sediments scoured from the riverbanks and lifted from the fields of Montana, Minnesota, and Ohio. The river channel had been confined and extended almost to the continental shelf, so material moving to the river mouth was not available for shoreline deposition. No longer was the river able to shift its channel at will and move its flows to other parts of the coastline. The natural processes that nourished the coastal shores no longer were taking place.

The upper Mississippi river basin is one of the most ecologically rich locations in the USA. Forty percent of North American waterfowl use the river corridor as a migratory flyway. Its aquaculture includes over 241 fish species. Large scale efforts to provide navigation and flood control to the upper basin have caused many of the same environmental problems experienced in the lower Mississippi valley. The most significant problems have been associated with the construction of locks and dams. While the pools behind the dams created lakes that support recreation as well as commercial navigation, they also inundated former wetland habitat, caused sediment from tributary river and streams to drop at their mouths and gradually back up these streams. Channel work between locks limited the lateral movement of the river and eliminated aquatic habitat. The navigation traffic itself caused problems with wake action on the shorelines and the continuous re-suspension of sediments caused by propeller wash. What was once one of the richest natural rivers in the USA, was experiencing severe degradation. Flood control levees, as in the lower valley, isolated bottomland areas from water and sediment recharge and eliminated habitat. Fifty-three percent of the floodplain from St Paul to St Louis was placed behind levees as was 83 percent of the floodplain in the middle Mississippi (Delaney & Craig 1997, Illston 1995).

## 6. Adjustments to original plans

### Cut-offs

Between 1929 and 1942, the Corps cut-off 16 river bends (loops) within the lower Mississippi valley. This action shortened the river length by 240 km. While these cut-offs lowered the flood stage in areas of the cut-off reach, by steeping the river gradient, they also increased the water velocity and increased riverbed erosion. The long-term result of these cut-offs was an increase in the sediment deposition and the flood stages in the reaches below the cut-offs and a considerable increase in the instability of the channel alignment in those reaches of the river where cut-offs had taken place. Since the initial construction period, no additional cut-offs have been attempted (USACE 1992, Schumm & Winkley 1994, Walters 1975, Robinson 1998).

### Channel stabilisation

The MRC learned from early work on the Mississippi with mat fascine made of willow brush and from use of timber dikes (groins) that bank erosion could be retarded and channel alignment improved. Rock dikes quickly replaced timber, and a specially designed articulated concrete revetment replaced the willow mattresses, with a resulting dramatic reduction in bank erosion. The river engineers of the MRC learned to work with the river. They placed dikes and revetments so as to build on the natural river sinuosity at critical river stages, forcing the river flows during low water into a narrower (and thus deeper) channel. In the early days, the MRC used dredges to maintain the channel and was continually excavating to achieve the required dimensions. The magnitude of this effort, however, was enormous and in low-water years the desired results were not achieved. Today, as a result of the success of the channel stabilisation programme, the annual dredging requirement has been significantly reduced. By the mid 90's, the number of dredging locations within the Mississippi had dropped from more than 30 to 12, resulting in only

23,000,000 cubic meters of dredging to maintain the mainstem channel (USACE 1992, Schumm & Winkley 1994, Walters 1975, Robinson 1998).

*Floodways*

While floodways performed well in relieving pressure on segments of the lower Mississippi levee system, one near-disaster did occur. During the 1950's engineers determined that an increasing volume of Mississippi flow was leaving the Mississippi at Old river and moving into the Atchafalaya. They postulated that if action was not taken to control this flow, during the next major flood, the Atchafalaya could 'capture' the Mississippi. This would substantially reduce the flows past New Orleans and Baton Rouge, endangering waterborne commerce and water supply for these centres of commerce and the region in between. The Congress quickly authorised construction of a control structure at the Old river and it was completed in 1961. In 1973, a major flood did occur and the pressure on Old River Control Structure was immense. The river forces rapidly began to undermine the structure and only a Herculean reinforcement effort by the engineers prevented its failure. Following the 1973 flood, the MRC developed plans for an auxiliary structure to support the original control structure, which was quickly stabilised. Construction on the auxiliary structure was completed in 1986 (USACE 1986, Robinson 1998).

*Non-structural approaches to flood damage reduction*

In its report to the White House in 1994, the study team chartered to examine the 1993 Mississippi flood as well as federal approaches to flood damage reduction, stated that the nation was not making full use of non-structural approaches to flood damage reduction. The team proposed that development in the floodplain should be avoided unless no alternative locations existed. When development is to take place, it is argued that the first method of reducing potential damages should be the retention of rain-water in the location in which it falls through use of land treatment and natural and artificial reservoirs. It then suggested that structures in the floodplain should be flood proofed, that where possible those at most risk should be relocated from the floodplain and that only after the first approaches had been attempted should levees and flood-walls be constructed. Much attention has been given to the report and several federal programmes are supporting its recommendations. Over 25,000 homes (13,000 in the upper basin) have been relocated from the floodplains in the USA since 1993 and thousands of hectares of marginally productive bottomland habitat have been transferred from agriculture to natural uses (Galloway 1995a, 1995a,b).

*Environmental impact mitigation*

As noted earlier, successes of the navigation and flood control programmes in the Mississippi river basin have been tempered by the environmental problems that have occurred. Had those responsible better understood the natural environment, many of these could have been avoided. In cases where that would not have been possible, steps to mitigate the impacts could have been taken.

Over the last two decades the Mississippi River Commission and the Corps of Engineers, working closely with state and federal natural resource agencies, have taken major steps to correct the situation in the lower valley. They seek to maintain control of the river and, at the same time, preserve its natural value. Where possible, damaged areas must be restored, and where feasible, in the process of carrying out their operation and maintenance activities, they seek to create new wetlands and wildlife areas and to ensure habitat survivability.

Wetland use is being managed through the previously mentioned national regulation programme. The focus of new flood control projects is being shifted to balance structural and nonstructural methods. Extreme care is taken in locating excavation areas used to obtain earth for the levee programme. The operating rules for dams, reservoirs, and other river facilities now take into account the natural life cycles of fish and wildlife affected by the contained rivers. Dike and revetment designs have been modified to increase the usefulness of dikes and revetment in developing habitat while at the same time preserving their channel stabilisation functions. A specially submerged bendway weir, designed by the USACE's St. Louis District, received a Presidential Design Award in 1994 for its contribution to both navigation and environmental enhancement (USACE 1994).

Considerable wetland loss has already occurred in the valley. Efforts are underway to remedy wetland problems created both by past work as well as those resulting from the natural processes of settlement and coastal movement. In Louisiana, a large structure has been built that permits diversion of fresh Mississippi river waters into an area south of New Orleans that has been subject to salt water intrusion. Not only will this reduce the encroachment of the seawater but it will also enrich the area with river sediments. Congressional authorisation has been given for the construction of two additional fresh-water diversion structures. Another programme involves the re-creation of 'lost" wetlands through use of dredged material placed in wet-sited disposal areas and enhanced by a vegetation seeding programme. More than 2,500 ha of wetlands have been created through this process along the outlet channels of the Mississippi to the Gulf of Mexico. In the Atchafalaya floodway, federal, state and local agencies have acquired interest in over 240,000 ha of bottomland forest habitat. A combined Federal and state interagency task force has been established to develop a Louisiana coastal protection plan. In co-operation with the US Fish and Wildlife Services and state agencies, all Corps construction projects in the lower Mississippi valley that involve wetlands or wetland associated areas normally include acquisition of lands to provide mitigation for any unavoidable environmental damage. These lands are developable as habitat and capable of supporting high quality fish and wildlife resources. These and other physical efforts are being guided by an extensive data gathering and processing programme and development of an environmentally focused geographic information system (USACE 1998, Robinson 1995).

In the upper basin, similar efforts to restore and enhance the natural environment have been underway. All of the federal environmental enhancement programmes have been put into action. Over $15 million dollars has been allocated to environmental studies as part of the review of upper Mississippi navigation. Congress authorised a long-term environmental management programme for the upper basin that involves not only the close monitoring of the environmental status of the riverine environment but also efforts to improve habitat and to adjust operations to assist in restoration of badly damaged areas. The Corps is experimenting with alternate methods of operation of the dams associated with navigation, has developed a new weir for use in bendways to reduce erosion and to improve habitat, and is rehabilitating and expanding natural areas behind levees. All new projects fully incorporate environmental designs (Robinson 1998).

## 7. Continuing issues

*Comprehensive planning*

The MRC's programme in the lower valley has been in existence for 70 years and has validated the effectiveness of comprehensive planning. From the beginning, the efforts to provide flood control and navigation for the lower valley were accomplished with the entire valley in mind. Projects in one area were rapidly related to projects in other areas. The inter-connection between navigation, flood control, channel stabilisation were easily seen and addressed as the times and dollars permitted. The needed advent of attention to environmental issues was also addressed in a comprehensive fashion. Impacts were seen as system-wide and not just related to the project area where they were discovered. Solutions could be accomplished on a system-wide basis. Other federal agencies and state and local officials were able to turn to one agency, the MRC to address the water challenges of the lower valley (Anderson 1998).

In contrast, the development on the upper Mississippi was not comprehensive. Only recently, in the on-going study of the navigation system, has a system-wide look been taken at the relationship between the environment and navigation. Flood control is still not considered as an upper-basin wide problem meriting comprehensive solution and management, and the results speak for themselves.

*Public involvement*

Water project development has always involved the public in its formulation but not at the scale now demanded by the public. When the lower valley project was put together in 1928, there was little consultation among the MRC, the USACE, state and local officials and the public. Today, in both the upper and lower valleys, public meetings are held to inform the public of issues under consideration and obtain the public's view on the efficacy of the proposed solutions. Full consultation among federal and state agencies is required and new information systems make project plans available instantly to all concerned. Non governmental organisations, representing a variety of interests groups, are also heavily involved in the process. With the objective of developing a consensus approach to solving water problems, those responsible have learned that more information availability produces better results than less.

## 8. Conclusions

Humans have been working with the Mississippi river since native Americans first encountered its waters. For three centuries, they have been attempting to control its movements. In the lower Mississippi valley they have been relatively successful over the past 60 years in dealing with the river but have had to adjust to its vagaries, learning each day. But, over the years, these same efforts seriously endangered the natural environment. They have developed advanced, work-with-nature, river engineering techniques, now use non-structural approaches to flood damage reduction, work towards environmental enhancement and impact mitigation and ensure increased public involvement. Recognising this, they now have prepared a comprehensive plan to continue their works on the Mississippi in a manner that not only will provide economic and social growth to the millions who work and live in the valley, but also will preserve the natural environment for future generations.

In the upper basin, the efforts are not as comprehensive but the goals are the same, providing for continued use of the river to benefit those who live along its banks while concurrently protecting and enhancing the natural environment for which they are ultimately responsible.

When humans took on the challenge of using the Mississippi river, they took on a challenge that will not cease. They grabbed a tiger by its tail and they cannot release this tiger. By working carefully with the river and its environment, they may be able to provide, for those who come after them, sustainable use of this mighty and historic river system. Perhaps they also may be able to convince Mark Twain, that while engineers may not ever tame the river, they may well be able to work with it in harmony.

## Acknowledgements

The author acknowledges the assistance in preparing this paper of LeHu Ti, UN Economic and Social Commission for Asia and the Pacific, Lieutenant Colonel J. Manous, the late Dr M. Robinson, P. Clark, C. Strauser, J. McCormick, D. Hanson, US Army Corps of Engineers, M. Robinson, Federal Emergency Management Agency, Dr R. Sparks, Illinois Historical Survey, and members of the Department of Interior and other federal agencies. The paper was also prepared, with modifications to emphasise institutional arrangements, for the Workshop on Regional Cooperation in Flood Control and Management for Improvement of Urban Environment in Asia and The Pacific (Bangkok, October 1998). The views in this paper are those of the author and do not represent necessarily the views of either the US Government or the International Joint Commission.

## References

Anderson, B. 1998. Mississippi Valley division. The Army Engineer 98/6: 21-25.
Barry, J. 1997. Rising tide. Simon and Schuster, New York.
Bhowmik, N.G. (Ed.), 1993. The 1993 flood on the Mississippi river in Illinois. Illinois State Water Survey Miscellaneous Publication 151. Illinois Water Survey, Urbana.
Delaney, R.L. & Craig, M.R. 1997. Longitudinal changes in Mississippi river floodplain structure. US Geological Survey, Upper Mississippi River Long Term Resource Monitoring Program, Onalaska.
Elliot, D.O. 1932. The improvement of the lower Mississippi river for flood control and navigation. Volumes I-III. US Waterways Experiment Station, Vicksburg.

Ellet, C. 1927. Senate Executive Document 20. US Senate, Washington.

Ferguson, H.B. 1940. History of improvement of the lower Mississippi river for flood control and navigation, 1932-1939. US Army Corps of Engineers, Vicksburg.

Fox, J. 1914. Mississippi river flood problem: How the floods can be prevented – A national duty. Mississippi River Levee Association, Memphis.

Galloway, G.E. & Manous, J.D. 1994. Balancing the environment, navigation, and flood control on the lower Mississippi river: A challenge for the 21st century. Proceedings of the 28th Congress Permanent International Association of Navigation Congresses (PIANC). PIANC, Brussels.

Galloway, G.E. 1995a. New directions in floodplain management. Water Resources Bulletin 31/3: 351-357.

Galloway, G.E. 1995b. Floodplain management: A present and a 21st century imperative. Universities Council on Water Resources Update 97: 4-8.

Harrison, R.W. 1961. Alluvial empire. Pioneer Press, Little Rock.

Holmes, B.B. 1979. History of Federal Water Resources Programs and Policies, 1961-70. Miscellaneous Publication 1379. US Department of Agriculture, Washington.

Humphreys, A.A. & Abbot, H.C. 1861. Report on the physics and hydraulics of the Mississippi river. Lippincott, Philadelphia.

Illston, T. 1995. The upper Mississippi river: Sustainable development alternatives. Fall 1994 Briefing Series. Northeast-Midwest Institute, Washington.

Robinson, M. 1995. An environmental tapestry. Briefing for Civil Works Directorate. US Army Corps of Engineers, Washington.

Robinson, M. 1998. Chief Public Affairs, Mississippi River Commission. Personal communication.

Schumm, S. & Winkley, B.R. (Eds.). 1994. The variability of large alluvial Rivers. American Society of Civil Engineers, New York.

Strauser, C.N. 1986. Restoration of the middle Mississippi river. Miscellaneous Paper. US Army Corps of Engineers, St. Louis District, St. Louis.

Twain, M. (Clemens, S. L.) 1883. Life on the Mississippi. Bantam Classic (1997), New York.

Tweet, R. 1984. A history of the Rock Island District, US Army Corps of Engineers, 1866-1983. US Army Engineer District, Rock Island, Rock Island.

US Army, Corps of Engineers. 1995. Floodplain management assessment. US Army, Corps of Engineers, Washington.

US Army, Corps of Engineers, Mississippi River Commission. 1972. Improvement of the Lower Mississippi River and Tributaries, 1931-1972. Mississippi River Commission, Vicksburg.

US Army, Corps of Engineers, Mississippi River Commission. 1973. Flood control: Lower Mississippi River Valley. Mississippi River Commission, Vicksburg.

US Army, Corps of Engineers, Mississippi River Commission. 1986. Mississippi River and Tributaries Project. Mississippi River Commission, Vicksburg.

US Army, Corps of Engineers, Mississippi River Commission. 1998. Command briefing. Mississippi River Commission, Vicksburg.

US Army, Corps of Engineers, St. Louis District. 1994. Bendway weirs. Submission for the Presidential Design Award. St. Louis District, St. Louis.

US Federal Interagency Floodplain Management Task Force. 1992. Floodplain management in the United States: An assessment report. Volume 2. Federal Emergency Management Agency, Washington.

US Floodplain Management Review Committee. 1994. Sharing the challenge: Floodplain management into the 21st century. Government Printing Office, Washington.

US National Park Service. 1992. Gateways to commerce: The US Army Corps of Engineers' 9-Foot Channel Project on the Upper Mississippi River. National Park Service, Denver.

Walters, W.H. 1975. Regime changes of the lower Mississippi river. Master Thesis. Colorado State University, Fort Collins.

# ELBE, ODRA, AND VISTULA: REFERENCE RIVERS FOR THE RESTORATION OF BIODIVERSITY AND HABITAT QUALITY

P.H. Nienhuis[1,7], J.C. Chojnacki[2], O. Harms[3], W. Majewski[4], W. Parzonka[5] & T. Prus[6]

[1] Department of Environmental Studies, Faculty of Science, University of Nijmegen, P.O. Box 9010, NL-6500 GL Nijmegen, The Netherlands;
[2] Department of Marine Ecology and Environmental Protection, University of Agriculture, Str. 4/H-19 K. Krolewicza, 71-550 Szczecin, Poland;
[3] Institut für Wasserwirtschaft und Kulturtechnik, University Karlsruhe, Kaiserstrasse 12, D-76128 Karlsruhe, Germany;
[4] Institute of Hydroengineering, Polish Academy of Sciences, P.O. Box 61, 80-953 Gdansk, Poland;
[5] Agricultural University, Plac Grunwaldzki 24, 50-363 Wroclaw, Poland;
[6] International Centre of Ecology, Polish Academy of Sciences, Ul. Marii Konopnickiej 1, Dziekanow Lesny n. Warsaw, 05-092 Lomianki, Poland;
[7] Member of the Netherlands Centre for River Studies (NCR), P.O. Box 177, NL-2600 MH Delft, The Netherlands

## Abstract

Ecological values of the Elbe, Vistula and Odra are recognized in theory, but in practice 'strong' economic imperatives are confronted with 'weak' ecological principles. Sound and internationally validated arguments to defend both environmental quality and biodiversity of the river basins are lacking. The rivers play an important role in the economic infrastructure of the Czech Republic, Germany and Poland. In terms of integrated river basin management the International Elbe Commission (IKSE) is the result of Czech-German policy agreement for the Elbe basin. Connected to the reunification of Germany in 1989 the unique historical opportunity arose to preserve the Elbe river which is still to a large extent influenced by river flood dynamics, although technological profits, mainly for navigation purposes, still play an important role in the discussion. The International Odra Commission (ICPO) is the central policy structure for the Odra; the international agreement, however, is still not ratified by the Polish government. For the Vistula catchment an integrated catchment management plan is lacking, but strategic plans for the upper, middle and lower Vistula are under construction. As for the Odra and the Vistula, mainly dominant technological solutions in favour of navigation and water storage, such as channelisation and the construction of weirs and reservoirs, are debated. Navigability and environmental protection are in many cases counteracting interests, but a sign in favour of ecology is also heard. A comparison between the river basin management of the Rhine on the one hand (where water quality has improved, but habitats have been annihilated), and of the Elbe, Odra and Vistula on the other hand (where, with the exception of the Elbe, water quality is still bad, but the diversity and integrity of habitats is large) leads to the confirmation of our hypothesis: the Western- and Central- European rivers can be used as reference rivers for the restoration of biodiversity and habitat quality of other European rivers which are economically highly developed but ecologically deteriorated.

*New approaches to river management, pp. 65–84*
*edited by A.J.M. Smits, P.H. Nienhuis and R.S.E.W. Leuven*
© 2000 Backhuys Publishers, Leiden, The Netherlands

## 1. Introduction

Rivers and floodplains of Europe, and particularly those of Western and Central Europe have been modified drastically during the past centuries. Almost eighty percent of the total water discharge of the main European rivers is more or less strongly affected by water regulation measures (Dynesius & Nilsson 1994). The main measures are visible in flow regulation, channelisation, fragmentation, land reclamation and consequent destruction of the original habitats, and water and sediment pollution. In practice most of the large European rivers have already been for more than 500 years manipulated systems, having lost their naturalness and ecological integrity. The indigenous flora and fauna of the large rivers has partially been replaced by allochtonous species. The overall process of disturbance by human influence has led to a levelling down of the original ecosystems.

Originally the river valleys in Western- and Central-Europe were covered with a luxuriant multi-species deciduous riverine forest. The mediaeval human colonisation brought about a considerable reduction of the forest acreage, mainly due to clear-felling and replacement of wooden areas by fields and meadows. Further land cultivation led to a reduction in the forest area and drainage of wetlands, which resulted in marked changes in the character of the remaining forests (IUCN 1995a,b).

A more careful look at the European river basins reveals a relation between economic prosperity and environmental quality. In this paper three Western- and Central-European rivers will be discussed, Elbe, Odra and Vistula (Figure 1). These rivers have a different historical background and are facing different economic developments. Our hypothesis is that these rivers can be used as reference rivers for the restoration of biodiversity and habitat quality of Western-European rivers, such as the Rhine and Meuse, which are economically highly developed but ecologically deteriorated. River catchment characteristics of Elbe, Odra and Vistula will be described first, followed by a brief survey of river management approaches. Finally, in the discussion economic imperatives are confronted with ecological principles.

## 2. River catchment characteristics

The landscapes of West- and Central-Europe have drastically changed over the centuries. The original temperate deciduous forests, characteristic of the first millennium, have gradually been replaced by man-made field crop and grassland ecosystems (Table 1). Although the overall area of woodland is larger than Table 1 suggests, only remnants of the original forests remained. The area of developed land, such as cities and infrastructural works is rapidly increasing (Revenga *et al.* 1998). The West- and Central-European rivers Elbe, Odra and Vistula are more or less comparable concerning their catchment, length and discharge characteristics.

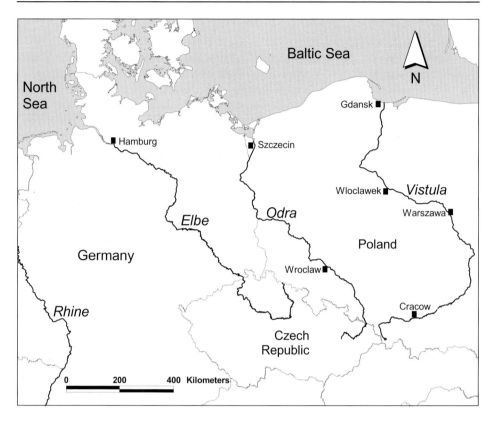

*Fig. 1.* The rivers Rhine, Elbe, Odra and Vistula in Europe. The tributaries are not indicated.

*Table 1.* River catchment characteristics of the Central European rivers Elbe, Odra and Vistula
+ = little; ++ = moderate; +++ = severe. (Revenga *et al.* 1998).

|  | Elbe | Odra | Vistula |
|---|---|---|---|
| Catchment ($10^2$ km$^2$) | 1,490 | 1,240 | 1,800 |
| Length (km) | 1,140 | 850 | 1,050 |
| Discharge (m$^3$ sec$^{-1}$) | 850 | 540 | 1,100 |
| Ice in lower basin | ++ | +++ | +++ |
| Loss original forest (%) | 75 | 72 | 82 |
| Cropland (%) | 74 | 79 | 80 |
| Developed land (%) | 21 | 17 | 15 |
| Population density (km$^{-2}$) | 164 | 117 | 131 |
| Large cities | 18 | 14 | 24 |
| Navigation | + | ++ | + |

## 2.1 Elbe

The Elbe is 1,140 km long, with the source being the "Riesengebirge" in the Czech Republic. Approximately two thirds of the catchment area of 149,000 km$^2$ is in Germany, one third is in the Czech Republic, and less than one percent is in Austria and Poland. A large part of the middle and upper Elbe run through the former countries Czechoslovakia and the German Democratic Republic. At Geesthacht, 15 km upstream of Hamburg, the only weir on the German river course marks the artificial limit of the estuarine, tidal brackish environment. Just before reaching Hamburg the river splits into the Norder- and Süderelbe, relics of a former inland delta, which now hosts the harbour district of Hamburg. Hamburg is one of the largests ports of Europe. This port is a huge sink for suspended material from the Elbe, and each year about 2.5 million tonnes of sediment have to be removed by dredging. The average discharge into the North Sea amounts to 850 m$^3$ sec$^{-1}$, with maximum and minimum value varying between 3,000 m$^3$ sec$^{-1}$ in spring after snow melt, and 150 m$^3$ sec$^{-1}$ in late summer (Adams *et al.* 1996).

After the German reunification in 1989 the former German Democratic Republic became part of Germany. This led to a complete shut-down of most heavy metal point sources in eastern Germany, and the beginning of effective municipal and industrial waste water treatment. The expected rapid reduction of the heavy metal concentrations of the Elbe sediments was not observed, owing to erosion and resuspension processes. In the 1985 ranking of large European rivers the Elbe showed very high concentrations for many heavy metals. Between 1972 and 1985, e.g., the mean mercury concentration in the sediments of the Rhine had decreased from 8.9 to 0.9 mg kg$^{-1}$, whereas in the Elbe an increase from 13.9 to 17.0 mg kg$^{-1}$ was registered. Only after 1991 concentrations of heavy metals started to decrease significantly (Müller & Furrer 1998). The same is true for inorganic nutrients and chlorinated hydrocarbons (Adams *et al.* 1996). Concerning the load of pollutants quite some progress has already been made. Illustrated by data over the period 1989-1994 the organic load of the Elbe basin has been reduced by 40%, and the mercury and cadmium load by respectively 80% and 20% (Adams *et al.* 1996). Improved wastewater treatment technology and the increase of the number of inhabitants connected to the wastewater treatment plants have resulted in a decrease of the nitrogen and phosphorus emissions from point sources in the Elbe basin. The emission reduction took especially place after the political changes in 1989: emissions from point sources decreased by about 65% for phosphorus and by 30% for nitrogen when the periods 1980-1989 and 1990-1995 are compared. The downward trend continued later in the nineties (De Wit 1999).

Oxygen concentration in the water, a good indicator for water quality, decreased after 1950 from 10 to 4 mg l$^{-1}$, and only after 1990 concentrations rose in a few years time again to values of 10 mg l$^{-1}$. Macrozoobenthos species such as molluscs, crustaceans and insects followed the same curve: from more than 100 species before 1950 down to 50 between 1950 and 1990, and an increase again to more than 70 after 1990 (Schöll *et al.* 1995). For the 30-year period from 1959 to 1989 the Elbe remained one of Europe's most strongly polluted large rivers, with an impoverished zoobenthic community consisting mainly of pollution-tolerant species (Adams *et al.* 1996).

The roughly 240 km of the Elbe running through the Czech Republic contains many weirs and barrages. The German Middle and Lower Elbe are rather unspoiled and contain only one weir at Geesthacht, near Hamburg. Although 80% of the original floodplains have been cut off from the river by levees, the remaining wetlands have still a high ecological diversity (Dahl & Flade 1994).

After great storm floods and notably after 1962, dikes along German estuaries and rivers entering into the North Sea were straightened and shortened. The result was that many marshlands were cut off from regular inundation, and that the floodplain character markedly altered. In the former Eastern German Republic, where a large part of the Elbe catchment is situated, the banks of the river basin remained rather unaltered and natural. In general the Elbe shoreline remains amongst the most natural landscapes of the land-water ecotone of the large European rivers, in particular within the reach of the biosphere reserve 'Mittlere Elbe'. Specific river-bound ecosystems are still to be found along part of the Elbe, natural levees consisting of sand-dunes and sand-ridges, dynamic erosion and sedimentation areas, extensive floodplain forests, and a relatively large area of shallow-water habitat for fish and other biota (Adams *et al.* 1996, Dahl & Flade 1994).

*2.2 Odra*

The Odra river is 850 km long, and has its source in the Czech Republic. The Lower Odra forms the geographic border between Germany and Poland. The river catchment of 124,000 km$^2$ (Revenga *et al.* 1998) has an important role for the water economy of the western part of Poland and the north-eastern part of Germany (Chojnacki & Kowalski 1997). The average discharge of the Odra to the sea amounts to 540 m$^3$ sec$^1$, but its hydrology is characterised by large variability in discharges. The mean annual discharge at Wroclaw is 170 m$^3$ sec$^{-1}$, and this is not sufficient for navigation in the free flowing middle Odra. The greatest flood in this century occurred in 1997, with a maximum discharge of 3,700 m$^3$ sec$^{-1}$ in Wroclaw. In the Upper Odra basin 22 barrages have been constructed in the course of time (Parzonka & Bartnik 1998). Owing to regulation works the course of the river Odra was shortened by 154 km. These works started already at the end of the 18th century and continued up to the early decades of the 20th century. The main aim was channelisation of the river bed for the purpose of better navigation by cutting off meanders, and reducing the length of the river considerably. The construction of regulation works in the upper, middle and lower Odra has caused large scale degradation of the river bed, *i.e.*, erosion and 1.5 to 3 m deepening of the river bed, and consequent lowering of the ground water table, which makes the waterway unusable during dry periods. Parzonka (1995) proposed a solution to this problem by suggesting supplementary 'feeding' of the river bed with sediment to compensate the erosion, similar to the feeding of the Rhine below the barrage of Iffezheim. These measures have not been brought into practice yet.

Recent hydraulic measures were not taken in the Odra basin, which means that notwithstanding the historical changes, large stretches of the Odra still have the characteristics of a natural river. Very important for the survival of the valley vegetation cover are the old river-beds and meanders, harbouring species rich communities (Macicka & Wilczynska 1993). In the Odra valley some natural fragments of riparian elm-ash forests survived with their rare raptors and hole-nesters, while in its lower course there are some willow-poplar and alder stands and extensive reed-beds and sedge associations still present. The Natural fragments of rivers serve as important staging sites for water fowl during their migration (300,000 over 25 species of wintering waterfowl; Tomialojc & Dyrcz 1993).

To avoid further geomorphological degradation of the river bed, the Polish water authorities have decided to construct another barrage downstream of the previous ones, notwithstanding the high ecological values of the river valley. However, this hydraulic construction will cause linear erosion in the course of time, analogous to the processes studied previously (Parzonka & Bartnik 1998).

The water quality of the Odra is classified as critically loaded with pollutants to strongly polluted (water quality class II to III; Dahl & Flade 1994). Intensification of human economic activity in the catchment of the Odra, expressed through the significant industrialization and urbanization of this area constitutes the main threat to the water quality in this region. This is particularly visible in the upper and middle Odra basin, where the most environmentally arduous industrial projects have been localized, near Wroclaw and Katowice. Waters of the lowest unclassified quality ('out of class') are carried in the upper and middle Odra, while downstream their quality systematically rises over the last ten years. The analysis of long-term quality changes shows a systematic improvement in the Odra river's waters in the region of the Polish-German border; in some cases indicators achieved standards which are close to the required levels. This denotes that with further regulation of the water supply and sewage disposal management in the upper and middle Oder basin, we should expect a significant water quality improvement in the upper and middle reaches (Soldan *et al.* 1994, IUCN 1995a).

## 2.3 Vistula

The Vistula is the largest river in Poland and has a length of 1,050 km, and is con-sidered as navigable over a stretch of 941 km from the Przemsza River to the Baltic Sea, but there is hardly any navigation along the river, mainly because of the irreg-ular water flows over the year, and the shallow thresholds. It is a unique feature in Poland, and to a great extent also in Europe, as it is one of the largest continental rivers which has maintained an almost natural character over a large part of its reach. Next to the Neva, the Vistula is the second largest river discharging into the Baltic Sea basin, and it plays an important role regarding the volume of the water conveyed, and the quantity of sediments transported to the sea. The Vistula drainage basin covers an area of 180,000 $km^2$, and of that area approximately 90% is situat-ed in Poland (Kajak 1993, Jedraszko-Dabrowska *et al.* 1995). The average dis-charge at the mouth amounts to 1,080 $m^3$ $sec^{-1}$, varying between a maximum of 7,840 $m^3$ $sec^{-1}$ and a minimum of 253 $m^3$ $sec^{-1}$ over the period 1951-1990 (Majewski 1998).

The Vistula river bed has only been channelized partially, chiefly in the upper and the lower river sections. Large water reservoirs and hydraulic power plants are mainly situated along the mountainous tributaries. In the lowlands there are embankments along wide stretches of the river valley to prevent floods. The middle part of the Vistula is dynamic, with braided channels, permanent and temporary islands and rich vegetation in the valley. Consequently the middle Vistula has retained its natural character, harbouring a diverse flora and fauna. This part is a very important habitat for breeding birds. It also forms an extremely important pathway for bird migration, harbouring the largest in Europe inland populations of rare tarns, gulls and waders (Tomialojc & Dyrcz 1993). Downstream from Wloclawek, the regulation works in the nineteenth century changed the braided type into the meandering type. In some places the banks are regulated, and partial dams are built across the river bed to straighten the channel (CML 1995).

The Vistula serves as a source of drinking water for most of the towns located along it. At the same time a total population of 24 million people live in the Vistula drainage basin, which discharge their mostly untreated sewage water in the river (CML 1995). Because of the fact that on average 70% of the sewage is untreated or treated unsatisfactorily, the concentrations of pollutants are very high and may affect human health (Dojlido & Woyciechowska 1989). The Vistula has become one of the most polluted rivers in Europe. In the Vistula, changes in water quality have been investigated carefully for over 30 years (Szymanska 1975, 1987). An analysis of physical-chemical data shows increasing degradation of the river until the 1990s, when a slight improvement was observed. The degradation was especially evident in the late 1970s and the early 1980s when all monitored waters were classified level III (bad quality) or below, "out of class" (very bad quality). Since the mid-1980s the length of both class II and "out of class" waters has increased. In 1991 77% of the total length of the river was out of any class (which means very bad quality) and none in the first class (which means good quality) (Central Statistical Office 1993), but dissolved substances characterising salinity, such as chlorides and sulphates, have a crucial impact on this classification. Elimination of these pollutants would shift over 50% of "out of class" river stretches to higher classes (Makinia *et al.* 1996).

Ecological studies of Kaniewska-Prus (1983) and others made clear that in the eighties water and sediments of large stretches of the Vistula river were heavily polluted. The pollution level is so alarmingly high that none of the cities downstream from Warszawa use the river water for drinking purposes. Due to chlorides, sulphates, heavy metals and toxic substances, the water is not only inappropriate for drinking, but also for irrigation as well (CML 1995). The water quality problem is strictly related to the problem of water resources. Because of the high demand for water from the Vistula (which is the largest source of water in Poland) and due to its irregular flow, there is a great need for water retention in several reservoirs along the Vistula. On the one hand these reservoirs may be regarded as positive, because they act like a natural settling pond, where pollutants can be stored and not need to be removed. Besides that, the contribution of the Vistula to the Baltic pollution is reduced. On the other hand, the sediments accumulating in the Wloclawek reservoir have already proved to be very dangerous. Due to dredging and consequent resuspension of particles with adhered pollutants, an ecological catastrophe took place in 1986, resulting in mass mortality of fish in the reservoir (Kajak 1993, CML 1995).

A problem specific to Poland is excess salinity concentration in the river water, which impairs water use in several ways, including reduction of self-purification processes in rivers, corrosion of water factories, ships and barges as well as water supply and cooling systems. The salinity of river water in Poland originates from the region of Upper Silesia (Southern Poland), mainly from coal mine water discharged to surface waters. The salt load discharged to surface waters is approximately 9,000 tons day[-1] and is still growing (MEPNR&F 1991). The largests loads (almost 50% of the Vistula catchment) come from five mines, and for the year 2000 a further increase with 60% to 15,000 tons day[-1] is anticipated. The concentration of sodium chloride in the river reach which passes Cracow, approximately 80 km away from Silesia, is higher than in the Baltic Sea. Construction of desalination plants for the five main contributing mines would reduce the load discharged to Vistula river with roughly 40% (Makinia *et al.* 1996).

Among all rivers in Poland, the two largest, the Vistula and the Odra, are of special interest as they discharge almost 90% of Poland's pollutant load to the Baltic Sea. Poland's potential impact on the Baltic sea is reflected in the facts that: (1) 99.7% of Poland's area belongs to the Baltic Sea drainage basin; (2) over 50% of the entire basin population live in Poland; and (3) approximately 40% of the entire basin's farmland is situated in Poland. The total annual runoff from Poland to the Baltic is approximately $62 \times 10^9$ m$^3$ per year, of which 50% and 34% are discharged by the Vistula and Odra rivers, respectively (MEPNR&F 1991). Poland's organic load, expressed as BOD5, is 22% of the total load discharged by all countries surrounding the Baltic. Nutrient leaching from the Polish land is also high, representing 30% and 40% respectively, of the total nitrogen and phosphorus discharged to the Baltic. The loads per Polish capita, however, are two to four times lower than those from all Scandinavian countries (Makinia *et al.* 1996).

The Baltic coast is an important tourist attraction, and the elimination of bacteriological contamination of the beaches of the Baltic has a high priority. The largest sources of bacteriological contamination are the direct sewerage outlets and small rivers and streams entering the sea. In recent years bacteriological contamination was the main reason for closing the beaches in the region of Gdansk (Olanczuk-Neyman *et al.* 1992), although some beaches in this area have been reopened since (Makinia *et al.* 1996).


## 3. River management

### 3.1 Elbe

Connected to the reunification of Germany in 1989 the unique historical opportunity arose to take measures for sustainable management of the Elbe basin and to preserve the river which is still to a large extent influenced by river flood dynamics. Already in 1993 the "Länder" governments decided to improve the Elbe river basin in order to let it be considered as a biosphere reserve (375,000 ha over 400 km river stretch) in the framework of the UNESCO "Man and Biosphere" programme. This reserve has been realized in 1998, and it will be one of the largests river oriented biosphere reserves in Europe (earlier the "Mittlere Elbe" area has already been designated as biosphere reserve). The free passage of migratory fish is one of the priorities in the Elbe management. The Elbe (Labe) stretch in the Czech Republic contains 24 barrages and weirs, including sluices for navigation; the majority contains (not optimally functioning) fish ladders. Existing passages will be improved and new ones will be built in the near future. The German Elbe stretch is free of weirs and barrages, except close to the mouth in Geesthacht there is a barrage, containing a fish passage, which has been newly rebuilt in 1998. The Elbe biosphere reserve finally aims at a drastic improvement of Elbe ecosystems, comprising long-term measures for conservation and rehabilitation of aquatic, semi-terrestrial and terrestrial ecosystems. One of the earlier aims of the Elbe action programme is the channelisation of the Middle and Upper Elbe for naviga-tion purposes. This economic target is in conflict with most ecological targets (IKSE 1997).

The 'Arbeitsgemeinschaft fur die Reinhaltung der Elbe' (ARGE-ELBE) started in 1977 on a national level, followed by the the IKSE, the 'Internationale Kom-mission zum Schutz der Elbe' in 1991 which extended its aims in the 'Aktions-programm Elbe'(IKSE 1995, 1997). A major aim of the 'Action Programme Elbe' is to reach a river basin comprising as natural as possible ecosystems and a high biodiversity. IKSE has an active policy to change the river floodplain into nature reserves. The following measures have been taken: (1) to execute a priority pro-gramme to reduce the load of pollutants; (2) to carry out a priority programme to conserve and rehabilitate the "Biotopstrukturen", biological communities and habi-tats; (3) to install an international warning and alarm system; (4) to set up an information network (INES); (5) to implement an international monitoring pro-gramme for water quality.

*3.2 Odra*

The Odra river with its tributaries constitute an international catchment. On the Polish side several administrative bodies, the Regional Board for Water Resources (RBWRM), act as management structures for this river. Its task is maintenance and utilisation of the river basin, together with flood control and conducting invest-ments. Within the sphere of influence of the RBWRM Szczecin modernisation and regulation of the river basin is necessary, with a strong focus on the navigability of the river. There are no hydro-engineering structures in the Odra headwaters, which means that ships have free access from the river to the Baltic sea. From the view-point of the river engineer the river bed should be adapted to the use of larger ves-sels, implying that sandbanks and meanders should be eliminated, in order to main-tain the necessary water depth for navigation, but also for flood and ice flow con-trol. The same is true in the RBWRM Opole, between Katowice and Wroclaw, where reconstruction and modernisation of the river channel together with the con-struction of new canals is under policy discussion (Anonymous 1998b).

The danger of extreme river discharges causing floods is a continuous threat in the Odra basin. The flood of 1997 has brought this problem fully in focus again. Retention of river water as a tool for protection against floods, can also be in favour of water supply during extremely dry periods. A programme for the construction of retention reservoirs started already 20 years ago. Skilful handling of these reser-voirs may significantly affect the regulation of the flood wave in the lower section of the rivers. It is also clear that only transboundary German-Polish co-operation can ease the impact of floods in the Odra basin (Dirksen 1997).

Navigability of the Odra river is still a prime objective of the Polish government. The government adopted in 1995 the Programme ODRA 2005 envisaging the adaptation of the main river and its tributaries to the navigation systems of Western Europe. The programme has been postponed owing to the extremely costs involved. The floods of 1997 induced the ODRA 2006 programme, with flood protection as a prime objective. The aims of ODRA 2006 programme are flood control, environmental protection and water management. In more detail ODRA 2006 aims at (1) the elimination of flood damages, (2) the construction of a passive and active flood control system, (3) protection and improvement of water quality and the natural environment, and (4) adaptation of the Odra waterway to international requirements (Anonymous 1998a).

To bring these conflicting interests into practice, first of all an international agreement in the International Commission for Protection of the Odra against Pollution (ICPO) is necessary. In 1996 the IOCP was signed by the participating countries. However, the Polish parliament has not yet ratified the document. In Germany the river Odra is under the federal board, whereas water management, just as in the Polish RBWRM's, lies in the competence of the provinces. The Poles maintain their banks and embankments and the Germans their's. The Germans have no interest in the continuity of the Odra waterway. They are more engaged in the modernisation of the Odra-Hawel canal and the realisation of the Berlin-Gartz canal, which will enable them to exit from the Oder's waterway onto the German canal (Anonymous 1998c).

Navigability and environmental protection are in many cases counteracting interests. Riparian habitats along the Odra, but also along other rivers, are under increasing threat of river-regulation projects, and of steady lowering of the water table in most of the river valleys, which leads to the replacement of riparian softwood stands by oak-hornbeam ones. River bed regulation diminishes physical diversity of the environment, hence affects diversity of (fish) communities. It is postulated therefore by Tomialojc & Dyrcz (1993): (a) to freeze all the river regulation projects and reconsider them by taking into account all the conflicting needs of the nature and of the various parts of human society, and (b) to establish a network of nature reserves and landscape parks of the river valleys, and (c) to start attempts for restoring some riverine forests, e.g. by constructing polders filled temporarily with flood waters.

### 3.3 Vistula

Poland is facing serious problems with water resources, and the Vistula is playing a central role in that process. The water demands doubled between 1960 and 1970 because of large industrial investments and the increase of the human population (Mikulski 1990). The relative water use in the industry is 2-3 times higher than in most industrialized countries. Inefficient use of water resources and the lack of a realistic pricing policy have led to high water demands. If nothing is done about this problem there will be an enormous water deficit in the next century which may inhibit further economic development (CML 1995, Majewski 1998).

One of the ways to manage the Vistula water quantities is the Lower Vistula Cascade project (LVC), meant to promote the socio-economic development of the

Lower Vistula region (CML 1995). In the lower section of the Vistula, between the cities Plock and Wloclawek, a dam reservoir has been built. This dam is part of the large-scale project called the Lower Vistula Cascade. The concept anticipates the building of seven large dams in the lower Vistula between Warszawa and Gdansk within 20 years. The project is controversial, because of the conflict between the supposed economic gains, generation of clean energy and better conditions for irrigation, and the irreversible changes provoked in the Vistula environment. But people agree that something should be done regarding flood risk control and water supply. An integrated catchment management plan, and not a lower Vistula plan only, may enhance solutions (Majewski 1998).

In the course of the years the Vistula river bed has silted up. At present scientists and engineers have contradictory opinions about the idea to restore the Vistula as a way of transport. Besides the management of the lower Vistula (the Lower Vistula Cascade project) there exists a plan to regulate the middle part of the river. This part of the river is to be included into a planned East-West water route which should connect the Odra river via Vistula basin to the Dniestr river in the Ukraine. The opponents of this idea are afraid that it might destroy the natural conditions of the river as well as its self-purification abilities (Niemirycz 1994). There is a great area of tension between the present economic growth in Poland and the ecological restoration of disturbed and polluted habitats, such as the river Vistula. Superimposed on that conflict are the drastic changes in environmental policy and management in Poland, affecting the management strategies to be preferred for river rehabilitation.

Until now an integrated management plan for the entire Vistula catchment is lacking, although the unidirectional flow of water necessitates a catchment approach. Water quality of the river Vistula will improve after the process of sewage purification by treatment plants is completed. Part of the town of Warszawa has treatment plants already, and others are under construction. There is an urgent need for sewage purification applying modern technology, but the situation is improving year after year. The most important action now is pollution control at the source. This should be incorporated in the ongoing privatization, restructuring and modernization of the individual water-use activities of farms, factories and municipalities. The pollution of diffuse sources is an important problem, especially with respect to the agricultural sector. According to Kindler (1994) protective measures should be taken against the uncontrolled rise in the use of chemical fertilizers.

In the framework of a better control of point sources, in 1990 the "list of 80" most polluting industrial plants in Poland was published, and among them many discharging on the Odra and Vistula basins. By decision of the respective voivodships (provinces) these factories are subjected to strict control measures of their activities. The plants were obliged to implement environmental-friendly technologies and to install environmental protection equipment. The results of these measures were considerable: a 70% lower chemical oxygen demand (COD) charge in waste water (RECCEE 1995). The introduction of a computer system to control water consumption by industries and communities, water quality, amount of wastes, charges for the water consumption and penalty fees for degradation is also a step forwards (Pawlowski & Dudzinska 1994).

## 4. Discussion

### *4.1 River management*

Since 1989 Poland is going through several political, social and economic changes. These developments initiated a process of evolution in water management: a new water law that applies to the new organisational water management structure, is emerging. Because of the changes in the organisation and contents of the water management, sometimes the division of responsibilities and tasks between different authorities and institutions is unclear. Three governmental levels can be distinguished in water management, national, regional and local level (RECCEE 1994 and 1995, CML 1995). The responsibilities of the separate authorities, especially with respect to local level activities, are rather diffuse. On the national level the Ministry of Environmental Protection is the key actor responsible for water management. The tasks of this Ministry are the setting of water quality standards, the implementation of plans on national level and the formulation of water quality objectives. The Ministry of Agriculture and Food Management is responsible for the management of the rural river stretches, for river regulation, land reclamation and flood protection (CML 1995).

On regional level a distinction can be made between general water management and river basin management. Regarding general water management, 16 voivodships are responsible for the regional water management, i.e. they have jurisdiction to provide licences, to implement the water law, in order to manage the water quality. River basins of Poland's main rivers are managed by the Regional Boards for Water Resources Management. This new administrative body was created in 1992 because of tuning problems between different voivodships and different governmental levels. Because river catchment boundaries did not correspond with administrative provincial units, the division of tasks between different voivodships was not clear (CML 1995, Nienhuis *et al.* 1998).

The ICPO, comprising the ODRA 2005 and ODRA 2006 programmes, is the central policy structure for the Odra. The international agreement, however, is still not ratified by the Polish government. For the Vistula catchment an integrated management plan is lacking, but strategic plans for the Upper, Middle and Lower Vistula are under construction (Table 2). The improvement of river basin management of the Vistula needs a clear study of the administrative structure of the water management. The Ministry of Environmental Protection published in 1996 a report about the present state of the water management in Poland and tendencies of change (Hydroprojekt 1996). After the flood of July 1997 flood protection is now one of the most important issues in the catchments of the Odra and Vistula, supported by subsidies of the European Commission.

At the moment the rivers Odra and Vistula are still heavily polluted and eutrophicated. The environmental quality should be improved in the near future under growing economic circumstances. Economic prosperity and water quality are positively related, as seems to be the "law" in countries of the European Union (Stanners & Bourdeau 1995). On the other hand both rivers are unregulated over large stretches and governed by natural processes, containing large wetlands, swamps and large meanders within the floodplain.

*Table 2.* Short history of integrated river basin management of Rhine, Elbe Odra and Vistula. Abbreviations see text.

|  | 1950-1970 | 1970-1990 | 1990-2000 |
|---|---|---|---|
| Rhine | IRC (1950) | RAP (1987) | AP Flood Defence (1998) |
| Elbe | – | ARGE-ELBE (1977) | IKSE (1990) |
| Odra | – | – | ICPO (1996) Not ratified ODRA 2005/2006 |
| Vistula | – | – | No integrated management plan |

According to IUCN (1995a,b) fragmentation of the environment is currently considered to be one of the main threats for the further existence of many plant and animal species. This is because the isolation of individual populations increases the risk of their extinction for demographic and genetic reasons. These adverse processes can be prevented by linking up isolated fragments of the natural environment (core areas) and, first of all, maintaining already existing connections between such patches. The ideal situation is when the link is composed of plant communities and associations similar to those present in the connected core areas. Such links are called 'ecological corridors'.

Vast tracts of the Vistula and the Odra have such value. The state of the Vistula is to a high degree a natural one, while in the case of the Odra river valley ecosystems have been better preserved, as large patches of the riverside were preserved during regulation works. Therefore the opinion of IUCN (1995a,b) is that everything should be done to maintain the still existing areas of high natural value in the river valleys and to begin the restoration of the ecological values of its degraded parts. This would enable the establishment of better-defined ecological corridors, stretching from the northern to the southern end of Poland, being main axes of ESOCH, an Ecological System of Protected Areas whose creation in Poland is now under way. The rivers also constitute important elements of EECONET (European Ecological Network; Liro 1995).

A preliminary survey of the landscapes and ecosystems in and along the Odra and the Vistula river is prepared by IUCN (1995a,b). It is difficult to compare the natural 'values' of the rivers with each other. We need sound and internationally validated arguments to defend both environmental quality and biodiversity of the Odra and Vistula basin. What is lacking in the literature are (1) indices to measure biodiversity and the quality and of ecosystems (size; naturalness; etc.), (2) monitoring systems to measure the degradation/improvement of ecosystems, (3) cohesion between policy considerations regarding nature, space, environment and water when decisions regarding the physical planning of ecosystems should be taken. Indices or indicators should be developed to measure and quantify the "value" of landscapes, ecosystems, communities and biota in the Odra and Vistula basins, and to compare those indicators in a context of other large international rivers (Elbe,

Rhine, Meuse, etc.). The aim of this important exercise is to provide the data on environmental quality of the Odra basin with an "objective" basis which can be used when conflicting interests should be judged.

The most important threat to the nature of the Odra valley is the planned restructuring of the river for the purpose of navigation of barges with a capacity of 3,000 tons. This would mean the necessity to build several new dams downstream of Brzeg Dolny, as well as to reconstruct most of the river meanders. Damming of the water will cause the inundation of most areas between levees, while the restructuring of the river bed will cause the destruction of many valuable ecosystems. The project aimed at restructuring the Odra for smaller barges (class III) is much less destructive, but also anticipates the construction of a couple of dams (IUCN 1995a). Similarly, huge damages to the valley biocenoses will be caused by the planned construction of the East-West waterway, through the Warta, Notec and Bydgoszcz channel and the Vistula and Bug rivers. This will particularly affect the area of peat-bogs and floodmeadows as well as populations of waterfowl.

IUCN (1995a) proposes to resign from the projects focused on the extension and reconstruction of the Odra river bed in order to improve its navigational conditions, its adaptation to larger barges and, related to this, a construction plan to build several dams on the stretch where there are no such constructions (between Brzeg Dolny and the river mouth). Construction of those dams would lead to the destruction of majority of forests and other valuable biotopes in the area between the levees. The proposed restructuring of the Odra is a very high risk project, economically speaking.

In Poland the area of tension between economic growth and ecological restoration is overshadowed by the drastic changes in environmental policy and management occurring since 1989. From a social point of view it is necessary to raise some questions: whether it is better to develop highways and road transport systems which are highly energy consuming and polluting the atmosphere, or develop river navigation? Is it better to build thermal or nuclear power plants, or develop hydraulic power plants producing ecologically clean and renewable energy? Poland cannot afford to have 'natural' rivers which bring only economic losses during floods.

Following the views of IKSE, the political changes in Eastern Europe provide a long-awaited opportunity for a policy of environmental conservation and recovery of riverine systems, particularly along the Elbe, and this may counteract some of the problems previously causing river deterioration. By preserving and improving the present conditions of the Elbe basin, difficult and costly future regeneration measures for the improvement of flood protection and the conservation of natural ecosystems may be avoided. Fortunately, the middle stretches of the Elbe are amongst the least channelled stretches of any of the major European rivers. It has been suggested that a lateral canal system, separate from the Elbe river itself, might be developed to carry commercial river traffic, but this would, however, reduce the natural annual flooding over the floodplains. Since annual floods are normal temporal events necessary to the proper functioning of the ecosystems, such a canal could indirectly and severely damage these important flood plain ecosystems (Adams et al. 1996).

According to Harms et al. (1998) the reconstruction of (a part of) the historical Elbe morphology and the serious habitat-loss which took place should guide further actions at the Elbe: (1) Today's morphology and habitats should be left and not further destroyed. This means that the utilisation of the Elbe should care for the ecology of this river; (2) Utilisation that interferes with the ecology must not further expand; (3) As long as navigation is necessary on the Elbe the possibility of bringing (back) structures into the river-bed is very limited. In contrast to this it might be possible to create alternative habitats for aquatic organisms in the waters of the floodplain (affluents, branches, standing waters) by reconnecting them with the river in different manners; (4) Using the data of historical analysis as a reference for the future development of the river, the conception and realisation of measures for the ecological improvement or correction of the river should be successful. Regarding the problems of flood protection and the agricultural land-use changes in the floodplain, the disposition of the levees should be taken into consideration to widen the space for more ecological morphology in the aquatic, amphibious and terrestrial Elbe-ecosystem.

*4.2 Reference rivers for biodiversity and habitat quality restoration*

It is clear that the ecological values of the Elbe, Vistula and Odra are fully recognized in theory, but in practice economic counteracting motives are still dominating. The rivers play an important role in the economic infrastructure of Germany and Poland. In this respect they can be compared to the river Rhine, that has an important infrastructural function in Europe. All four rivers systems are roughly under the same cold temperate climatic regime, but have a completely different historical background. During the nineteenth century most of the large European rivers, including the Rhine, were being regulated by numerous longitudinal levees, and lateral dams and weirs, mainly for navigation and transport purposes (Nienhuis & Leuven 1998, Havinga & Smits 2000). The surface area of the floodplains along the Rhine has drastically been diminished during the nineteenth and intensively during the twentieth century. The upper and the middle Rhine between Bodensee and Rastatt contains numerous weirs and barrages. The larger part of the middle and lower Rhine was harnessed between high levees, which do not allow the natural dynamic morphological processes anymore. The Rhine delta has been changed completely owing to the building of massive flood-control dams in the mouths of the estuaries. The larger tributaries of the middle Rhine, Neckar, Mosel and Main contain many weirs and are only disposable for restricted navigation purposes, and most floodplains have been enclosed (Tittizer & Krebs 1996).

Compared to the Rhine, the river basins of Elbe, Odra and Vistula are still rather natural and dynamic ecosystems. As the Eastern German and Polish economic development during the past 50 to 70 years diverged negatively from the expansion in Western European states, only a few regulation works were built, in contrast to the Rhine where, both in the upper and lower stretches, during the last 50 years massive dams and regulation works have been erected. Consequently the Elbe, Odra and Vistula have maintained part of their natural, unregulated character, comprising flood plain forests and connected wildlife, mainly in the middle and lower sections of the rivers. Our hypothesis is confirmed, stating that these rivers can be used as reference rivers for the restoration of biodiversity and habitat quality of other European rivers which are economically highly developed but ecologically deteriorated.

Figure 2 shows the tentative and hypothetical relation between economic prosperity in the catchments of Rhine, Elbe, Odra and Vistula and water quality and biodiversity and habitat quality. The experience after the second World War shows that
technological improvements, stemming from economic prosperity, quickly enhance
the quality of river water and – more slowly – underwater sediments. At the same
time the effects of urban and infrastructural expansion, and expensive river regulation works destroy natural or semi-natural ecosystems. A comparison between the
river basin management of the Rhine on the one hand (where water quality has
improved, but habitats have been annihilated), and of the Elbe, Odra and Vistula on
the other (where, with the exception of the Elbe, water quality is still bad, but the
diversity and integrity of habitats is large) leads to a firm conclusion: a wise decision does not comprise the irreversible destruction of the floodplains along Elbe,
Odra and Vistula for short-term economic profits, but intends to save the river
basins for future long-term profits. These long-term profits comprise healthy and
complete ecosystems, spawning grounds for migratory fish, "spongy" wetlands for
quantitative water management, self purification properties, and nature conservation perspectives.

History learns us that river environments are often irreversibly abused in favour
of economic growth. Large rivers are economic arteries in almost all countries, and
this is true for Elbe, Odra and Vistula. The demand on space in the catchments of
these rivers for navigation, housing, working and traffic will only increase in the
near future. Occupation of space means an absolute and irreversible loss of landscape and ecosystems, and hence irreversible deterioration of the natural environment. Loss of space is generally irreversible. Changing occupied land or removing
civil engineering constructions such as dams and weirs in favour of the rehabilitation or restoration of "natural" landscape, means destroyal of economic capital, and
that is against the rules in market economies.

In international river policy approaches, however, a tendency from technological to ecological river management is noticeable. This historical change from 'technology' to 'ecology' is a very recent development, occurring in economically rich
countries. In the United States of America (USA) some experiments to remove old

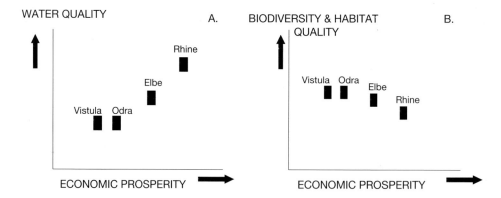

*Fig. 2.* Tentative relation between economic prosperity and water quality (a) and biodiversity and
habitat quality (b) of four European rivers.

dams from rivers have been carried out. Dam removal has received increasing attention over the last years as a viable alternative to rehabilitation of unsafe dams. Environmental considerations for assessing dam removal alternatives for river restoration were also at stake, as many hydroelectric dams come up for relicensing in the USA. A number of small dams in several USA rivers have been removed recently in favour of the natural flow of the river and in favour of restoring the migration route of fish and habitats of wildlife (Shuman 1995). The final aim of these experiments is to restore the ecological corridor, the natural river continuum from its source to the final receiving water body.

It is not unusual that after a serious accident or disaster the running environmental policy will suddenly change: 'lock the stable door after the horse has bolted'. The activities of the International Rhine Commission (IRC) offer some good examples. Already since 1950 the IRC co-ordinated a water quality monitoring programme (Table 2). The discussion to change the operative policy in the catchment of the river Rhine gained only momentum in 1986 after the Sandoz fire, which chemical spills killed almost the entire aquatic ecosystem of the river Rhine. This accident gave rise to the Rhine Action Programme (RAP) in which closure of point sources of chemical pollution in the Rhine basin, and the rigorous treatment and cleaning of the polluted Rhine-water became priority number one (Dieperink 1999).

After the narrow escape from disastrous river floods in the Rhine basin in 1993 and 1995, flood protection rose high on the political agenda of the IRC. In 1998 the Action Plan on Flood Defence (IRC 1998) was launched, comprising the widening and deepening of river beds, and constructing overflows, flood plains and agricultural land available in case of extremely high water. These policy decisions meant a cultural change in the Rhine basin: after one thousand years of embanking flood plains and channelling rivers, and gaining land on the river and the sea, the policy is slowly changing in favour of natural ecological processes. Technological solutions to fight excess river water, such as weirs, dams, and ever higher levees are in the process of being abandoned now in favour of ecological solutions, such as wider, more natural river beds.

Concerning the river Rhine the 'technology – ecology controversy' is switching now in favour of ecological solutions. Concerning the Elbe river the historical opportunity to turn the key in favour of ecology is under discussion, although technological profits, mainly for navigation purposes, still play an important role in the discussion. As for the Odra and the Vistula, mainly dominant technological solutions in favour of navigation and water storage, such as channelization and the construction of weirs and reservoirs, are debated, although a sound in favour of ecology is also heard (IUCN 1995a,b). The relation between economic prosperity, water quality and biodiversity conservation is a deadlock for sustainable integrated water management. We may only hope that the German and Polish authorities promote the wise use of water resources of the Elbe, Odra and Vistula rivers, and concomitant preservation of river ecosystems. We also hope that the Dutch and German endeavours to restore the strongly depleted habitats along the Rhine river will be persistently continued and successful.

# References

Adams, M.S., Kausch, H., Gaumert, T. & Krüger, K-E. 1996. The effects of the reunification of Germany on the water chemistry and ecology of selected rivers. Environmental Conservation 23: 35-43.

Anonymous. 1998a. Complex Development Programme. Life for the Odra river region. MATRA, Program Polska-Holenderskiej Wspolpracy Instytucjonalnej w Dorzeczu Odry, April-June 1998. p. 5.

Anonymous. 1998b. Regional management of water economy in Szczecin. MATRA, Program Polska-Holenderskiej Wspolpracy Instytucjonalnej w Dorzeczu Odry. p. 13-14.

Anonymous. 1998c. I want to see changes on the Odra. MATRA, Program Polska-Holenderskiej Wspolpracy Instytucjonalnej w Dorzeczu Odry. p. 3.

Central Statistical Office. 1993. Environmental Protection, Warsaw.

Chojnacki, J.C. & Kowalski, W. 1997. The present status of the Lower Odra ecosystem and the Odra estuary. Third Annual Meeting SC of ICE-PAS, 8-9 December 1997. Szczecin Branch ICE-PAS, Szczecin. pp. 1-23.

CML. 1995. Lower Vistula management: towards sustainable development. Centre of Environmental Science (CML), European Postgraduate Course Environmental Management, Leiden University. pp. 1-108.

Dahl, H-J. & Flade, M. 1994. Die Elbe und ihr Schutz – eine internationale Verpflichtung. Natur Landschaft 69/6: 239-250.

De Wit, M.J.M. 1999. Nutrient fluxes in the Rhine and Elbe basins. PhD Thesis Utrecht University, Utrecht.

Dieperink, C. 1999. From open sewer to salmon run: lessons from the Rhine water quality regime. J. Water Policy 1/5: 471-485.

Dirksen, W. 1997. Transboundary cooperation only can ease impact of floods on the river Odra. Land and Water Management in Europe, ERWG Letter 4: 3-4.

Dojlido, J. & Woyciechowska, J. 1989. Water quality classification of the Vistula river basin in 1987. Ekologia Polska 37: 405-417.

Dynesius, M. & Nilsson, C. 1994. Fragmentation and flow regulation of river systems in the Northern third of the world. Science 266: 753-762.

Harms, O., Kiene, S. & Nestmann, F. 1998. The analysis of historical river morphology, reference for the future development (Elbe – Germany). In: Gayer, J., Scheuerlein, M. & Starosolszky, O. (Eds.) – Proceed. Internat. Conference European River Development, Budapest. pp. 225-232.

Havinga, H. & Smits, A.J.M. 2000. River management along the Rhine: a retrospective view. In: Smits, A.J.M., Nienhuis, P.H. & Leuven, R.S.E.W. (Eds.). New approaches to river management. Backhuys Publishers, Leiden. pp. 15-32.

Hydroprojekt. 1996. Strategia Gospodarki Wodnej w Polsce. Warszawa (in Polish).

IKSE. 1995. Aktionsprogramm Elbe. Internationale Kommission zum Schutz der Elbe (IKSE), Magdeburg. pp. 1-22 + Anlagen (in German).

IKSE. 1997. Bericht über den Stand der Umsetzung der Oekologischen Sofortmassnahmen zum Schutz und zur Verbesserung der Biotopstrukturen der Elbe. Internationale Kommission zum Schutz der Elbe (IKSE), Magdeburg. pp. 1-32 + Anlagen (in German).

IRC. 1998. Action Plan on Flood Defence. International Commission for the Protection of the Rhine (IRC), Koblenz.

IUCN. 1995a. Oder as an ecological corridor; state – functioning – threats. International Union for the Conservation of Nature – IUCN-Program Europy. Fundacja IUCN Poland, Warszawa, Poland. pp. 1-266.

IUCN. 1995b. Vistula as an ecological corridor; state – functioning – threats. International Union for the Conservation of Nature – IUCN-Program Europy. Fundacja IUCN Poland, Warszawa. pp. 1-195.

Jedraszko-Dabrowska, D., Bukacinski, M., Bukacinski, D. & Cygan, J.P. 1995. Vistula river (Poland) - concepts of management. Arch. Hydrobiol. Suppl. 101, Large Rivers 9: 675-678.

Kajak, Z. 1993. The river Vistula and its floodplain valley (Poland): its ecology and importance for conservation. In: Boon, P.J., Calow, P. & Petts, G.E. (Eds.), River conservation and management. Wiley, Chichester. pp. 35-49.

Kaniewska-Prus, M. 1983. Ecological characteristics of the polysaprobic section of the Vistula river below Warsaw. Pol. Arch. Hydrobiol. 30: 149-163.

Kindler, J. 1994. Some thoughts on the implementation of water quality management strategies for Central- and Eastern-Europe. Water Science Technology 30: 15-24.

Koblak-Kalinska, E. 1992. Problems of water protection against pollution. Gospodarka Wodna 10: 222-229 (in Polish).

Liro, A. (Ed.). 1995. National Ecological Network EECONET-Poland. IUCN European Program. International Foundation for the Conservation of Nature – IUCN, Warszawa. pp. 1-66.

Macicka, T. & Wilczynska, W. 1993. Aktualna roslinnosc doliny srodkowej Odry i jej zagrozenia. In: PAN Komitet Ochrony Przyrody (Eds.), Nature and Environment Conservation in the Lowland River Valleys of Poland. Krakow. pp. 49-60 (in Polish).

Majewski, W., 1998. Comprehensive management of the Lower Vistula. In: Gayer, J., Scheuerlein, H. & Starosolszky, O. (Eds.), Proceed. Internat. Conference European River Development. Budapest. pp. 285-291.

Makinia, J., Dunnette, D. & Kowalik, P. 1996. Water pollution in Poland. Europ. Water Pollut. Control 6: 26-33.

MEPNR&F. 1991. Regulation of the Ministry of Environmental Protection, Natural Resources and Forestry (MEPNR&F), concerning water classification and conditions required for wastewater discharged to water and ground. Dziennik Ustaw 116/1001, pos. 503.

Mikulski, Z. 1990. Water resources and management in Poland. In: Mitchell, B. (Ed.), Integrated water management, international experiences and perspectives. Belhaven Press, London. pp. 172-187.

Müller, G. & Furrer, R. 1998. Pollution of the river Elbe – past, present and future. Wat. Qual. Intern. 2: 15-18.

Niemirycz, E. 1994. The Vistula river of Poland, environmental characteristics and historical perspective. Plenary Present. Intern. River Quality Symp., Portland, Oregon, USA, March 21-25, 1994.

Nienhuis, P.H. & Leuven, R.S.E.W. 1998. Ecological concepts for the sustainable management of river basins: a review. In: Nienhuis, P.H., Leuven, R.S.E.W & Ragas, A.M.J. (Eds.), New concepts for sustainable management of river basins. Backhuys Publishers, Leiden. pp. 7-33.

Nienhuis, P.H., Hofman, N.J.W., Rietbergen, M.G., Ligthart, S.S.H. & Prus, T. 1998. Water quality management of the lower reach of the Vistula river in Poland. In: Nienhuis, P.H., Leuven, R.S.E.W & Ragas, A.M.J. (Eds.), New concepts for sustainable management of river basins. Backhuys Publishers, Leiden, Netherlands. pp. 332-332.

Olanczuk-Neyman, K., Czerwionka, K. & Gorska, A. 1992. Bacteriological pollution of coastal water and sand in the region of the Gdansk Bay. Proceed. Symposium Research on Hydraulic Engineering, University of Zagreb, Zagreb. pp. 165-169.

Parzonka, W. 1995. Modelling of the bed load movement in degraded rivers. Scientific papers, Agricultural University Wroclaw, Conferences X, 2: 73-79.

Parzonka, W. & Bartnik, W. 1998. Degradation of Middle Odra caused by regulation works. In: Gayer, J., Scheuerlein, H. & Starosolsky, O. (Eds.), Proceed. Intern. Confer. River Development, Budapest, Hungary, April 16-18, 1998. VITUKI, Budapest. pp. 345-352.

Pawlowski, L. & Dudzinska, M.R. 1994. Environmental problems of Poland during economic and political transformation. Ecol. Engineering 3: 207-215.

RECCEE. 1994. Government and Environment, a directory for Central and Eastern Europe. Regional Environmental Centre for Central- and Eastern-Europe (RECCEE). Contacts for Government Ministries with Environmental Responsibilities, Budapest.

RECCEE. 1995. The Emerging Environmental Market. A survey in the Czech Republic, Hungary, Poland and the Slovak Republic. Regional Environmental Centre for Central- and Eastern-Europe (RECCEE), Budapest.

Revenga, C., Murray, S., Abramowitz, J. & Hammond, A. 1998. Watersheds of the world: ecological value and vulnerability. World Resources Institute, Washington D.C. pp. 1: 1-33; 2: 1-164.

Schöll, F., Behring, E. & Wanitschek, M. 1995. Faunistische Bestandsaufnahmen an der Elbsohle zur ökologischen Zustandsbeschreibung der Elbe und Konzeption von Sanierungsmassnahmen. UBA-Texte 64, 1995 (in German).

Shuman, J.R. 1995. Environmental considerations for assessing dam removal alternatives for river restoration. Regul. Rivers: Res. Manag. 11: 249-261.

Soldan, P., Svrcula, J., Ibrekk, H.O. & Kallqvist, T. 1994. Abatement strategies in the Odra river basin. Wat. Sci. tech. 29: 347-349.

Stanners, D. & Bourdeau, P. 1995. Europe's Environment. The Dobris Assessment. European Environment Agency, Copenhagen.

Szymanska, H. 1975. Comparison of the Vistula water purity in years 1964-1972. Gospodarka Wodna 5: 166-168.

Szymanska, H. 1987. Comparison of the Vistula water purity in years 1972-1983. Gospodarka Wodna 12: 282-285.

Tittizer, T. & Krebs, F. 1996. Ökosystemforschung der Rhein und seine Auen – eine Bilanz. Springer, Berlin. pp. 1-468.

Tomialojc, L. & Dyrcz, A. 1993. Przyrodnicza wartosc duzych rzek i ich dolin w Polsce w swietle badan ornitologicznych. In: PAN Komitet Ochrony Przyrody (Eds.), Nature and Environment Conservation in the Lowland River Valleys of Poland. Krakow. pp. 13-38 (in Polish).

# MANAGEMENT OF THE MEKONG RIVER BASIN

N.N. Quang
*Resources Development Division, Mekong River Commission Secretariat,
P.O. Box 1112, Phnom Penh, Cambodia*

## Abstract

The Mekong river runs from Tibet through China, Myanmar, Laos, Thailand, Cambodia and Viet-nam, into the South China Sea. The river has great potential in terms of water and related resources, such as hydropower, agriculture, fisheries, forestry (wetland diversification) and navigation. Taking into account economic and social changes in the region, four riparian countries of the Lower Mekong Basin, assisted by the United Nations Development Programme, have signed an Agreement on Co-operation for the Sustainable Development of the Mekong River Basin and a Protocol on the Establishment and Commencement of the Mekong River Commission. This paper briefly describes the hydrological, economic and ecological characteristics of the Mekong river basin and discusses the origin and activities of the Mekong River Commission. Special attention is paid to the preparations for the Basin Development Plan and the Water Utilisation Programme.

## 1. Introduction

In view of recent economic and political changes in the region, Cambodia, Laos, Thailand and Vietnam, assisted by the United Nations Development Programme (UNDP), have been developing a new framework for the management of the Mekong Basin since 1992. As a result of over three years of negotiations, the four riparian countries signed on Agreement on the Co-operation for the Sustainable Development of the Mekong River Basin and a Protocol on the Establishment and Commencement of the Mekong River Commission (MRC), on April 5, 1995. This marked a new phase in the co-operation for joint development and management of the Mekong basin.

This paper describes the hydrology of the Mekong basin and its ecological and economic values. In addition, it briefly presents the history of the establishment of the MRC and its mandates to co-operate and to promote, in a constructive and mutually beneficial manner, the sustainable development, utilisation, conservation and management of the Mekong river basin water and related resources for naviga-tional and non-navigational purposes, for social and economic development and for the well-being of all riparian states, consistent with the needs to protect, preserve, enhance and manage the environmental and aquatic conditions and to maintain to the ecological balance exceptional to this river basin. The paper also addresses the methods and measures the MRC has used to implement the Agreement in its initial days. The main highlights in terms of river management are the preparation of a

*New approaches to river management, pp. 85–96
edited by A.J.M. Smits, P.H. Nienhuis and R.S.E.W. Leuven*
*© 2000 Backhuys Publishers, Leiden, The Netherlands*

Strategic plan for the Implementation of the Agreement, the preparation of the Basin Development Plan (BDP) with participatory approach, the design of the Water Utilisation Programme (WUP), including drawing up and monitoring the implementation of Rules for Water Utilisation and Inter-basin Diversion, and strengthening the capability of the MRC Secretariat and the National Mekong Committees in the member countries.

## 2. The Mekong river basin

Originating in Tibet, the Mekong river, ranked as the 12th longest river in the world with total length of 4,800 km, runs across the territories of six countries (China, Myanmar, Laos, Thailand, Cambodia, Vietnam) before discharging into the South China Sea. The total area of the basin is 795,000 km$^2$, ranking as the 21st largest river in the world. The lower part, with an area of 606,000 km$^2$, known as the Lower Mekong basin, covers almost the entire territories of Laos and Cambodia, one third of Thailand and two-fifths of Vietnam (Figure 1). The upper Mekong basin is located in China and Myanmar, accounting for 24% of the total area and 18% of the annual runoff. Every year, about 475 billion m$^3$ (ranking 8th in the world) of almost unregulated river water flows into the sea.

The flow in the Lower Mekong Basin is mainly created by rainfall, which varies from 1,000-1,200 mm per year in North-eastern Thailand and amounts over 3,000 mm per year in the eastern mountain range. The approximate acreage of the catchment areas and the flow distributions of the Mekong river in its riparian countries are presented in table 1.

In terms of water and related resources, the Mekong river has great potential. Because of the favourable hydrological and topographical conditions, about 30,000 MW hydropower capacity and an annual amount of 170,000 GWh can be generated in the lower part of the Mekong basin, in an economically viable and environmentally sound way. The upper part, in the Chinese province of Yunnan, has a potential of 246,700 GWh per year. Nearly half of the Mekong hydropower potential is located along the main stream, while the remaining potential is situated along the numerous tributaries in Laos.

*Table 1.* Approximate catchment area and flow distribution of the Mekong river.

| Country | Catchment area (km$^2$) | Percentage (%) | Average flow (m$^3$s$^{-1}$) | Percentage (%) |
|---|---|---|---|---|
| China | 165,000 | 21 | 2,410 | 16 |
| Myanmar | 24,000 | 3 | 300 | 2 |
| Laos | 202,000 | 25 | 5,270 | 35 |
| Thailand | 184,000 | 23 | 2,560 | 17 |
| Cambodia | 155,000 | 20 | 2,860 | 19 |
| Vietnam | 65,000 | 8 | 1,660 | 11 |
| Total | 795,000 | 100 | 15,060 | 100 |

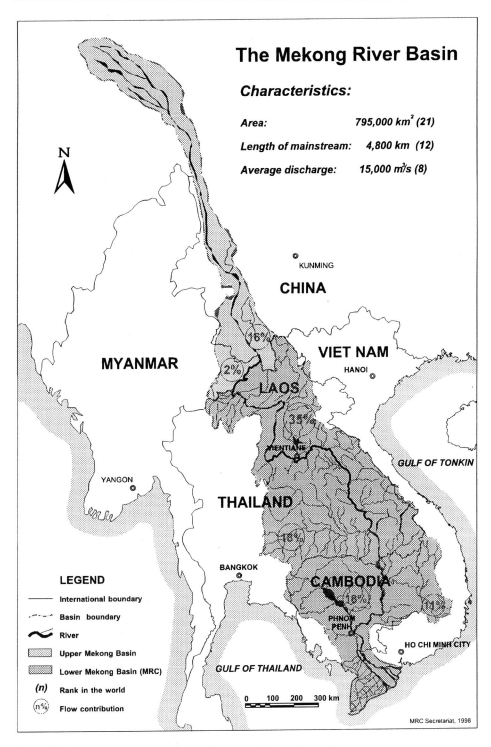

*Fig. 1.* The riparian countries and large tributaries of the Mekong river basin.

The Mekong basin can be divided into six principal land type divisions, including: Lancang river basin (Yunnan), Northern Highlands (Laos, Myanmar, Yunnan, Thailand), Korat Plateau (Thailand) and Sakon Plateau (Laos), Eastern Highlands (Laos, Vietnam), Southern Uplands (Cambodia) and Lowlands (Cambodia, Laos, Vietnam). About 13 million ha in the lower Mekong basin allow cultivation, including about 8 million ha in the Northeast of Thailand and about 5 million ha in the Mekong delta.

In the basin, wetlands areas are located along the river and its tributaries, housing about a thousand fish species. Fish are also an important source of nutrients for the rural population. Annual catches of inland fisheries are estimated at about one million metric tons, of which about 300,000 to 400,000 tons are caught in Cambodia. In addition, the river is a useful and cheap transport route, whose upper stretches can be used for inland navigation while the delta branches can accommodate for coastal and seagoing vessels. Forestry potential in the region is great but is threatened by slash-and-burn practices, which have many harmful effects on agricultural production and the environment, including water shortages, soil erosion and flash floods.

## 3. Establishment of the Mekong River Commission

Over a century ago, the French intended to use the Mekong as a transport route to Yunnan, (China) but soon abandoned this ambition due to the many obstacles such as rapids, water falls and shallows. In 1950, the Americans conducted a brief preliminary survey in the lower Mekong basin, which resulted in further studies of flood control by the then Economic Commission for Asia and the Far East (ECAFE).

In 1957, under the auspices of ECAFE (now Economic and Social Commission for Asia and Pacific or ESCAP), the four riparian countries of the lower Mekong basin agreed to integrate their efforts to develop the water and related resources by establishing the Committee for Co-ordination of Investigations of the Lower Mekong Basin (the Mekong Committee). Over the period 1957-1975, much was achieved by the joint efforts of the four countries, which were supported by the international donor community. These accomplishments included the basic system data, the 1970 Indicative Basin Plan and many other water resource projects implemented in Thailand and Laos (Committee for Co-ordination of Investigations of the Lower Mekong Basin 1970). The first difficult period for the Mekong co-operation was that of 1975-1977 when, due to political changes in the region, no meetings of the Mekong Committee were held. However, the activities of the Mekong Secretariat continued. In 1978, three of the riparian countries, namely, Laos, Thailand and Vietnam, resumed their co-operation by forming the Interim Mekong Committee (Interim Committee for Co-ordination of Investigations of the Lower Mekong Basin 1978).

The reactivation of the Mekong Committee was completed in 1991, when Cambodia officially requested to rejoin the Committee. In preparation for its rejoining, Cambodian representatives had already taken part in some meetings of the Interim Mekong Committee. However, due to disagreement among the parties concerned on the preparation and interpretation of the 'basic documents', the Mekong co-operation entered a second crisis period. In 1992, with the assistance of UNDP, two Mekong Consultative Meetings of the four countries were held in Hong Kong and Kuala Lumpur. At the Mekong Consultative Meeting it was decided to set up a Mekong Working Group, composed of representatives of the four lower Mekong riparian countries, whose mandate was to prepare a new framework for future co-operation among the countries of the lower Mekong basin, which could respond to the recent and rapid economic and environmental changes in the region.

On April 5, 1995, in Chiang Rai, Cambodia, Laos, Thailand and Vietnam signed on Agreement on the Co-operation for the Sustainable Development of the Mekong River Basin and a Protocol on the Establishment and Commencement of the Mekong River Commission (MRC). This marked a new phase in the co-operation for joint development and management of the lower Mekong basin. The Agreement incorporated three significant elements (Mekong River Commission 1995):

1. the concept of sustainable development, together with a recognition of the importance of protecting the environment and the ecological balance;
2. the use of a Basin Development Plan (BDP) as a tool and process to identify, categorise and prioritise projects and programmes;
3. the establishment of Rules for Water Utilisation to maintain the required flow regime in the Mekong river.

## 4. Mandate, structure and mode of operation of the MRC

As stated in the Agreement, the four member countries agree "to co-operate in all fields of sustainable development, utilisation, management and conservation of the water and related resources of the Mekong river basin, including but not limited to irrigation, hydropower, navigation, flood control, fisheries, timber floating, recreation and tourism, in a manner to optimise the multiple use and mutual benefits of all riparian states and to minimise the harmful effects that may result from natural occurrences and man-made activities". For this purpose, MRC's mandate is "to co-operate and promote in a constructive and mutually beneficial manner, the sustainable development, utilisation, conservation and management of the Mekong river basin water and related resources for navigational and non-navigational purposes, for social and economic development and the well-being of all riparian States, consistent with the needs to protect, preserve, enhance and manage the environmental and aquatic conditions and to maintain of the ecological balance exceptional to this river basin". The MRC is a three-level inter-governmental organisation with an international status. The highest level, the Council, is a policy-making body consisting of one member from each country at the ministerial level. The second body, the Joint Committee, is the implementing level, consisting of one member from each country at the departmental level. The Chairmanship of both these bodies is rotated annually by the alphabetical order of member countries' names (normal order for the Council and reverse order for the Joint Committee). The third body of the MRC is the Secretariat, headed by a Chief Executive Officer, serving as the technical and administrative arm of the Joint Committee and the Council. The MRC Headquarters, after forty years of being located in Bangkok (Thailand), has just been relocated to Phnom Penh (Cambodia) on the basis of a decision made by the Council in late 1996.

The priority issues for implementing the Agreement are to prepare the Basin Development Plan (BDP) and to draw up the Rules for Water Utilization and Inter-basin Diversion. A Sub-Committee on BDP and a Sub-Committee on the Rules for Water Utilization and Inter-basin Diversion have consequently been established. Since water quality is a very important issue, a Sub-Committee for Rules on Water Quality was established as well. The Sub-Committees on Water Quantity and Water Quality will conduct their studies in parallel and submit their results for the Joint Committee's consideration.

## 5. Strategic Plan for Implementation of the 1995 Mekong Agreement

Throughout its history, there have been periods during which the Mekong Committee and the Interim Mekong Committee were mainly funded by a wide range of supportive multi-lateral and bilateral development partners. During these periods, donor funding was reasonably regular and predictable, as the Mekong Committee was a convenient institution through which development funds could be channelled, especially to those member countries in transition. Consequently, there was little incentive to plan strategically. Operations and organisations were designed basically to cope with the various programmes and projects initiated by the Secretariat, the four member countries and occasionally by donors.

Many donors supporting the MRC have expressed concern that the MRC operations seemed to lack vision and that their investments in the MRC were not being used as effectively and efficiently as they would like, in the interests of the basin's people. At the same time, some other Mekong regional development initiatives were emerging, all competing for scarce development funds in the same geographic area. In short, the pressure of all factors, including significant international and regional change in the political, social and scientific environments, the uncertainty of future funding support, and the imminent relocation of the MRC Headquarter to Phnom Penh has led to the development of a Strategic Plan. The MRC's Strategic Plan has been given top priority. It will allow the MRC to concentrate its efforts to manage an international river – the Mekong – in a comprehensive and integrated manner according to reasonable and realistic timing sequences, in accordance with the actual capacity of the MRC Secretariat and four National Mekong Committees.

With clear visions, goals, strategies and, importantly, the continuity provided by the Strategic Plan, the MRC will be able to develop prioritized, logical, future programmes which will contribute directly to agreed goals and visions, and will reassure donors that their funds will be used for focused and co-ordinated programmes for sustainable development in the Mekong river basin. Outcomes of the study include "An economically and socially prosperous, environmentally sound Mekong river basin" as a vision of the Mekong river basin and "A world class river basin organisation, financially secure, serving the riparian countries to achieve the basin vision" as a vision of the MRC.

Since "to promote and co-ordinate sustainable management and development of the basin's water and related resources for the well-being of the basin's people through the provision of objective scientific information and policy advice in accordance with the 1995 Agreement" is the long-term mission of the MRC, it plans, between now and the year 2003, to achieve the following five short- and medium-term goals:

1. to establish and implement Rules for Water Utilisation and Inter-basin diversion;
2. to formulate a Basin Development Plan to provide an effective planning and process tool for sustainable management and development;
3. to establish an integrated, basin-wide, environmental monitoring network for the use and conservation of water and related resources;
4. to stimulate and evaluate the effectiveness of the ongoing programmes and projects, and progressively initiate new development activities in accordance with the Strategic Plan;
5. to improve the capacity of the MRC to implement its mission and to play the leading role in co-ordinating the basin's water-related activities and meet stakeholders' expectations.

To achieve these goals, four Key Result Areas (KRAs) have been defined:

1. Natural Resources Planning and Development;
2. Environmental Management and Social Considerations;
3. Databases and Information Systems;
4. Organisation, Management and Co-operation.

The challenge will be to remain focused on these goals while maintaining the flexibility to cope with the inevitable short-term pressures that will demand attention and perhaps re-alignment of strategies from time to time. The long-term goal to the year 2015 is having a financially secure MRC to operate programmes and projects contributing to the improvement of the livelihoods of the basin's inhabitants, consistent with clean and safe water resources and a healthy eco-environment.

## 6. The MRC's Annual Work Programme

In the past, the annual Mekong "Work Programme" document was basically drafted as a list of proposals for potential donor funding. Some proposals sat on the list, without being funded, for many years. Earlier "Work Programme" proposals were not prioritised and for the most part had no clear focus. In the light of the Strategic Plan, the MRC has started to "overhaul" its Work Programme, by restructuring it through the four Key Result Areas. From a Work Programme consisting of a number of single projects, the current Work Programme of the MRC has developed to comprise several inter-linked and integrated programmes (Mekong River Commission 1998a,b). The 1999 Work Programme must very much be seen as the first part of a transition in which the Basin Development Plan (BDP) and Water Utilisation Programme (WUP) will be given more attention (Mekong River Commission 1998c). The BDP and WUP will be discussed in detail in sections 7 and 8.

In addition to the BDP and WUP, the 1999 MRC Work Programme includes several basin-wide projects and programmes with the aim to seek funds from interested donors. The implementation of these projects and programmes, whether funds for them have already been secured or not, is one of the five goals of the Strategic Plan. Some of the programmes highlighted here are the Mekong Environment Programme, the Fisheries Programme, the Watershed Management and Forestry Programme, the Agriculture and Irrigation Programme, the Hydropower Programme, the Navigation and Transport Programme and the Human Resources Development Programme.

The main objective of the Mekong Environment Programme is to integrate environmental aspects in the development of the Mekong river basin water and related resources at all steps of the project cycle. The programme has found support from the Swedish International Development Agency and the Danish International Development Agency.

The Fisheries Programme aims at promoting economic and sustainable fish production systems throughout the Mekong river basin. The programme is currently being supported by the Danish International Development Agency and has four main components:
1. the management of capture fisheries;
2. the development of small-scale aquaculture;
3. the strengthening of institutions;
4. the co-ordination and exchange of information.

The Watershed Management and Forestry Programme comprises a watershed classification project, a forest cover assessment and monitoring project, and a project for the sustainable management of resources. This programme is currently being supported by the Swiss Agency for Development Co-operation and the German Development Co-operation through the Deutsche Gesellschaft für Technische Zusammenarbeit.

In the past, a Mekong Irrigation Programme, which consisted of several irrigation projects in Northeast Thailand and Laos, was formulated with financial assistance from the Government of the Netherlands. At present, with the assistance from Denmark, the MRC Secretariat is co-ordinating with line agencies in four riparian countries to conduct an Expert Consultation, aimed at formulating a MRC agriculture and irrigation programme which would be attractive to donors.

According to the Hydropower programme, the hydropower potential in the lower Mekong basin is estimated at about 30,000 MW, with a possible average annual production of 170,000 GWh. The installed capacity of tributary projects ranges from 20 MW to about 700 MW and those on the main channel from 600 MW to 3,300 MW. Over one third of the potential is located on the main channel and the remainder on the major tributaries, particularly in the Laos PDR. To date, 12 hydropower projects have been built on the tributaries of the Mekong river, with a total capacity of 450 MW (45% being located in the Laos PDR). Four projects, totalling 1,140 MW, are under construction. Many other tributary hydropower projects and inter-linked transmission lines have been studied by the MRC and other initiatives, such as the ADB-Greater Mekong Sub-Regional Co-operation (GMS) and the WB. Apart from some dams constructed in upper stretch of China, no dam has been built in the main channel of the Mekong river since 1957. Despite their economic attractiveness, shown by many studies at various levels, some large main channel hydropower projects such as Pa Mong could not be implemented for a number of reasons, relating to environmental problems, resettlement and power demands.

In order to enable the MRC to make appropriate decisions on hydropower projects, the MRC has approved principles for hydropower development in which state-of-the-art assessment of cumulative environmental impacts and socio-economic aspects, as well as mechanisms for public participation by stakeholders in hydropower planning and development are to be applied by the MRC, in its efforts to promote the most effective use of the natural resources in the lower Mekong basin. The MRC is to encourage the private sector to join in developing the Mekong hydropower potential with proper consideration for the environment and the well-being of the people living in the region. Based on these principles, a study of the MRC Hydropower Development Strategy has been proposed and included in the Work Programme (Phanrajsavong 1996).

Navigation and Transport is another important sector, which includes several projects, including updating the hydrographic atlas, studying the port system along the Mekong river, harmonising navigational aids, strengthening the Mekong navigation training, training to construct bank protection, upgrading ferry facilities, studying the river channel access, and studying the hydraulics and morphology of the river. Current donors for this sector are Denmark, Belgium, Finland, and Australia.

## 7. Basin Development Plan

After the Indicative Basin Plan (IBP), which was drawn up by the Mekong Committee in 1970 and the Revised IBP (Perspectives for Mekong Development) developed by the Interim Mekong Committee in 1987, this is the third time that riparian countries of the Lower Mekong Basin have decided to draw up a Basin Development Plan (BDP). In the 1995 Mekong Agreement, the BDP is referred to as "the general planning tool and process that the Joint Committee of the MRC would use as a blueprint to identify, categorise and prioritise the projects and programmes to seek assistance for and to implement the plan at the basin level". In other words, the BDP is to be developed in line with the principles of the Agreement, which relate to sustainable development, utilisation, management and conservation of the water and related resources, the protection of the environment, natural resources, aquatic life and conditions, and the ecological balance of the Mekong river basin, the reasonable and equitable use of the waters, etc.

Several water-related sectors, for which development and management strategies will have to be prepared, have been identified (Mekong River Commission 1997). Two cross-sector themes will be integrated into all analyses and outputs: the environmental and ecological balance (which would include not only an analysis of environmental conditions in the Mekong river basin but also considerations of appropriate measures of response to environmental changes and impacts) and human resource development (in the water-related sectors).

Unlike what happened on previous occasions, the MRC has proceeded with caution in preparing of the BDP proposal, in which the concept of public participation (participatory approach) has been incorporated. In some countries in the region, this concept may to some extent be a novelty, and it will therefore take some time for all stakeholders to be appropriately involved in the planning process. In other words, the participatory approach to the planning of water resources and related resource development and management in the Mekong basin is rather new to many people in the region. The national policies, strategies and plans in each of the member countries, as well as the initiatives by other institutions such as the Asian Development Bank, the World Bank, the Association of Southeast Asian Nations and other regional programmes which could affect the future of the Mekong river basin are to be taken into consideration. Environmental and social considerations are integral parts of the planning process. The BDP will involve the national planning agencies and active public participation. "Don't plan for us without us" is a concern that has been expressed during the course of BDP preparation.

## 8. Water Utilisation Programme

At present, there are many on-going and planned projects in the MRC Work Programme that relate to water utilization. In order to assist the MRC Secretariat in preparing an overall programme framework to improve the co-ordination of the various projects and programmes, a Water Utilisation Programme has been proposed. The Water Utilisation Programme is conceived as a long-term programme aiming to develop, maintain and implement rules for water utilisation as well as related procedures and processes that would be needed to support their implementation. The Water Utilisation Programme should be seen as an umbrella programme which covers five broad areas:
1. overall co-ordination and capacity building;
2. basin modelling and analytical tools;
3. hydrological monitoring and data collection co-ordination;
4. formulating the rules;
5. strengthening the MRC's basin management functions to implement the rules.

Donors for the Water Utilisation Programme are the World Bank (under the Global Environment Facility grant financing), Japan (for water quantity), France (for water quality) and Finland (for modelling). Regarding the Rules for Water Quantity, Japan is the first donor to have committed itself to support part of the study. France also explores its readiness to co-finance, probably together with Sweden, the preparation of Rules for Water Quality. The World Bank is considering supporting the preparation of the project document on the Water Utilisation Programme to provide a framework to cover both quantity and quality aspects.

## 9. Other initiatives

In addition to the MRC, there are other regional initiatives, such as the Greater Mekong Sub-regional Co-operation (initiated by the Asian Development Bank), the Forum for Comprehensive Development of Indochina (initiated by Japan) and the Association of Southeast Asian Nations-Mekong Basin Development Co-operation. Through these initiatives, the Mekong co-operation includes not only water and land resources but also other economic sectors. Geographically, these initiatives cover not only the Mekong basin but also almost the whole five of the countries as well as China's Yunnan province. While these regional initiatives mainly relate to investment through loans or joint ventures, the MRC's activities mainly focused on the pre-investment phases, including strategic studies, basin-wide database collection and resource development activities, using grants from external donors. Immediately after its establishment, the MRC has invited two upstream countries, i.e., China and Myanmar, to participate in its meetings as observers. Subsequently, the co-operation has been strengthened through a mechanism of dialogue meetings between the MRC, China and Myanmar, in which these two upstream countries were adequately informed of the activities of the MRC and participated in relevant activities of the MRC projects. At present, a detailed proposal for co-operation in some specific areas is being prepared.

## 10. Challenges for the future

The signing of the Agreement on Co-operation for the Sustainable Development of the Mekong River Basin is a great achievement of the MRC member countries. However, the successful implementation of the Agreement in terms of river management will not be an easy task. The implementation also depends on the goodwill and constructive co-operation of all parties concerned in utilising and protecting the precious and fragile common assets of the Mekong, and also on the support from the community of donors. Developing and managing water and related resources in the Mekong river basin requires a long-term development plan and an institutional framework of co-operation acceptable to all countries, in which participation of all stakeholders concerned is one of the conditions for success. The MRC has been entrusted this challenging task by its member countries and will draw on the valuable experiences learnt from other international river basins, especially those with similar conditions as the Mekong river basin.

## Disclaimer

This paper expresses the view of the author and does not necessarily reflect the vision of the Mekong River Commission Secretariat.

## References

Committee for Co-ordination of Investigations of the Lower Mekong Basin. 1970. Report on Indicative Basin Plan. The Mekong Secretariat, Bangkok.
Interim Committee for Co-ordination of Investigations of the Lower Mekong Basin. 1978. Perspectives for Mekong development. The Mekong Secretariat, Bangkok.
Mekong River Commission. 1995. Agreement on Co-operation for Sustainable Development of the Mekong River Basin signed by Cambodia, Laos, Thailand and Vietnam. Mekong River Commission Secretariat, Phnom Penh.
Mekong River Commission. 1997. Final Report on Mekong River Basin Diagnostic Study. Mekong River Commission Secretariat, Phnom Penh.

Mekong River Commission. 1998a. Annual Report 1997. Mekong River Commission Secretariat, Phnom Penh.

Mekong River Commission. 1998b. Annual Report 1998. Mekong River Commission Secretariat, Phnom Penh.

Mekong River Commission. 1998c. The 1999 Work Programme. Mekong River Commission Secretariat, Phnom Penh.

Phanrajsavong, C. 1996. Hydropower development in the lower Mekong basin. Briefing Note Workshop on Development Dilemmas in the Mekong Subregion. Monash University, Melbourne.

# ECOLOGICAL BASIS FOR THE MANAGEMENT OF THE PANTANAL - UPPER PARAGUAY RIVER BASIN

C.J. da Silva
*Proj. Ecologia do Pantanal, Instituto de Biociências, Universidade Federal de Mato Grosso, 78.060-900 Cuiabá, Mato Grosso, Brazil*

## Abstract

The present paper summarises ecological data on the Pantanal Mato Grossense - upper Paraguay river basin (Brazil). In addition, it presents general information on land and water use in the headwaters of the Pantanal. Recommendations and strategies for sustainable river management and protection of the region are discussed, in view of the need to increase the ecological data base, to assess the present model of land and water use and to empower the local communities to participate.

## 1. Introduction

The Pantanal, the world largest floodplain, with an area of about 138,183 km$^2$, is composed of a mosaic of different environments, sustaining rich aquatic and terrestrial biota. The fragile equilibrium of the Pantanal ecosystems, maintained by the flood pulse, is threatened by the new direction of economic growth, principally deforestation, modification of the hydraulic geometry of the rivers and alterations to the natural area. These tendencies are more evident in the catchment area of the upper Paraguay river basin, from where the waters flow to the Pantanal. Ecological studies about the Pantanal are still incipient, but already permit a general understanding of the system. However, there is a need to organise the existing data in order to assess which studies or study focus and sites should be investigated. There are various interest groups in the Pantanal; First of all, it is considered a national patrimony in the Brazilian Constitution of 1988, so all Brazilians have an interest in and concern for its fate. Locally, various groups can be identified: the Indians, first to inhabit the region; traditional communities of Indian, African and European descendants; the Pantanal farmers, who have been there since the 18th century; the Plateau farmers, who arrived in the 1970s; the population of the urban areas close to the Pantanal and finally those dependent on the region for tourist and navigation activities.

The aim of this paper is to outline the ecological basis of and suggestions for the management of the Pantanal Mato Grossense in the upper Paraguay river basin. The geographical position of the Pantanal is described in section 2. Section 3 describes, based on the available literature, the region's main physical characteristics (hydrol-

*New approaches to river management, pp. 97–117*
*edited by A.J.M. Smits, P.H. Nienhuis and R.S.E.W. Leuven*
© *2000 Backhuys Publishers, Leiden, The Netherlands*

ogy, geomorphology and soils) and its biota (composition, diversity). The function-
ality of the Pantanal is also described, using the flood pulse concept (Junk *et al.*
1989). Section 4 discusses the various social groups within the basin as well as the
development of economic activities. The environmental problems resulting from
these activities are outlined. Section 5 discusses strategies to conduct sustainable
management policies, considering three conditions (or pillars) as the basis for management: production and organisation of the ecological data, the present model of
land and water use and the role played by society. Mechanisms to strengthen these
pillars, either already in use or as alternatives, complete this paper.

## 2. Location of the Pantanal

The Pantanal Mato Grossense is located in the Paraguay river basin, in the central
part of South America, between longitudes 16° to 22° and latitudes 55° to 58°, and
includes parts of Brazil, Paraguay and Bolivia (Figure 1). The Paraguay river
stretches over a distance of 2,800 km, from its source in the Serra de Tapirapuã,
Mato Grosso state (Brazil) to where it discharges into the Paraná river in the cities
of Corrientes and Resistencia in Argentina, draining an area of 1,095,000 km². The
Paraguay river is divided into three sections. First, the upper Paraguay, which starts
at the source and runs over a distance of 1,873 km, crossing Brazil, Bolivia and
Paraguay, until it joins the Apa river. Then the middle Paraguay, which crosses
Paraguay and flows over 797 km before reaching the Tebicuary river. Finally, the
lower Paraguay, which leaves Paraguay and joins the Parana river in Argentina after
a run of 130 km (Figure 1).

The upper Paraguay river basin (UPRB) drains an area of 496,000 km² of which
351,000 km², (around 71%), is in Brazil (Mato Grosso and Mato Grosso do Sul
states), while 145,000 km² or about 29% is in Bolivia and Paraguay. The UPRB can
be subdivided into three areas according to their topography: the "Planalto" or
Plateau, the water head region, with altitudes ranging from 750 to 250 m; the
"depressão" or depression with altitudes between 250 and 180 m; and the Pantanal,
between 180 and 150 m, the area where extensive seasonal flooding occurs
(Alvarenga *et al.* 1984). The Pantanal region is situated on a low relief area, where
flooding by the Paraguay and its tributaries is seasonal (Figure 2). It is surrounded
by the Upper Paraguay Depression between the Brazilian Shield and the Andes.

## 3. Ecological description of the Pantanal region

The Pantanal climate is hot and humid with a rainy season in the summer and a dry
season in the winter (Köppen 1948). The mean annual temperature is 25°C.
Summer occurs when the continental equatorial air mass reaches the region and the
winter is due to the polar air mass producing the "friagem" phenomenon, when cold
air masses may cause temperature to drop to as low as 0°C for short periods
(Valverde 1972). Precipitation varies between 1,250 mm per year in the northern
and 1,100 mm in the southern region. Evaporation exceeds precipitation for 6 - 12
months per year, only permitting the growth of savannah vegetation. The rainy sea-

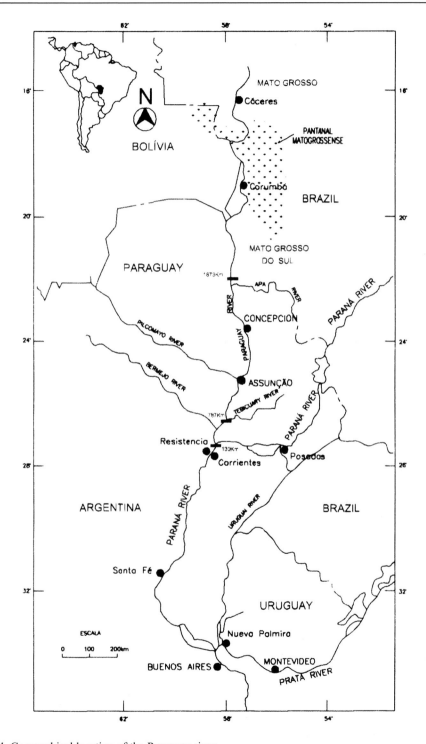

*Fig. 1.* Geographical location of the Paraguay river.

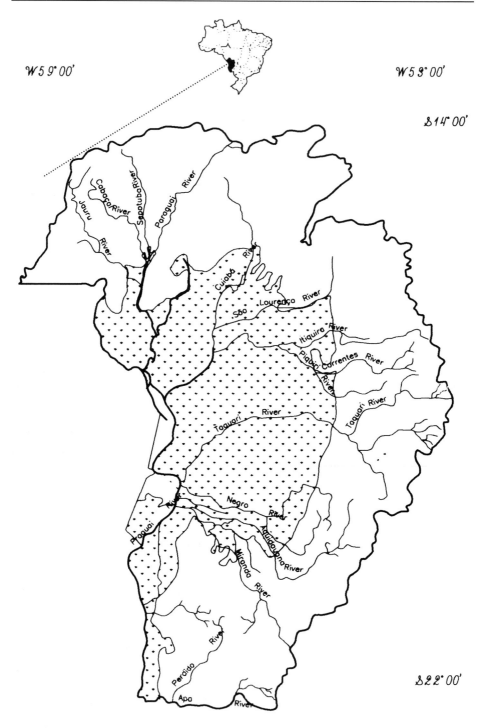

*Fig. 2.* The upper Paraguay river basin showing the Pantanal region (shading) and catchment area (light).

son extends from October to April, with a maximum rainfall of 213 mm per month, and the dry season from May to September, with a minimum rainfall about 5 mm per month (Tarifa 1986).

Since the Quaternary Era, the Paraguay river and its tributaries have deposited their sediments on the Pantanal floodplains. As a consequence, the soils vary according to the origin and age of the sediments. Recent sediments are found only along the rivers. Most of the soils of the Pantanal are composed of old nutrient-poor sediments, which were periodically lixiviated by the rains and floodwater. Extensive dry periods caused by the alternation of glacial and interglacial periods resulted in sediment consolidation and partial lateritisation (Amaral Filho 1986).

The Conservation Plan (PCBAP 1997a) catalogued the various soil types of the upper Paraguay basin into 3 geomorphologic units: the Pantanal inundation plain, residual relief and adjacent depressions, and the plateau. Quartz sands and latosoils (deep red and yellowish red) are most abundant on the plateau. The deep red latosoils exhibit a low base saturation and low water and nutrient retention, and are highly susceptible to erosion. These soils are generally used for soya bean and corn production as well as for pasture. The quartz sands show a low humidity retention capacity, intense lixiviation and high erosion susceptibility. The predominant soil types in the depression and residual relief are younger in characteristics than those of the plateau. In the Pantanal floodplain, hydromorphism is predominant.

On the basis of the range of geological formations and geomorphologic units, and the various drainage sub-basins and flood levels, different Pantanal types have been identified by Pantanal inhabitants and researchers. Because of these differences, some authors have adopted different classifications for various Pantanal types: Alvarenga *et al.* (1984) identified 13 types of Pantanal, based on the interpretation of radar imagery (side-looking airborne radar); Adamóli (1981) classified the Pantanal into 10 different types, using mainly political and river boundaries; Hamilton *et al.* (1996) distinguished 10 subregions, using passive microwave remote sensing, field studies and flood patterns.

In the Pantanal, flood levels vary in both time and space, as a result of the large expanse of the territory and the complex regional hydrological system. In the northern part of the Pantanal, in the state of Mato Grosso, flooding occurs from January to March, concurrently with the rainy season (October-April). In the Southern Pantanal, in the state of Mato Grosso do Sul, mainly in the Paraguay river, there is a lag-time of about two or three months between the rainy season and the peak of flooding (May-July). The water coming from the upper Pantanal (near the town of Cáceres) takes this time to reach the lower region (near the town of Corumbá). This is due to the low inclination of the Paraguay river and its tributaries within the Pantanal (Carvalho 1986) and to the geomorphologic controls succeeding one another down the upper Paraguay river channel. These controls, identified as rocks outcrops, at places such as Refúgio Trés Bocas-Amolar, Ladário-Porto da Manga and Fecho dos Morros-Porto Murtinho, are considered responsible for the present hydrological configuration of the Pantanal (Ponce 1995).

In addition to the annual flood pulse, inter-annual periods of pronounced dry and wet phases are frequent in the Pantanal (Figure 3). They influence the expansion and regression of water, flora, fauna, and types of soil use. According to Veloso (1972), the last dry phases which occurred in the 1960s, favoured some species of plants,

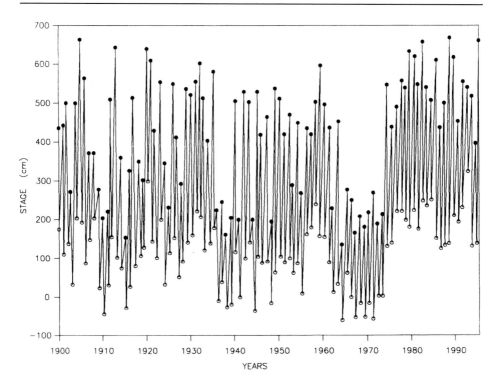

*Fig. 3.* Inter-annual water fluctuations in the upper Paraguay river at Ladário city (Southern Pantanal).

like *Vochysia divergens* which expanded and increased their dominance over the landscape. When pronounced flooding began in 1974, the water entered the flood-plain and many lakes then increased their surface area and volume, causing the extinction of many plant communities (Da Silva 1990, Da Silva & Esteves 1995).

In the Pantanal Mato-Grossense, the annual water level fluctuation, of variable duration and extent, causes a series of functional and structural transformations in the ecosystems and influences the spatial organisation of diversity. The form and persistence of the connections between the lakes, locally known as "baías" (small shallow lakes) and the rivers, or floodplains, also contributes to the spatial organi-sation of diversity. As a consequence, ecological processes (such as productivity, decomposition, biomass and nutrient import/export, nutrient concentration/dilu-tion), limnological variables and the spatial organisation of the biological commu-nities vary in time (high/low water periods) and in space (Da Silva 1990).

The available data regarding nutrients indicates large variations of nutrient con-tents of the water column. The concentration of mineral salts in the northern tribu-taries varies from 5 to 340 μS cm$^{-1}$ (Junk & Furch 1980, Wantzen 1998). The high-est dissolved ion values (1594 - 5200 μS cm$^{-1}$) are found in a special type of lake, called "salinas", which occurs in the southern part of the Pantanal (Mourão 1989) and also in lakes (850 μS cm$^{-1}$) surrounded by "ninhais", habitats where colony-breeding birds reproduce (Da Silva & Oliveira 1998). Large seasonal variations in electrical conductivity in the water column have been reported for the lakes and the floodplains of the Pantanal (Da Silva & Esteves 1995, Heckman 1994, Hamilton *et al.* 1999). In some lakes, drained by the Cuiabá river (the main Paraguay river tributary on the left margin), the dry period and rapid evaporation contribute to the increase in nitrogen and phosphate concentrations, whilst calcium, magnesium and potassium contents increase in the rainy season (Da Silva & Esteves 1995). On the other hand, electrical conductivity in the Bento Gomes river (another tributary of the upper Paraguay river) is higher during the dry season (Heckman 1994). The presence of easily weathered carbonate rocks in some of the upland watersheds surrounding the floodplains and concentration of solutes in some closed or semi-closed lakes due to evaporation have been found to be linked to this variation (Da Silva & Esteves 1995, Hamilton *et al.* 1999). The amount of total suspended matter is generally higher during the high water period (Wantzen 1998, Espindola *et al.* 1999a,b, Oliveira & Calheiros 1999).

The production, growth and decomposition rates of aquatic macrophyte biomass are higher during the high water period (Da Silva & Esteves 1993, Penha *et al.* 1998a,b, Penha *et al.* 1999). The life cycle of the aquatic macrophyte *Pontederia cordata* var. *ovalis* (Mart.) Solms is closely linked to oscillations in water level and depends on the recurrence of the dry phase, indicating the importance of the annual water level variations (Penha *et al.* 1998b). The effects of concentration and dilution, during the dry and inundation periods respectively, have been documented with respect to phytoplankton, zooplankton, fish and bird communities (Espindola *et al.* 1999a,b, Rezende *et al.* 1996, Strussman 1991).

According to Ab'Saber (1988), the present biotic framework of the Pantanal Mato Grossense is a consequence of the Quaternary climatic fluctuations in South and Central America, which provoked changing conditions that have had a repercussion on the spatial and temporal distribution of the flora and fauna. According to Pott & Pott (1999) the plants species are distributed in the savannas and in semi-deciduous and evergreen forests. The semi-deciduous forests emerge from some rather particular Pantanal features such as: 'Capões' – forested islands that are round in shape and not inundated, 'cordilheiras' – sandy elongated paleo-levées which rise about 1 to 3 m above the level of the floodplain, and 'morrarias' (hills) of some 200 to 300 m in height, surrounded by floodplains partly covered with deciduous forest. The evergreen forests are located in the seasonally flooded areas. The species richness is shown in table 1, based on existing studies.

According to PCBAP (1997b), mammals species that are threatened in other Brazilian regions, such as the Giant anteater (*Myrmecophaga tridactyla*), the Giant

*Table 1.* Species richness in the Pantanal wetlands.

| Group | Number of species | Source |
|---|---|---|
| Plants | 1,863 | Pott & Pott (1999) |
| Mammals | 122 | Fonseca *et al. (*1996) |
| Reptiles | 93 | PCBAP (1997b) |
| Fish | 264 | Britski *et al.* (1999) |
| Birds | 656 | Cintra & Yamashita (1990), PCBAP (1997b) |

otter (*Pteronura brasiliensis*), the Jaguar (*Panthera onca*), the Puma (*Felis concolor*) and the Southern river otter (*Lutra longicaudalis*) are still being observed in the Pantanal. According to PCBAP (1997b) abundance estimations, there are about 3,5 million caimans (*Caiman crocodilus yacare*), the species that most captures the attention of visitors to the Pantanal. According to Coutinho & Campos (1996) the intensity and duration of the floods influence the reproductive success of this species, with brief less extensive floods leading to reduced reproduction rates.

Many fish species show annual lateral migrations between the river channel and the floodplain and longitudinal migrations from the headwaters to the lower courses, depending on fluctuations in the water level and the behaviour of the species. Feeding habits, reproduction, growth, and migration are strongly influenced by the flood cycle. Ferraz de Lima (1986) reports that during high water there is trophic migration, because many shrubs and trees in the Pantanal are fruiting. Silva (1985) observed that fruits and seeds are the most important food items of *Piractus mesopotamicus* (Pacú; a commercial fish species) during high water levels. During that period, the species accumulates fat for gonad development, to be used in times of low water levels when food availability is scarce and during rising water for spawning migration.

The numbers of aquatic birds seem to be higher in the Pantanal than in the floodplains of the large central Amazonian white-water rivers. This is probably due to the large flood amplitude and the dense forest cover of the 'várzea', which hamper large wading birds (Junk & Da Silva 1995). Of the total number of bird species, 156 live or depend on wetland habitats while 32 feed mostly on fish (Cintra & Yamashita 1990, Cintra & Antas 1996).

## 4. Land and water use

Most of the inhabitants of the upper Paraguay river basin (about 2 million people) live on the plateau and in depressions that surround the Pantanal. This is also the region where the tributaries originate. In the plateau municipalities, population density varies from 2.1 to 50 inhabitants per km$^2$. In the Pantanal, density is lower than 2 inhabitants per km$^2$ (PCBAP 1997a).

The main economic activities in the Plateau region and depressions are agriculture (Soya bean, corn, sugar cane and polyculture), cattle raising and mining. In the Pantanal, the main activities are extensive cattle raising, fishing and, more recently tourism. There are many other economical activities, such as transport, energy and urbanisation. The plateau farmers, mainly from Southern Brazil, arrived in Mato Grosso in the 1970s, stimulated by public policies such as POLOCENTRO (Programme for the Development of the Cerrado) and in the 1980s, POLONOROESTE (Integrated Development Programme for Northwest Brazil) and by some private initiatives. These farmers developed an industrial agriculture based on soya bean, aimed at the external market and supported by agricultural mechanisation and tax incentives. Gold mining started with the colonisation of the region in the 17th century. More recently, there was a spate of diamond mining. In the beginning, mining was generally characterised by small-scale exploitation. Nowadays, both gold and diamond mining are in decline.

According to Da Silva & Silva (1995), indians have lived in the Pantanal, on the plateau and in depressions since time immemorial, fishing, gathering and living of subsistence agriculture. The farmers of the Pantanal arrived in the region about 200 years ago. Following PCBAP (1997a) the mean cattle density has been 16 heads per km$^2$, representing some 2,225 million animals.

Fishing has evolved in 3 different modes: 1) subsistence fishing employed by indians and mixed descendants of indians, blacks and whites, who live along the river margin; 2) sport fishing employed by tourists from urban areas or from other states and 3) professional fishing, generally employed by traditional fishermen, an activity that maintains around 3,500 families (Da Silva & Silva 1995, PCBAP 1997a). Professional fishermen are organised into colonies and have a profound knowledge of fish ecology and management. On the Cuiabá river, the main tributary on the left margin of the upper Paraguay river, the professional fishermen know about fish habitats, the spawning period of the year, migration and feeding. They also use sophisticated fishing strategies involving cosmological knowledge (such as moon and hydrologic phases), technology (bait, fishing nets, hooks, harpoons, bow and arrows, each technique adapted to specific species, habitats and periods of the year), ecological knowledge (fish habitat, fish feeding habits as well as biological processes such as reproduction and migration) and management skill (various techniques to increase fish densities and catches) (Da Silva & Silva 1995).

The potential tourist attraction of the upper Paraguay river catchment area resides in its scenic beauty and leisure potential, which includes waterfalls, rivers, streams, canyons, monuments of cultural value, handicraft, folklore and traditional events. The main tourist activities on the Pantanal floodplain include observing the fauna and flora, and recreational and sports fishing (PCBAP 1997a).

The main transport routes in the region are roads and rivers. The roads were designed to carry agricultural products from the plateau and depressions and, in the Pantanal, to transport cattle. The Paraguay and Cuiabá rivers were intensively used to transport cattle, timber and cement before the roads were built. Nowadays, some enterprises are trying to transform the upper Paraguay river into a waterway for soy bean transport. The energy potential of the UPRB is about 1,325 MW, of which 240 MW are already are being used or about to be used with the construction of several hydroelectric facilities, one of which is quite a sizeable plant. The increase in the number of urban nuclei and population has initiated the arrival of the process of urbanisation. PCBAP (1997a) shows that in the 1970s, there were 3 main urban concentrations; at present there are 8.

In Brazil, Law No. 9,433 on water resources regulates water management (Brasil 1998a). The law is based on the following fundamental principles: that water is a limited public good with economic value; that the watershed is the water management unit; that rivers must be managed for multiple uses and finally, that management ought to be decentralised and participatory. In Brazil, the public authorities are responsible for water management through basin committees, forums in which the public authorities, the end-users, and communities can decide on matters of water provision. However, the basin committees are still at an initial stage. The upper Paraguay river basin is regarded as a Federal river, since it runs between two Brazilian states (Mato Grosso and Mato Grosso do Sul) and marks the border with Paraguay and Bolivia. The Upper Paraguay River Integrated Committee (locally named CIBHAP) is composed so far to represent the Federal and State Governments, the end-users (farmers, industrialists, and fish raisers), the State Environmental Council (an independent government organ) and society at large, all nominated by the Brazilian President.

At the international level, the Prata Basin Treaty, signed by Argentina, Bolivia, Brazil, Paraguay and Uruguay, regulates UPRB activities. The treaty promotes the identification of the common interests of the signatories, studies, programmes, works and the formulation of operational tools or legal instruments that the respective parties consider necessary. The administration of this treaty is the responsibility of the Co-ordinating Intergovernmental Committee, composed of members of the signatories (Brasil 1998b).

Environmental problems which affect the Pantanal Mato Grossense are the result of the inadequate management concepts applied in the catchment area of its various tributaries. The substitution of savanna, deciduous and semi-deciduous forests by large scale soya bean plantations and pastures were stimulated in the early 1970s by projects like POLOCENTRO (Programme for the Development of the Cerrado) and in 1980s by POLONOROESTE (Integrated Development Programme for Northwest Brazil) and by some private initiatives. The rise of agriculture has led to the fragmentation of the cerrados (savanna), loss of biodiversity, erosion and sedimentation in the headwaters and to an increase in the sediment load of the tributaries of the Pantanal (Da Silva 1998, PCBAP 1997a). Large land areas have been degraded as the result of these processes (PCBAP 1997a).

Sediments deposited within the Pantanal are changing the drainage system and the pattern of inundation. Because of the flat topography, small changes in water level affect large areas (Junk & Da Silva 1995). According to Ponce (1995), modification of the river sediment loads will drastically affect the functioning of the Pantanal system. Its complex drainage system and flat relief cannot accommodate large sediment loads, which will result in modification of the hydraulic geometry of the system by obstructing drainage channels. For example, the erosion and sedimentation processes resulting from the present land use of the catchment areas have caused the channels of some of the main tributaries of the upper Paraguay river, such as the Taquarí river and the São Lourenço river, to shift their positions with increasing frequency. This has resulted in the destruction of their levees (PCBAP 1997a, Hamilton *et al.* 1998, Oliveira & Calheiros 1998).

Wantzen (1998) has demonstrated in small tributaries of the São Lourenço river that the increase in sediment loads has affected the benthos community. The instability of the river channel and the coverage of the bottom by moving sediments cause benthos habitat destruction. According to Oliveira & Calheiros (1999), the increased sediment load of the Taquarí river in Mato Grosso do Sul has changed the temporal and spatial patterns of suspended matter, dissolved material, water transparency and chlorophyll content, interfering with processes and organisms involved in primary production.

Furthermore, the establishment of soya bean mono-cultures has brought with it the application of fertilisers and pesticides. The pollution of the environment by pesticides and their transport into the Pantanal has not yet been quantified. In the State of Mato Grosso (Northern Pantanal), in the headwaters of the São Lourenço river, the following pesticides are being used in the soya bean culture, according to an in situ survey by Blumenschein *et al.* (1996): insecticides such as Dimilin (diflubenzurone), Dissulfan UBV, Endosulfan 350 C, Thiodan (organochlorinated), Azodrin 400, Curacron 500, Nuvacron 400, Tamaron Br (organophosphorated), Karate 50 Ce, (synthetic piretoids) Carbofuran Fersol 350 Sc (carbamates); herbicides Blazer Sol., (difenil eter), Flex (organochlorinated) Gramaxone 200, Regione (bipiridilios) Basagran 480 (tiadiazines), Corsum, Laço CE, Boxer (triazines) Glicosato Nortox, Roundup (organophosphorated); fungicides Tecto 100 (benzimidazóis). In the lysimeter pilot study made in the Oxisol of the headwaters of the São Lourenço river, by Laabs *et al.* (1999), the relative contamination potentials of pesticides were ranked as follows: metolachlor > atrazine = simazine > monocrotofos > endosulfan >chloropyrifos > trifluraline > cyhalothrin.

In relation to nutrient input into the system, calculations for soya bean culture have shown that about 400 kg per ha of nitrogen, phosphorus and potassium are used to correct savanna soil fertility. Some 0.3 - 0.5 ton per ha of lime are also used to lower the aluminium toxicity in the soil (Blumenschein *et al.* 1996).

In the Pantanal lowlands, the subdivision of large farms into smaller ones has led to pasture exhaustion in the seasonally inundated fields, forcing some farmers to deforest areas that are such as "cordilheiras" to increase the pasture area (PCBAB 1997a). This has resulted in the introduction of exotic species to these areas and consequently in the loss of biodiversity.

Some problems of the Pantanal are related to mining, for example, the increase in sediment load and mercury pollution. Since the beginning of the 1980s, gold extraction in the municipalities of Poconé and Livramento on the periphery of the Pantanal (depression area) has led to the contamination of the Bento Gomes river with mercury, as well as to the degradation of the landscape there. According to Nogueira *et al.* (1997) high total mercury levels were detected in suspended matter and in the sediments of a floodplain lake (baía) formed by a widening of the Bento Gomes river, since it acts as a sink for mercury. The floodplain lake stores 26% of the mercury transported in the water and 41% of the mercury transported in suspended matter.

The impact of urbanisation is well supported by evidence of water quality analyses. Studies by FEMA (1997) indicate that most streams of the catchment area of the upper Paraguay river comply with the oxygen norm of a minimum of 5 mg l⁻¹, established by CONAMA (National Environmental Council) for rivers of second quality, a class that includes all UPRB rivers. This class includes waters intended for domestic use, protection of aquatic communities, bathing, irrigation of gardens and aquaculture for human consumption. The Coxipó river in Cuiabá city shows values higher than the limit during the rainy season, because of high organic pollution. Bacteria counts are high in the Paraguay, Bento Gomes, and São Lourenço rivers (with counts of up to 50,000 per 100 ml water in the urban area of Cuiabá) due mainly to faecal contamination. These numbers exceed the limit of 1,000 bacteria per 100 ml water allowed by CONAMA. Turbidity values and the amounts of solids in the São Lourenço river and its tributary, the Vermelho river, also go beyond the CONAMA limits during the rainy season (100 NTU and 500 mg l⁻¹, respectively). Total nitrogen concentrations were higher than the limits indicated by CONAMA in the Cuiabá, Coxipó, and Vermelho rivers. All the rivers studied demonstrated phosphorus levels higher than that recommended by CONAMA (0.025 mg l⁻¹).

The main problem associated with the road network in the plateau area is inadequate bridges. They are narrower than the river channel widths and consequently retain water and sediments, drowning riparian forests. Hamilton (1999) shows that scenarios in which this river stage is decreased from 20th and 80th percentile values (as purposed by Waterway Paraguay River for improving navigation in the upper Paraguay river) result in large potential impacts on inundation. Stage decreases of 0,10 and 0,25 m would reduce the total flooded area by 1430 and 3830 km$^2$, at low water, and by 2410 and 5790 km$^2$, respectively at high water. According to Wantzen *et al.* (2000), present-day navigation in the upper Paraguay river, with barges wider than the channel width in some stretches of the river, is tearing the levees, especially in tight meanders, provoking the destruction of gallery forests and archaeological sites.

The main problem related to fisheries is the growth of the pressure on the aquatic ecosystem due to the increase in professional, sports and subsistence fishing (PCBAP 1997a). The growth of fishing reduces the food of fish-eating birds and increases social conflicts with respect to fish resources (Da Silva & Silva 1995). The introduction of exotic species and species from other basins for aquaculture can also cause problems when eggs or even fish escape to the rivers. The introduction of exotic species can produce diseases in native species or even dislocate them from their natural habitats (PCBAP 1997a). Tourism has increased pressure on the land, causing speculation and the construction of hotels and tourist resorts in fragile areas - even those protected by environmental law. The increase in the number of motorboats to transport tourists causes high waves that are responsible for the erosion of the channel levees and consequently for extra sedimentation (Da Silva & Silva 1995). The recent construction of dams for power generation can cause alterations to the river hydraulic geometry of the river and to the flood pulse in the Pantanal. Table 1 summarises the main environmental concerns associated with economic activities.

## 5. Proposals for sustainable river management

A proposal for the sustainable management of rivers in the Pantanal has to include the catchment area. Some recommendations for management and research strategies can be suggested, based on three pillars: the ecological basis (including hydrological data), the use of land and water, and participatory mechanisms (Figure 4).

The stability of the Pantanal system largely depends on the flood pulse, which regulates the functioning of the wetlands during the dry and inundation phases. In the Pantanal Mato Grossense, plants and animals are adapted to the annual dry and flooding periods. Additional events, such as inter-annual variations in dry and flooding periods represent additional stress to the organisms. The lack of data on the impact of these periods on the native plant and animal communities precludes detailed assessment, but cattle losses during the large flood events as well as during prolonged dry periods readily demonstrate this stress increase. Even then, however, the structure and function of the system are maintained as long as flood pulse is not modified (Junk & Da Silva 1999).

*Table 2.* The main problems associated with economic activities in the upper Paraguay river basin.

| Economic activities | Plateau / Depression | Pantanal |
|---|---|---|
| Agriculture and cattle raising | Deforestation; savanna fragmentation; erosion; loss of soil fertility; loss of diversity in landscape, habitat and species of aquatic organisms; pollution from biocides | River silting; increased number of islands and increasing size of existing islands; pollution by biocides. Cattle raising: deforestation of "cordilheiras" (sandy paleo-levées), alteration of original landscape; loss of tree diversity in the capões (forested islands that are round in shape) and invasion of flooded fields by invasive tree species |
| Fishery | Introduction of exotic species | Introduction of exotic species; increasing pressure on food for birds and on the eggs of birds laid on the beaches |
| Tourism | Increased deforestation and erosion in fragile areas | Increased pressure on fishing, erosion of banks and silting of river banks and rivers, disturbance of birds nests on river beaches |
| Gold and diamond mining | Degradation of landscape; loss of soil; silting; mercury contamination | Water, sediment and aquatic biota contamination by mercury; increased sedimentation |
| Transport | Increased erosion and silting of rivers; loss of gallery forests through permanent flooding and loss of species susceptible to prolonged flooding near bridges connecting the roads | Changes in the direction of water flow, transformation of seasonal wetlands into permanently flooded areas through the construction of roads and dikes; erosion of riverbanks caused by barges on the upper Paraguay river |
| Urbanisation | Water, air and soil pollution by deficient sewage systems; | Water pollution by deficient sewage systems; |
| Energy | Altered river flow pattern and sedimentation through hydroelectric dams; point contamination by organic residues from alcohol factories; fish mortality | Flood pulse altered by hydroelectric dams |

The available ecological data on the Pantanal has been largely obtained since the 1970s, when the Pantanal had already entered a phase in which the flooded land areas were larger than in the 1960s. The existing data, published in scientific jour-

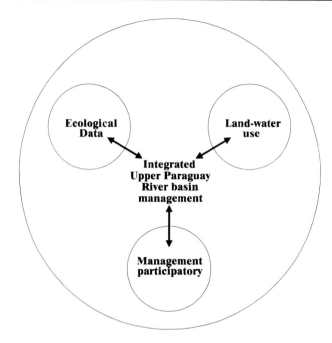

*Fig. 4.* Conceptual Scheme to discuss upper Paraguay river basin management.

nals, theses and monographs or collected in the Conservation Plan of the upper Paraguay river basin (PCBAP 1997) still focus on an ecological description of the system. There is a need to place an emphasis on ecosystem structure and function. Some studies have been published on the ecology of vertebrates by the EMBRAPA-CPAP (Brazilian Agency for Agriculture Research, Centre of Research on the Pantanal) scientists, as well as some on ecological changes in the functioning of the flood pulse and on the environmental impacts of gold-mining and erosion by scientists of the Pantanal Ecology Project of the Mato Grosso Federal University. Table 3 summarises the major studies or current projects in the region.

The application of ecological concepts on river management is still incipient in Brazil. In Europe, where this is more common, there are some differences in the management forms. According to Nienhuis & Leuven (1998), the Netherlands uses the AMOEBA method to manage its rivers. This is a general method for ecological description, in which the ecotope is the unit of space, using the River Ecotope System (RES) for the spatial classification of rivers. The United Kingdom has adopted the System for Evaluating Rivers for Conservation (SERCON). In this system, the habitat is the unit of space and the spatial classification of river uses the River Habitat System (RHS). In both cases the authors recommend a more thorough analysis of the ecotope vs. habitat concepts for river management. The use of these European management instruments in the upper Paraguay river basin could only be introduced with some caution, in view of the length of the river segment (1,800 km) and its great spatial heterogeneity. Efficient management of a heterogeneous river

*Table 3.* Main studies or current projects in the Pantanal region.

| Project | Execution/promotion | Reach | Status/situation |
|---|---|---|---|
| PEP2-Pantanal Ecology Project-SHIFT Programme | Mato Grosso Federal University/CNPq-IBAMA-BMBF-Brazilian-Germany Agreement | Pantanal and catchment area in Mato Grosso State | Public policy, 2nd phase (1997-2001) |
| Long term ecological changes to inter-annual water fluctuations | EMBRAPA-CPAP / CNPq-National Council of Research and Technologic Development | Pantanal – Paraguay river | Public policy approved |
| Sustainable management of the upper Paraguay river basin | Local NGOs and environmental agencies GEF/UNEP/BIRD/ Brazilian Environmental Ministry | Pantanal and catchment area in Mato Grosso and Mato Grosso do Sul states | Public policy approved |
| Pantanal Project – Sustainable Development of Pantanal | IBAMA and environmental agencies of Mato Grosso and Mato Grosso do Sul states / IDB | Pantanal in Mato Grosso and Mato Grosso do Sul states | Public policy approved |
| Ecological Changes | EMBRAPA-CPAP, Wageningen University and European Union | Pantanal in Mato Grosso do Sul state | Public policy submitted for approval |

requires the creation of a relevant classification scheme for the different aquatic habitats along the various reaches of the river, taking into consideration various geological, geomorphological and hydrological aspects, the variation in the vegetation, migratory birds and fish routes and the reproductive behaviour of animals. Thereafter, such a classification system could be extended to the entire Paraguay river, down to its point of discharge into the Prata river.

Jongman (1998) suggested the concepts of ecological corridors and metapopulation as useful ecological principles for the management of rivers. Ecological corridor concepts are useful for the upper Paraguay basin and were recommended by Brazilian scientists and NGOs that are active in the Pantanal during the workshop "Priority Actions for the Conservation of Biodiversity in the Cerrado and the Pantanal". The corridors identified cover the north-south and east-west axes of the UPRB. The first axis includes the Paraguay and Jaurú rivers down to the Apa river region. The second includes the Cuiabá, São Lourenço and Piquiri rivers and the Negro and Miranda rivers (Brasil 1999).

On the whole, current economic activities in the basin cause serious environmental problems. As for the various management and development plans for the Pantanal, it is important to pay close attention to those including items which interfere with the flood pulse, such as drainage canals, waterways and large hydroelectric dams. It is important to realise that the aim of these interventions (mainly in the transport and energy sectors) is to support cereal agriculture that affects the Pantanal. This industrial agriculture, developed in the catchment area since the 1970s, constitutes the region's mainstay economic activity and as such is the source of environmental problems (erosion, sedimentation, pollution) that directly affect the Pantanal downriver. Furthermore, it has brought social problems such as the concentration of land and capital, leading to social exclusion in the region. It is well known that social exclusion is also a source of environmental degradation .

Any management strategy has to be based on ecological and conservation concepts that are in tune with the region in terms of the flood pulse, ecological corridors and factors associated with landscape ecology. In the catchment area, a possible strategy would be the use of the River Continuum Concept, the preservation of landscape and biological diversity through the association of landscape units such as the official riparian forest reserves and the savanna surrounding or merging with cultivated and degraded areas. This would maximise the interaction between landscape units, contribute to the maintenance of the flow in the main rivers and minimise negative border effects (erosion, tree fall in riparian forests, pesticide and nutrient entry).

It is important to safeguard present-day biodiversity, water resources and the various forms of use of both of these, in order to optimise ecological potentials, socio-cultural opportunities and economic opportunities. The region's ecological potential has allowed various economic activities favouring the development of each social group in the basin. For example, the associated tourism, fisheries and cattle raising can benefit indian people and traditional communities and farmers. To sustain the ecological potential, it is necessary to implement public policies requiring that subsidised activities maintain this potential. For example, the financing of industrial agriculture has to be linked to the adoption of soil water conservation practices by the farmers. Beyond this, the amplification of existing alternative product markets such as tourism and traditional fishery structures contribute to the maintenance of ecological potential. A variety of economic factors have to be taken into account in this process.

In relation to the participatory management of rivers, Brazil can contribute on the world scene with new approaches. The Brazilian experience in the Amazon basin rivers and more recently in the Parana-Paraguay basin is rich and diverse. Successful management of the Pantanal requires scientific knowledge in conjunction with ample societal participation. In the region, there is a clear action-reaction interplay on the part of the various social groups (stakeholders) with regard to impacting economic activities. This scenario requires a participation space for the various stakeholders, mainly in all the decision phases of public policies which may have a socio-environmental impact on the region, such as the Paraná-Paraguay Waterway Project.

There are in the Pantanal region various representative forums such as the Forum for Environment and Development of Mato Grosso and Mato Grosso do Sul states, organised by NGOs; and the Upper Paraguay Basin Integrated Committee (CIBHAP). This Committee is composed of representatives of society, states and the Federal Environmental and Planning Agencies and of members of the business community. Nowadays, the activities of the Living River Coalition (formed by NGOs from Brazil, Paraguay, Bolivia, Uruguay and Argentina associated with the Paraguay river, and others from North America and the Netherlands) is steadily strengthening social participation in the management of the rivers in the MERCO-SUL region. The usefulness of the coalition's actions is illustrated by the role it has played in the discussions concerning the Parana-Paraguay Waterway Project. In the short term it appears important to bring together these various representatives to enhance the efficiency of decision making. The Basin Committees currently being established under state law (which is a copy of the Federal one) might achieve this feat. However, the most serious challenge to the representative forums is popular education, as the vast majority of the UPRB people do not feel involved in the questions under debate. As this vast silent majority becomes more involved and concerned, it may become more active in the representative forums, and the emergence of a public opinion on the fate of the Pantanal might exert pressure on local and national politics. This is of course a long-term effort.

The organisation of existing ecological data, the production of new data, the strengthening of low impact and ecologically sustainable economical activities and the creation of more effective stakeholder participation mechanisms require the establishment of strategies and priority actions for the short, medium and long term. Taking into account the main socio-economic activities of the UPRB, and the temporal dynamics of its ecosystem functions, table 4 summarises the broad research priorities and socio-economic management strategy recommendations compatible with the UPRB/Pantanal ecology.

## 6. Conclusions

It can be concluded that the policy and development processes in Pantanal management have to incorporate ecological concepts, mechanisms to assess current projects and economic activities as well as more efficient participatory management. This requires the improvement of the Pantanal ecological databases using information needed for sustainable management. Also, it is indispensable to develop and use readily available ecological concepts and management methods adapted to heterogeneity.

The predominant economic activities in the plateau area (catchment area) are the sources of the present environmental problems in the Pantanal floodplain. Thus, it is essential to assess the current land and water uses, and to stimulate those that are adequate for the Pantanal ecological conditions.

The uniqueness and fragility of the Pantanal system, the diversity of interlocutors and the dimension of the environmental problems in the region necessitate the introduction by governments and multilateral agencies of mechanisms that facilitate a greater and more active community participation in the decision making process concerning all phases of the design and development of public policies producing socio-environmental impacts in the region.

## Acknowledgements

This article is the result of my research on the Pantanal Ecology Project at Universidade Federal de Mato Grosso, in Cuiabá, Brazil and the SHIFT Programme managed by CNPq/IBAMA/BMBF (Brazilian - German Agreement). I am particularly grateful to Dr P. Girard for his helpful comments and translation efforts.

*Table 4.* Recommendations for research priorities and strategies for the sustainable management of the Pantanal.

| Activities | Research priorities | Strategies for management |
|---|---|---|
| Conservation and preservation | Biological indicators of environment quality of the water, flood pulse and landscape units; Assessing the structure and functioning of the landscape units in ecological corridor concepts; Ecology of invader and coloniser species and their role in the succession in the floodplain areas; Assessing fragmentation effects on the fluvial regime; Defining ecological classifications and protocols for rivers and floodplains | Adding impact assessment of the proposed project on the flood pulse process and the economic values of the ecological functions to the environmental impact studies; Environmental compensation should be paid on a yearly basis and not just once at the start of operation of the impacting activity and these resources should also be applied in research and management projects; Adopting the ecological classification for river management |
| Agriculture and cattle raising | Applying research to adjust the existing soil conservation techniques to the plateau and depression soils | Adopting soil conservation practices to reduce soil loss; Monitoring suspended sediments, pesticides and nutrients levels in water bodies |
| Gold and diamond mining | Selecting fast growing species to favour ecological succession in degraded areas; Defining protocols and indicator organisms to monitor mercury contamination in rivers and water bodies | Applying the law with regard to the recuperation of mining districts once the exploitation phase is over; Monitoring mercury levels in river water and indicator organisms downstream of mining |
| Fishery | Relating fish growth rates, reproduction, population productivity and ecological adaptations using the river continuum concept for headwaters and the flood pulse concept for floodplains; Food web studies | Specifying a closed season for each commercial species in the fishery law; Creating jobs for the local fishermen during the closed season; Reducing catch quotas for tourist fisheries |
| Tourism | Geotechnical and ecological studies to support zoning | Defining appropriate zones for tourism; Regulating and enforcing regulation in tourist zones |
| Urbanisation | Alternative sewage strategy studies; Geotechnical and ecological studies to support zoning | Defining appropriate zones for urbanisation; Regulating and enforcing regulation in urban zones |

*Table 4.* Continued.

| Activities | Research priorities | Strategies for management |
|---|---|---|
| Transport | Research on type and size of boats that can navigate on the Paraguay river between Cáceres and Corumbá cities during low and high water periods without causing bank erosion and sediment re-suspension; Surveying of the coloniser species in susceptible erosion/ sedimentation areas; Evaluation studies of the ecological functioning of rivers | Regulating boat sizes to adapt to the river's ecological conditions; Implementing river margin conservation practices to minimise bank erosion; Maintaining stream geometry; Avoiding channel rectification |
| Energy | Evaluation studies of the ecological functioning of rivers | Maintaining the flood characteristics; Avoiding dam construction |

# References

Ab'Saber, N.A. 1988. O Pantanal Matogrossense e a teoria dos refúgios. R. Bras. Geogr. 50/2: 9-57. (in Portuguese).

Adamoli, J. A. 1982. O Pantanal e suas relações fitogeográficas com os cerrados. Discussão sobre o conceito de "Complexo do Pantanal". In: Separata dos Anais do XXXII Congresso Nacional de Botânica, Sociedade Brasileira de Botânica,Universidade Federal do Piaui, Teresina. pp. 109 – 119. (in Portuguese).

Alvarenga, S. M., Brasil, A.E., Pinheiro, R. & Kux, H.J.H. 1984. Estudo geomorfológico aplicado a Bacia do Alto Paraguai e Pantanais Matogrossenses. B. Téc. Projeto RADAMBRASIL, sér. Geomorfologia Salvador 187: 89 - 183. (in Portuguese).

Amaral Filho, Z.P. 1986. Solos do Pantanal Matogrossense. In: Anais do Simpósio Sobre Recursos Naturais E Sócio-Econômicos do Pantanal. EMBRAPA, Brasília. pp. 29-42. (in Portuguese).

Brasil. 1998a. Politica Nacional de Recursos Hídricos. Ministério de Meio Ambiente dos Recursos Hídricose da Amazônia legal. (in Portuguese).

Brasil. 1998b. Tratados Internacionais deRecursos Hídricos. Caderno Legislativo 3. pp. 61-73. (in Portuguese).

Brasil. 1999. Ações Prioritárias para a Conservação da Biodiversidade do Cerrado e Pantanal. MMA, FUNATURA, Conservation International, Fund.Biodiversitas Universidade de Brasilia. (in Portuguese).

Blumenschein, M., Neuburger, M. & Rempis, M. 1996. O espaço rural na bacia do Alto Rio Paraguai A. Transformações sócio-espaciais. SHIFT- Studies on Human Impact on Forests and Floodplains in the Tropics (CNPq/ IBAMA/BMBF/DLR) UFMT/UT, Cuiabá-Tubingen. (in Portuguese).

Britski, H.A., Silimon, K.Z.S. & Lopes, B.S. 1999. Peixes do Pantanal. Manual de identificação Brasília. EMBRAPA- SPI, Corumbá EMBRAPA CPAP. (in Portuguese).

Carvalho, N.O. 1986. Hidrologia da Bacia do Alto Paraguai. In: Anais do Simpósio Sobre Recursos Naturais E Sócio-Econômicos do Pantanal, 1. Corumbá, EMBRAPA, Brasília. pp. 43-48. (in Portuguese).

Cintra, R. & Yamashita, C. 1990. Habitats, abundância e ocorrência das espécies de aves do Pantanal de Poconé, Mato Grosso, Brasil. Papéis Avulsos de Zoologia 37/1: 1-21. (in Portuguese).

Cintra, R. & Antas, P.T.Z. 1996. Distribuição geográfica, história natural e conservação das espécies de aves da região do Pantanal no Brasil. In: Resumo do Segundo Simpósio sobre Recursos Naturais e Sócio-econômicos do Pantanal. Manejo e Conservação. EMBRAPA, Brasília. (in Portuguese).

Coutinho, M. & Campos, Z. 1996 Effects of habitat and seasonality on the densities of caiman in southern Pantanal, Brazil. Journal of Tropical Ecology 12: 741-747.

Da Silva, C.J. 1990. Influência da variação do nível dá água sobre a Estrutura e funcionamento de uma área alagável do Pantanal Mato Grossense (Pantanal de Barão de Melgaço, Municipio de Santo Antônio.de Leverger e Barão de Melgaço - MT). Thesis, Universidade Federal de São Carlos, Departamento de Ciências Biológicas. (in Portuguese).

Da Silva, C.J. 1998. A planície de inundação da Bacia do Alto Rio Paraguai O Pantanal Mato Grossense. In: Anais do IV Simpósio de Ecossistemas Brasileiros. Academia São Paulo de Ciências. pp. 258-272. (in Portuguese).

Da Silva, C.J. & Esteves, F.A. 1993. Biomass of three macrophytes in the Pantanal of the Mato grosso, Brazil. Int. J. Ecol. Environ. Sci. 19: 11-23.

Da Silva, C.J. & Esteves, F.A. 1995. Dinâmica das caracteristicas limnologicas das baías Porto de Fora e Acurizal em função da variação do nível da água ( Pantanal de Mato Grosso). Oecologia Brasiliensis I. Estrututura, funcionamento e manejo de ecossistemas brasileiros. pp. 47-60. (in Portuguese).

Da Silva, C.J. & Oliveira, D.M.M. 1998. The role of aquatic birds in the lake nutrient dynamics at the Pantanal Mato Grossense, Brazil Book of Abstracts. XXVII SIL Congress, Dublin. p. 281.

Da Silva, C.J. & Silva, J.A.F. 1995. No rítmo das águas do Pantanal. NUBAUP/USP.

Espindola, E.G., Matsumura-Tundisi, T. & Moreno, I.H. 1996a. Efeitos da dinâmica hidrológica do sistema Pantanal Mato Grossense sobre a estrutura da comunidade fitoplanctônica da Lagoa Albuquerque (Pantanal Matogrossense), Mato Grosso do Sul, Brasil. Acta Limnologica Brasiliensia 8: 13-27. (in Portuguese).

Espindola,E.G., Matsumura-Tundisi.T. And, Moreno, I.H. 1996b Efeitos da dinâmica hidrológica do sistema Pantanal MatoGrossense sobre a estrutura da comunidade de zooplancton da Lagoa Albuquerque ( Pantanal Mato Grossense), Mato Grosso do Sul, Brasil. Acta Limnologica Brasiliensia 8: 37-57. (in Portuguese).

FEMA - Fundação Estadual de Meio Ambiente. 1997. Qualidade da água dos principais rios da bacia do Alto Rio Paraguai: 1995-1996. FEMA MMA-PNMA. Cuiabá-MT. FEMA. (in Portuguese).

Ferraz de Lima, J.A. 1986. A pesca no Pantanal de Matop grosso (Rio Cuiabá: importância dos peixes migradores). Acta Amazônica 16/17: 87-94. (in Portuguese).

Fonseca, G.A.B., Herrmann, G., Leite, Y.L.R., Mittermeier, R.A., Rylands, A.B. & Patton, J.L. 1996. Lista anotada dos Mamiferos do Brasil. Occasional papers in Conservation Biology 4: 1-38. (in Portuguese).

Hamilton, S.K., Sippel, S.J. & Melack, J.M. 1996. Inundation patterns in the Pantanal wetland of South America determined from passive microwave remote sensing. Archiv für Hydrobiologie 137/1: 1-23.

Hamilton, S.K., Corrêa de Souza, O & Coutinho, M.E. 1998. Dynamic of floodplain inundation in the alluvial fan of the Taquari river (Pantanal, Brazil). Verh. Internat. Verein. Limnol. 26: 916-922.

Hamilton, S.K., Sippel, S.J., Calheiros, D.F. & Melack, J.M. 1999. Chemical characteristics of Pantanal. Waters. In: Anais do Segundo Simpósio sobre Recursos Naturais e Sócio - econômicos do Pantanal. Manejo e Conservação. EMBRAPA, Brasília. pp. 89-100.

Hamilton, S.K. 1999. Potential effects of a major navigation project (Paraguay-Paraná Hidrovia) on inundation in the Pantanal floodplains. Regulated Rivers: Research and Management 15: 289-299.

Heckman, C. 1994. The seasonal succession of biotic communities in wetlands of the tropical wet and dry climate zone: I. physical and chemical causes and biological effects the Pantanal of Mato Grosso, Brazil. Int. Ver. Gesamten Hydrobiol. 79/3: 397-421.

Jongman, R.H.G. 1998 Rivers: key elements in European ecological networks. In: Nienhuis, P.H., Leuven, R.S.E.W. & Ragas, A.M.J. (Eds.). New concepts for sustainable management of river basins. Backhuys Publishers, Leiden. pp. 53-66.

Junk, W.J., Bayley, P.B. & Sparks, R.E. 1989. The flood pulse concept in river-floodplain systems In: Dodge, D.P. (Ed.). Proceedings of the international large river symposium (LARS). Canadian Special Publication of Fisheries and Aquatic Sciences 106: 110-127.

Junk, W. J. & Da Silva, C.J. 1995. Neotropical floodplains: A comparison between the Pantanal of Mato Grosso and the large Amazonian river floodplains. In: Tundisi, J.G., Bicudo, C.E.M, Tundisi, T.M. (Eds.). Limnology in Brazil. Brazilian Academy of Sciences, Brazilian Limnological Society, Rio de Janeiro. pp. 195-217.

Junk, W.J. & Da Silva, C.J. 1999. "O conceito do pulso de inundação"e suas implicações para o Pantanal Mato Grossense. Anais Segundo Simpósio sobre Recursos Naturais e Sócio - econômicos do Pantanal. Manejo e Conservação. EMBRAPA, Corumbá, Brasil. pp. 17-28. (in Portuguese).

Junk, W.J. & Furch, K. 1980. Quimica da água e macrófitas aquáticas de rios e iguarapés na Bacia Amazonica e nas áreas adjacentes parte I: trecho de Cuiabá-Porto Velho- Manaus. Acta Amazônica 10/3: 611-633. (in Portuguese).

Köppen, G.W. 1948 Climatologia. Fundo de Cultura Econômica. México. pp. 242-248. (in Spanish).

Laabs, V., Amelung, W., Pinto, A., Altstaedt, A. & Zech, W. 1999. Leaching and degradation of cornand soybean pesticides in an Oxisol of the Brazilian Cerrados. Journal Chem.: 1-9.

Mourão, G.M. 1989. Limnologia comparativa de três lagoas (duas "Baías e uma "Salina") do Pantanal de Nhecolândia, MS. São Carlos, UFSCAr. (in Portuguese).

Nogueira, F.M.B., Castro, E., Silva, E.C. & Junk, J. 1997. Mercury from gold mining in the Pantanal of Poconé ( Mato Grosso, Brazil). Int. Journal of Environmental Health Research 7: 181-191.

Nienhuis, P.H. & Leuven, R.S.E.W. 1998. Ecological concepts for the sustainable management of lowland river basin: a review. In: Nienhuis, P.H., Leuven, R.S.E.W. & Ragas, A.M.J. (Eds.). New concepts for sustainable management of river basins. Backhuys Publishers, Leiden. pp. 7-33.

Oliveira, M.D. & Calheiros, D.F. 1998 Transporte de nutrientes e sólidos suspensos na bacia do Rio Taquari ( Mato Grosso do Sul). Acta Limnologica Brasiliensia 10/2: 35-45. (in Portuguese).

Oliveira, M.D. & Calheiros, D.F. 1999. Avaliação preliminar das caracteristicas limnológicas da bacia do Rio Taquari. In: Anais do Segundo Simpósio sobre Recursos Naturais e Sócio - Econômicos do Pantanal: Manejo e Conservação. EMBRAPA, Brasilia. pp. 137-149. (in Portuguese).

PCBAP - Plano de Conservação da Bacia do Alto Paraguai ( Pantanal). 1997a. Análise Integrada e Prognóstico da Bacia do Alto Paraguai III. Ministério do Meio Ambiente, dos Recursos Hidricos e da Amazônia Legal. (in Portuguese).

PCBAP - Plano de Conservação da Bacia do Alto Paraguai ( Pantanal) 1997b. Diagnóstico dos Meios Físico e Biótico- Meio Biótico II. Ministério do Meio Ambiente, dos Recursos Hidricos e da Amazônia Legal. (in Portuguese).

Penha, J.M., Da Silva, C.J. & Bianchini, I. 1998a. Análise do crescimento da macrófita aquática Pontederia lanceolata em áreas alagáveis do Pantanal Mato Grossense, Brasil. Ver Brasileira de Biologia 58/2: 287-300. (in Portuguese).

Penha, J.M., Da Silva, C.J. & Bianchini, I. 1998b. Impacto da variação do nível de água no ciclo de vida da macrófita aquática *Pontederia cordata* var. *ovalis* (Mart) Solms, em área alagável do Pantanal Mato Grossense. Brazilian Journal of Ecology 2: 30-35. (in Portuguese).

Penha, J.M., Da Silva, C.J. & Bianchini, I. 1999. Productivity of the aquatic macrophytes *Pontederia lanceolata* Nutt. (Pontederiaceae) on the floodplains of the Pantanal Mato-grossense, Brazil. Wetlands Ecology and Management 7/3: 155-163.

Ponce, V.M. 1995. Estudos Hidrológicos e Ambiental da Hidrovia Paraná-Paraguai no Pantanal Mato Grossense. Um Estudo de Referência. San Diego State University, San Diego. (in Portuguese).

Pott, A. & Pott, J.V. 1999. Flora do Pantanal - Listagem atual de fanerógamas. In: Anais do Segundo Simpósio sobre Recursos Naturais e Sócio – econômicos do Pantanal: Manejo e Conservação. EMBRAPA, Brasilia, Brasil. pp. 297-325. (in Portuguese).

Rezende, E.K., Pereira, R.A.C., Almeida. V.L.L. & Silva, A.G. 1996. Alimentação de peixes carnívoros da planície inundável do rio Miranda, Pantanal, Mato Grosso do Sul, Brasil. EMBRAPA,CPAP. Boletim de pesquisa, 3: 1-36. (in Portuguese).

Silva, A.J. 1985. Aspectos da alimentação do pacu adulto Colossoma mitrei (Berg. 1985) Pisces, Characidae, no Pantanal de Mato Grosso. Thesis. UFRJ, Rio de Janeiro. (in Portuguese).

Strussman, C. 1991. Predation on avian eggs by the boid snake, *Eunectes notaeus*. Herp. Review 22/4.

Tarifa, J.R. 1986. O sistema climático do Pantanal. da compreensão do sistema à definição de prioridade de pesquisa climatológica In: Anais do Simpósio Sobre Recursos Naturais E Sócio – Econômicos do Pantanal, EMBRAPA, Brasília. pp. 9-27. (in Portuguese).

Valverde, O. 1972. Fundamentos geográficos do planejamento rural do Município de Corumbá. R. Bras. de Geogr. 34/1: 49-144. (in Portuguese). Veloso, H.P. 1972. Aspectos fito-ecológicos da Bacia do Alto Paraguai. Biogeografia. (in Portuguese).

Wantzen, K.M. 1998 Effects of siltation on bentic communities in clear waters streams in Mato Grosso, Brazil. Verh. Internat. Verein. Limnol. 26: 1155-1159.

Wantzen, K.M., Da Silva, C.J, Figueiredo, D.M. & Migliacio, M.C. (2000). Recents impacts of navigation on the upper Paraguay river. Revista Boliviana (in press).

# NEW APPROACHES TO RIVER MANAGEMENT IN THE UNITED STATES OF AMERICA

C.E. Hunt
*World Wildlife Fund-US, Freshwater Ecosystem Conservation, 1250 24th Street, NW Washington, DC 20037, The United States of America; Present address: World Wide Fund for Nature, Living Waters Campaign, Boulevard 12, NL-3700 AA Zeist, The Netherlands*

## Abstract

River management in the United States (US) is evolving from a product-oriented, engineering approach to a dynamic, multiple objective management approach. Historically, river managers have focused on the design and construction of projects, which then move into the less glamorous phase of operation and maintenance. The modern framework for river management more resembles a continuous loop than an assembly line. Under a process known as "adaptive management," river managers are continually adjusting their actions in response to monitoring data which alerts them to changing environmental and economic conditions and social preferences. Water resources agencies no longer dominate the decision-making process, but have begun to serve a technical support function to a more democratic process of negotiation among various interests affected by water resource management. Water projects are less frequently designed for single purposes, such as flood control or environmental restoration, and more frequently encompass a number of objectives including flood damage reduction, navigation enhancement, water supply, water quality, and biodiversity conservation.

This new framework for river management requires sophisticated technical capabilities. The static engineering approaches that dominated the twentieth century are gradually giving way to systemic models that have the ability to simulate the complex hydrodynamic processes that characterise water and sediment movement through an entire catchment. The output from the hydrologic models are used to provide input to water quality and ecological models so that water managers can assess the likely results of a variety of river management alternatives. This model-based approach also provides interest groups with an ability to assess various alternatives for river management, thus providing them with a platform for informed negotiation. Such a capacity reduces the reliance on power politics that have historically polarised interest groups and frequently stymied water resources development and management. More and more, negotiated agreement is becoming the venue of choice for resolving water resource conflicts in the US.

The concepts of multiple objective management, systemic approaches, adaptive management, hydrologic modelling, and democratic process are illustrated with a number of US examples, including the Mississippi river basin, Everglades restoration, water allocation negotiations in the Southeastern US and artificial flooding of Colorado river.

## 1. Introduction

River management in the US is evolving rapidly. Historically, river management has been characterised by structural engineering approaches that alter the environment

*New approaches to river management, pp. 119–139*
*edited by A.J.M. Smits, P.H. Nienhuis and R.S.E.W. Leuven*
*© 2000 Backhuys Publishers, Leiden, The Netherlands*

to provide for a narrow range of uses. Modern river management is more likely to include options that maintain or restore the natural functions of the river and catchment and are designed to meet a broader range of objectives. River management agencies are increasingly moving from an engineering and construction role to that of an information provider and consensus-builder. These changes are being driven by an increasing awareness of the full costs of traditional water resources management approaches, an increase in leisure time and growing demand for environmental protection, and new technological capabilities that support highly complex decision-making processes.

The economic driving forces behind the changes in river management are considerable. Some of the costs of historic approaches are related to their environmental impacts. Examples of high cost, environmental impacts for which river management strategies are largely responsible include the decline of a fishery worth $1 billion per year in the Pacific Northwest (National Research Council 1996a), the subsidence of land in the Mississippi river delta, and the intrusion of saltwater into the aquifer that supplies the rapidly growing Miami metropolitan area (US Army Corps of Engineers & South Florida Water Management District 1999). Other costs are evidence that the river management approaches themselves are not succeeding and need to be rethought. Such evidence includes the fact that, according to data compiled by the National Weather Service flood damages in the US increased 268 percent in real dollars between 1916 and 1985 despite a steady increase in flood control expenditures. For the five ten-year periods from 1936 to 1985, average annual Federal flood control expenditures increased by 103% after adjusting for inflation (Eiker 1986). Trend data for the past decade have not yet been compiled, but would certainly show an upward trend as a result of the many multi-billion dollar flood events of recent years. Reasons for increased flood damages include floodplain construction, alteration of watershed hydrology, river channel modification, and climatic changes.

The costs of operating and maintaining navigable waterways have also increased significantly over the past century. Dredging costs are growing because of increased sedimentation from altered watersheds, increased bed and bank erosion resulting from river channelisation and normalisation, the exhaustion of near-channel disposal sites, the costs of special treatment and disposal for contaminated sediments, the increase in vessel draft, and the increase in traffic density on some waterways.

Some of the new approaches that are being implemented in the US to increase the benefits and reduce the costs of river management are described below and illustrated with case studies. These include systemic thinking (Redwood river basin), public participation (Everglades/South Florida), adaptive management (the Apalachicola-Chattahoochee-Flint and Alabama-Coosa-Tallapoosa river systems), and natural flow regimes (the Colorado and Snake river basins). Figure 1 presents the geographical locations of the case study sites.

## 2. The Era of new approaches

The realisation that the traditional engineering approaches may be incurring unnecessary costs and may not be optimising the benefits of river management have

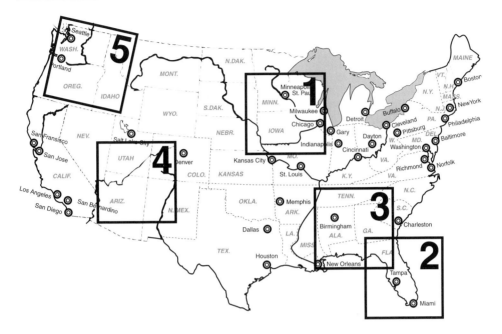

*Fig. 1.* Geographical positions of the case study areas in the United States of America. 1: Redwood river basin; 2: Everglades/South Florida; 3: Apalachicola-Chattahoochee-Flint and Alabama-Coosa-Tallapoosa river systems; 4: Colorado river and Glen Canyon Dam; 5: Snake river basins.

opened the door for the application of new concepts. These include an expanded geographic frame of reference that takes the entire catchment into consideration. New concepts also include procedural ideas such as increased public participation throughout the process, approximations of natural flow regimes, and the use of monitoring networks to provide managers with a basis for modifying their actions as necessary to respond to changing conditions.

*Systemic thinking: The Redwood river basin*

The trends in increasing river management costs have led the US to view water issues in a more systemic context that links the watershed, floodplain, and river channel. Rather than viewing a problem and its potential solution as confined to a single stretch of river, managers are more likely to look at cause and effect relationships that may take place many miles away from the river channel.

The Redwood river basin in South-western Minnesota provides an example of how considering cause/effect relationships throughout a watershed can reduce the costs and increase the rewards of river management. The Redwood river basin is part of the upper Mississippi river basin (Figure 2). Before Europeans extensively settled the upper Mississippi river basin, it was characterised by extensive wetlands. The hummocky land surface left by retreating glaciers markedly retarded run-off and enhanced the ponding of water (Winter 1992). Prairie ecosystems, dominated by perennial grasses, ranged from mesic to wetland communities in a gently rolling landscape where defined stream channels were rare and marshy swales conveyed

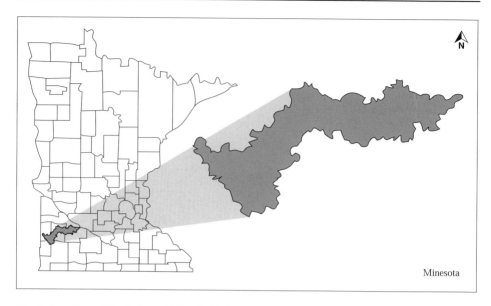

Minesota

*Fig. 2.* Location of the Redwood River basin in Southwestern Minnesota. Source: Minnesota River Basin Data Center (http://www.mrbdc.makato.msus.edu).

water downstream. The prairies formed deep root systems that served to hold the topsoil layer together, conduct water into the ground, and built up substantial quantities of organic material in the soil structure which acted like a sponge in absorbing water during precipitation events. The roughness provided by prairie grasses obstructed the movement of run-off, and the leaves and stems of the grasses increased evapotranspiration. The prairie and wetland communities that characterised much of the upper Mississippi river basin acted in concert to reduce and smooth out flood peaks, while ensuring a steady base flow of water stored in the aquifer into streams during the dry season (Hunt 1997).

European settlement drastically changed the hydrologic characteristics of the upper Mississippi river watershed. Wetlands were drained for crop production. This drainage had the effect of connecting closed basins that had historically filled with snowmelt and rainwater in the spring, later losing the water to evaporation, evapotranspiration, and groundwater infiltration, directly to surface water systems through drainage tiles or ditches. The result was more a rapid and complete discharge of run-off into the tributaries of the Mississippi river. In addition, row-crop farming removed the prairie vegetation from most of the Mississippi's catchment. Soils which had been bound and fertilised by the growth of perennial grasses were frequently cleared of vegetation completely during the winter and early spring, contributing to high rates of run-off and soil erosion. Less run-off infiltrated into the groundwater table, and there was therefore less water available to support river flows during the dry season. The hydrology of the upper Mississippi river basin has become significantly flashier than it was under natural conditions. The changes in the hydrologic characteristics of the catchment, along with changes in floodplain and channel morphology and in climate, have contributed to significant alterations of the flow regime in the Mississippi river. Flood peaks on the Mississippi river are higher in stage and volume than under pre-settlement conditions. The Mississippi also carries less water under low flow conditions than it did under pre-settlement conditions (Belt 1975).

South-western Minnesota is part of an epicentre of heavy precipitation events that covered much of the Midwestern US during 1993 (Wahl *et al.* 1993) and has shown a trend in increasing precipitation and increasing flood frequency over the past century (Chagnon & Kunkle 1995). The upland portions of the upper Mississippi river basin incurred most of the agricultural damages during the flood, including 70 percent of US Department of Agriculture disaster assistance payments and 80 percent of Federal crop insurance payments (Scientific Assessment and Strategy Team 1994). Over half of the total flood damages were in agricultural areas (Ayers 1993). GIS data compiled by government scientists suggest a high correlation between counties with the highest levels of flood-related crop losses, Federal crop insurance and disaster assistance payments, and the presence of drained hydric soils (Scientific Assessment and Strategy Team 1994).

The 179,415 ha Redwood river watershed begins on the "Coteau du Prairie", a rolling plateau punctuated with numerous small lake and wetland basins, and drains into the Minnesota river, a major tributary of the Mississippi. Before agricultural drainage, wetlands covered roughly 43 percent of the catchment. More than 82 percent of the catchment is now used for agriculture, indicating extensive drainage of wetlands. Before drainage for agriculture, many of the wetlands in the catchment were closed basins that stored rainfall and snowmelt and did not contribute directly to river flows (National Research Council 1997). Local officials believe that increased drainage of former wetlands in the 1970s and 1980s has led to increased flooding throughout the basin (R. Finley, personal communication). The headwaters of the Redwood river drain past the town of Marshall, Minnesota, which experiences periodic flooding. During 1993, Marshall was flooded by three separate rainfall events that triggered floods ranging in frequency from estimated 20 to 50 year events. Lyon County, where Marshall is located, received nearly $17.5 million in Federal Aid in response to the 1993 floods, more than $14.5 million of which was for agricultural damages (Phillipi 1995).

Government agencies have planned traditional flood control projects for the catchment, but the projects have faced political opposition because they would provide benefits only to the town of Marshall while imposing costs on other portions of the basin. The US Army Corps of Engineers and Soil Conservation Service studied the Redwood river basin in the 1980s and identified several potential dam sites, but none of them were economically feasible according to federal guidelines. One of these sites, on the South Branch of the Redwood river, was subsequently adopted by a county-level organisation that planned to build a dam there. This dam has been stalled because of the potential adverse impacts to a state-owned wildlife area and because of the objections of local residents. The Corps has produced a plan for a project that would divert water from the Redwood river at Marshall to nearby Cottonwood river during high flood stages. The residents of the Cottonwood river basin have resisted this proposal.

For the past four years, a number of organisations and federal agencies, including World Wildlife Fund, have been exploring alternative approaches that would use restoration of the natural hydrologic characteristics of the catchment to reduce flood damages, improve water quality, and provide habitat for wildlife. Measures used would include wetland restoration and the installation of soil and water conservation practices. Initial modelling efforts indicate that the restoration of all small wetlands in the Redwood basin, along with closing off the outlets from half of them, would reduce the 100 year flood peak at the mouth of the Redwood river (downstream from Marshall) by 16 percent. The hydrologist who performed the model believes that the model probably underestimated the amount of storage that the wetlands in the catchment would provide if they were restored, because the graphic information used in the model was not sufficiently detailed to elucidate the depth of the pothole wetlands. A recent study of a subbasin draining into the Redwood river suggests that the addition of other small-scale watershed management practices, such as no-till farming, contour plowing, terracing, installation of check dams, and intercropping could significantly increase the watershed's potential to store floodwaters (Jacobson 1999).

The US Army Corps of Engineers has recently joined the project, bringing the ability to model water, sediment and nutrient transport throughout the catchment and to extrapolate the findings of the Redwood study to other parts of the Minnesota river basin. The Corps' Waterways Experiment Station (WES) intends to use this catchment as a pilot for a new Land Management System programme. Through this project, WES will develop conceptual and simulation model systems for increasing understanding of watershed processes and the effects of land management measures on aquatic ecosystems. The emerging approach to reducing flood damages in the Redwood basin would reduce flood costs in agricultural areas as well as in the city of Marshall while providing additional water quality and wildlife benefits. It could well prove far more cost effective than dams and diversion projects.

*Engaging the public: The Everglades/South Florida Restoration Project*

In 1992, Congress authorised the Corps of Engineers to re-examine the flood control and water supply infrastructure serving central and southern Florida to determine the feasibility of structural or operational modifications to the project essential to restoration of the Everglades and Florida Bay ecosystems while providing for other water-related needs (US Army Corps of Engineers 1994). The pre-drainage wetlands of southern Florida covered an area estimated at approximately 8.9 million acres. This region was a complex system of hydrologically interrelated landscapes, including expansive areas of sawgrass (*Cladium jamaicicense*) sloughs, wet prairies, cypress (*Taxodium ascendens*) swamps, mangrove (*Rhizophora mangle* and *Avicennia germinans*) swamps, and coastal lagoons and bays.

The biodiversity harboured by this landscape was phenomenal. The Everglades ecosystem alone provides habitat for 56 federally listed threatened or endangered species, including the Florida panther (*Felis concolor coryi*), Key deer (*Odocoileus virginianus*), American crocodile (*Crocodylus acutus*), and Wood stork (*Mycteria americana*). Florida Bay is home to the Manatee (*Trichecus manatus latirostris*) and Bottlenose dolphin (*Tursiops truncatus*) and supports commercial and recreational fisheries and a diving industry on the only coral reef system in the US.

As a result of land use and water management practices during the past 100 years in southern Florida, the defining characteristics of the regional wetlands have been severely altered. Roughly half of the Everglades system was drained to create land for agriculture and urban development. The hydrology of the system has been significantly altered (Figure 3). Rather than storing wet weather flows in the extensive wetland system, the drained system dumped excess water to tide. The sudden flushes of freshwater into the South Florida estuaries upset the salinity balance and damaged the ecology of these ecosystems. The lack of water storage availability in the peninsula caused lower dry-season flows, decreased wading bird habitat in the Everglades, increased salinity in Florida Bay, and a reduction in hydraulic head for the groundwater supply in Southeast Florida, which both reduces water availability and permits saltwater intrusion into the aquifer.

The fundamental tenet of the Central and Southern Florida restudy project is that hydrologic restoration is a necessary starting point for ecological restoration. The ecological goal of the south Florida ecosystem restoration is to recreate, on a somewhat smaller scale, a healthy ecosystem large enough and diverse enough to survive the natural cycles of droughts, floods, and hurricanes and to support large and sustainable communities of native vegetation and animals. Economic goals include increasing the water supply in the metropolitan south-eastern portion of the

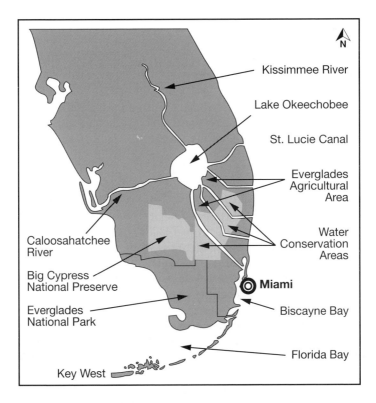

*Fig. 3.* Map of South Florida ecosystem. Source: South Florida Restoration Task Force (http://www.sfrestore.org/documents).

peninsula, reducing flood damages, increasing the basis for recreation and tourism in South Florida and Florida Bay, and restoring commercial fish harvests in the Bay.

The Corps is working on the restudy and on a vast array of related activities with a wide range of federal and non-federal partners. The project's local sponsor is the South Florida Water Management District, a regional organisation responsible for drainage, flood control and stormwater management. Other partners include the National Park Service, US Fish and Wildlife Service, National Marine Fisheries Service, US Geological Survey, US Environmental Protection Agency, US Department of Agriculture, a number of state agencies, Native American tribes, and private sector groups. Governor Lawton Chiles oversees the Governor's Commission on Sustainable South Florida, an effort to promote sustainable development in the region through an integration and balancing of environmental and economic interests. The Governor's Commission has adopted a conceptual plan as a framework for guiding development and ecosystem restoration (Governor's Commission on Sustainable South Florida 1996). The Corps used this document as a basis for the feasibility stage of the restudy. The federal agencies have developed an inter-agency budgeting process through which they support each other's requests for appropriations giving the project a distinct advantage in competing for money and political support (South Florida Ecosystem Restoration Program 1999).

The public participation process for the restudy has been particularly outstanding. Numerous public participation workshops were held early in the process to gather comments on the restudy. In 1993 and 1994, the Corps and partner agencies held three rounds of large-scale public meetings. Smaller "focus group" sessions were held in 1997 to discuss specific issues in the plan with agricultural, urban, environmental, and other interest groups. Also in 1997, the Corps and South Florida Water Management District established an internet web site for the restudy (http://www.restudy.org). The agencies have posted the various alternatives under consideration for the restudy on the web site. The postings include detailed descriptions of the structural components of the alternatives and outputs from hydrologic modelling of each alternative and comparisons of projected flow patterns under the various alternatives with the natural, or pre-disturbance flow regime. The base hydrologic model is the South Florida Water Management Model (SFWMM), which was developed by the South Florida Water Management District. SFWMM is a regional-scale computer model that simulates the hydrology and the management of the water resources system from Lake Okeechobee to Florida Bay. The model simulates the major components of the hydrologic cycle in South Florida and incorporates current or proposed water management control structures and operating rules. This model is used to simulate the hydrologic effects of the various alternatives under consideration as part of the restoration study (for more information, see the restudy web site at http://www.restudy.org).

The outputs of the SFWMM for each alternative are fed into a series of ecological and water quality models. These models help the project managers assess the effects of each alternative on key environmental indicators, such as populations of endangered species, the fish forage base for wading birds, the areal extent of specific ecological communities, and concentrations of nutrients in the water column of Lake Okeechobee and of wetlands in the Everglades system. The output of the ecological and water quality models are used to compare the predicted conditions in the South Florida/Everglades ecosystem with project goals. All of these outputs are available for public review and comment on the web site.

The technical meetings of the interagency restudy team are also open to the public. Representatives of interest groups can actually sit with agency staff and discuss alterations to the proposals under consideration. Representatives of the World Wildlife Fund have convinced the restudy team to make specific alterations to the favoured alternative during these meetings, fine-tuning the alternative to more fully support biodiversity conservation objectives.

### Adaptive management: The ACT and ACF river basins

Water stress and over-allocation of water resources, particularly during droughts, are not problems unique to arid regions of the world. These phenomena are now experienced in the South-eastern US, a region that receives over 127 cm of rainfall on an average, annual basis. Water withdrawals to support the growing municipal and industrial water demands of the rapidly expanding city of Atlanta (Georgia) have triggered intensive negotiations on water allocation between the states of Alabama, Georgia and Florida. The negotiations involve two relatively large river basins, the Apalachicola-Chattahoochee-Flint (ACF) and Alabama-Coosa-Tallapoosa (ACT) systems (Figure 4). These river basins support some of the most diverse aquatic ecosystems in the world, as well as extremely productive estuaries in Apalachicola Bay and Mobile Bay (Olson & Dinerstein 1998).

The population of Atlanta has steadily increased from less than one-half million in 1950 to almost 3 million in 1990. This concentration of people has produced a commensurate demand on the water resources of the two basins. As a result, reservoirs in Georgia that were initially constructed to provide flows for navigation, hydropower, and flood storage volume have been used primarily to store water as a buffer against drought and for municipal and industrial consumption. The state of Alabama filed suit against the US Army Corps of Engineers in 1990, claiming that reallocation of reservoir storage was a violation of the federal laws that authorised construction of the dams. The Corps and the three affected states decided to settle the water allocation dispute through a process of negotiated agreement, rather than through litigation.

In 1997, the state legislatures of Alabama, Florida and Georgia passed laws authorising water allocation compacts for the two river basins. These compacts were passed by the US Congress later that year, and signed into law by the President of the US in November as Public Laws 105-104 and 105-105. The compacts create interstate administrative agencies, the ACF and ACT basin Commissions, which are composed of the governors of the effected states (Alabama and Georgia on the ACT; Alabama, Georgia, and Florida on the ACF) and a Federal Commissioner appointed by the President of the US. The compacts direct the parties to the compact to "...develop an allocation formula for equitably apportioning the surface water of the ACF[and ACT] basin among the States while protecting the water quality, ecology, and biodiversity of the ACF [and ACT]...".

Environmental issues have taken an increasingly prominent role in public policy debates since the last compacts were negotiated. The majority of water allocation compacts that have been established in the US have dealt primarily or exclusively

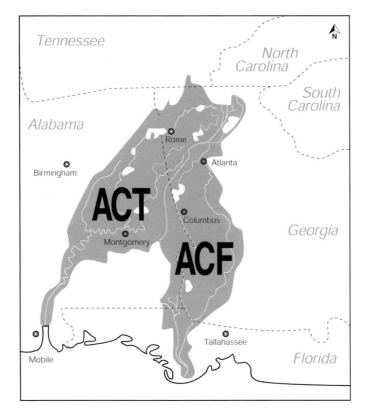

*Fig. 4.* Location map of the Apalachicola-Chattahoochee-Flint (ACF) and Alabama-Coosa-Tallapoosa (ACT) river basins.
Source: US Army Corps of Engineers (http://www.sam.usace.army.mil/sam/pd/actacfeis).

with water quantity issues. These compacts have varied in their terms from an apportionment of a percentage of stream flow to a flat delivery requirement of a given number of acre-feet at a specified point on the stream (Meyers *et al.* 1988). Interstate water compacts in the US require congressional consent. Those that contain numerical delivery requirements are therefore difficult to amend once the apportionments have become law. The compacts for the ACT and ACF are unusual because they don't include water allocation formulae. The parties to the compacts have therefore managed to maintain considerable flexibility in the negotiation process so far.

Environmentalists have been lobbying for the incorporation of several relatively new concepts into the water allocation negotiations. These include demand-side management, or limits to water consumption (as an alternative to setting minimum instream flow requirements); consideration of water quality; natural flow regimes (see the following section) and adaptive management. Initial concepts and proposals put forward by the states of Alabama and Florida include some form of these concepts.

Adaptive management is an approach to planning and executing programmes involving natural resources where outcomes may be difficult to predict and choices are controversial (National Research Council 1998). This approach to natural resource management views projects as a sequence of experimental designs and the results of each experiment are used in a learning process to improve subsequent designs. Monitoring, assessment, feedback, and adjustments are integral parts of the resource management process. Thus, it is vital to the concept of adaptive management that resource managers maintain flexibility to respond to changing environmental conditions, social conditions, or social preferences in the system.

Taking a truly adaptive approach to the management of the ACT and ACF systems requires a significant departure from traditional water allocation negotiations. First, in an adaptive management approach, there is no final agreement on how the system will be managed. Management regimes are applied and then amended as necessary in response to feedback from the ecosystem and the public. Second, an adaptive management approach requires consideration of the entire river basin as a system. The system perspective requires that state negotiators move beyond the negotiation of state line flows and consider cause and effect linkages throughout the system. Third, adaptive management requires that monitoring systems be established and maintained in order to gauge the river system's response to management actions. Management must then be ready to change in response to incoming information. While many environmental management programmes currently have associated monitoring programmes, few of them effectively make use of information gathered through monitoring efforts to adapt management to changing conditions. Fourth, many river management regimes have been established to serve a minimum number of functions, such as water supply and flood control. An adaptive management process integrates a wider range of concerns and evaluates interrelationships between different components, such as water flow and water quality, water quality and estuarine productivity, or water flows and riverine ecology.

A model of the river systems often forms the foundation for an adaptive management process. While all ecosystem models are imprecise and somewhat unreliable, the construction of a model and its associated data base provides an opportunity for interested stakeholders to develop a shared vision of what is being managed and how the management should be done, *i.e.*, as a basis for negotiating. In addition, models and their associated data bases provide a consistent framework for comparing alternative courses of action (Lee 1993).

In the ACF system, a "shared vision" model has been developed (Leitman & Starnes undated). Shared vision models are computer simulations of water systems that are built, reviewed, and tested collaboratively with stakeholders through a shared vision process. The shared vision process includes both decision makers and key interest groups in the development of models in order to more accurately reflect the operational aspects of the system and to increase acceptance of the model. The ACF model has been designed to represent the water system infrastructure and operation and the interrelationships between various water demands. Shared vision models take advantage of new, user-friendly graphical simulation software that is flexible and accessible to users with relatively minimal training. The shared vision model for the ACF was developed with significant input from environmental organisations, leaders of lakeside homeowners organisations, navigation trade organisations, water managers from local and regional governments, and other stakeholders (Anonymous 1995).

The existence of a model that facilitates systemic perspectives and provides river managers with some predictive ability, in combination with an ongoing monitoring programme, is a useful tool in designing adaptive management "experiments" and evaluating their results. The model can be used to predict, for example, the response of Apalachicola Bay to a reduction in low flows during the summer. Should a management plan be implemented that reduces summer low flows to the bay, data can be collected by the monitoring programme on the response and compared to predictions. The model can then be recalibrated as necessary, and management regimes altered to accommodate the new knowledge.

*Natural flow regimes: the Colorado and Snake river basins*

The need to manage rivers in a manner protective of biological diversity has driven many debates over instream flow allocations in recent years. For the most part, the success of a negotiation has been judged on the guarantee of a minimum flow to support fish and other aquatic organisms. The desire to conserve an entire range of species dependent on a river system has posed a problem for resource managers, however, because it is virtually impossible to manage a river in a way that optimises conditions for all species at all times. In addition, there is relatively little known about the specific flow requirements of different taxa.

Within the past two decades, biologists have learned that variability is equally important to maintaining aquatic biodiversity as is the establishment of a minimum flow. Species and ecosystems respond to both high flows and low flows. They also respond to the timing of flows of various magnitudes, and to the rate of change in magnitude of flows. High flows trigger migration in many species of fish, for example. Low flows allow the establishment of moist soil vegetation on floodplains; an important source of food for waterfowl and wading birds and a source of nutrients for the aquatic system. Flood flows reset the entire river system by scouring some areas, depositing silt on others, and moving organic debris and bottom materials. The latest theories of aquatic resource management include the hypothesis that the best way to optimise conditions for the suite of species that have evolved with a river is to maintain or restore the natural flow regime (Michener & Haeuber 1998).

Poff *et al.* (1997) have suggested that at least partial restoration of the natural flow patterns of a river is important to the restoration of riverine ecosystems. The authors recommend the development of quantitative, river specific standards based on the reconstruction of the natural flow regime using historic hydrologic data, where such data exists and relying on reference streams or models where data is scarce. Restoration guidelines based on this philosophy should be viewed as experiments to be monitored and evaluated in an adaptive management approach to river management.

Poff *et al.* (1997) label the idea of replicating hydrologic variability as the "natural flow regime." Richter *et al.* (1997) provided a methodology for translating the natural flow regime into river management targets by decomposing the temporal complexity inherent in a stream flow regime into ecologically meaningful parts. The authors suggest that the natural flow characteristics of rivers fall into five major categories: magnitude, duration, frequency, predictability, and rate of change. In applying this approach to management of a river, the managers statistically derive thirty-two ecologically relevant hydrological parameters for each year of stream flow record for a selected reference period or data series. Measures of the central tendency and dispersion are computed from the annual series for each of the thirty-two parameters and used to characterise interannual variation. The fundamental concept is that the river should be managed in such a way that the annual value of each of these parameters falls within the range of natural variation for that parameter. Thus, the parameters that characterise a natural flow regime for a river can be used to check the ecological viability of a river management regime.

River managers in the US are increasingly looking for ways to manage river systems with more natural flow patterns, primarily in an attempt to conserve and restore biological diversity. Approaches include watershed management (see the Redwood river case study, above), changes in dam operations, and dam removal.

*The Colorado river experimental flood*

A significant trend in water resources management in the US is an apparent decrease in priority given to navigation, power production and flood control functions and an increase in priority for recreation and biodiversity conservation. These changing priorities motivated the artificial flood which was staged in the Grand Canyon below Glen Canyon Dam in the Spring of 1996 (Figure 5). The Grand Canyon has become an important site for both recreation and biodiversity conservation. Grand Canyon National Park receives approximately 5 million visitors per year. Roughly 25,000 people raft the Colorado river through the Grand Canyon every year. These rafters camp on beaches, which have been eroding since the dam began operation. The Grand Canyon segment of the Colorado river is designated as critical habitat under the federal Endangered Species Act for two endemic, endangered fish species – the razorback sucker (*Xyrauchen texanus*) and the humpback chub (*Gila cypha*). The decline of these species is thought to have resulted from the construction and operation of dams, and resulting habitat changes. Riparian vegetation along the Colorado river in the Grand Canyon has been proposed as critical habitat under the Endangered Species Act for the endangered Kanab ambersnail (*Oxyloma hydeni kanabensis*) and the South-western willow flycatcher (*Empidonax traillii*) (Schmidt *et al.* 1998). The decline of these species is also related to the loss of habitat. The lower Colorado river supported more than 3,237 ha of native cottonwood communities in the 1600s. By 1977, only 1,133 ha remained. Overgrazing and tree cutting to supply fuel to steam boats contributed to the loss of riparian habitat, but the biggest factor in its decline has been the construction of dams and subsequent cessation of flooding (Hunt 1988).

Prior to the construction of Glen Canyon Dam, the Colorado river through the Grand Canyon was very much a flood-driven system. Before the dam was constructed, peak discharge occurred in late spring following snowmelt in the Rocky Mountains. The magnitude of the two-year recurrence flood for the period 1921 through 1962 was 2,150 m$^3$sec$^{-1}$, and flows exceeding 1,250 m$^3$sec$^{-1}$ were typically sustained for 30 days or more. Short duration floods occurred in the Fall (Schmidt *et al.* 1998). Steep tributaries emptying into the Colorado river created debris fans as their waters slowed upon reaching the mainstem. These debris fans

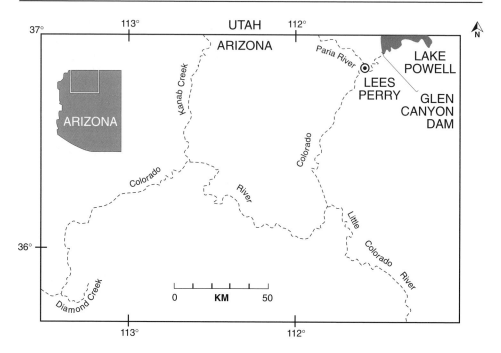

*Fig. 5.* Location map of the Colorado River and Glen Canyon Dam. Source: Colorado River Resources (http://www.mwd.dst.ca.us/pr/crr/cr2.html).

created turbulence directly downstream of the mouth of the tributaries. Eddies formed on the downstream side of these rapids, allowing sediments to settle out of suspension and formed sandbars. Behind the sandbars, quiet backwaters formed and provided safe haven for breeding fish. During heavy floods, the river would flush the debris fans out of the channel and from the river bottom. The deposition of sediments from the bottom of the river channel on river terraces that were normally not inundated created large expanses of beaches along the canyon walls.

Construction of Glen Canyon Dam was completed in 1962. The dam was operated primarily to control the distribution of water between the upper and lower Colorado river basins in accordance with water allocation compacts and subsequent law, and to provide flood control. Hydropower generation was considered an "incidental" by-product of dam operations, but was important to the economic viability of federal irrigation projects in the Colorado river basin. The benefits of operating the dam to achieve these objectives included the measured distribution of approximately 15 billion $m^3$ of water, the generation of hydropower worth up to $100 million per year, the maintenance of a cold-water trout fishery, and recreation in the reservoir created by the dam. The environmental costs of the dam include the suppression of native fishes adapted to warm water environments, the erosion of beaches that are important for recreational purposes, and the degradation of riparian habitats (National Research Council 1996b).

Significant hydrologic and ecological alterations have taken place in the Grand Canyon stretch of the Colorado river as a result of dam construction and operation.

The dam now traps most of the sediment, 66 million tons per year, that once flowed through the canyon. The Paria and Little Colorado rivers supply the majority of sand that enters the Canyon since Glen Canyon Dam was constructed (Collier *et al.* 1996). These two tributaries supply sediment loads of sufficient quantity to provide a net accumulation of sediment in the river canyon. Sand bars and beaches that erode are not being replaced by new formations, however, because flows in the managed system are not high enough to mobilise sand from the river bottom and redeposit it on the channel margins.

The daily and seasonal operating regimes of the Glen Canyon Dam were challenged in the early 1980s by constituencies calling for the moderation of operating regimes in recognition of values other than hydropower production. In 1982, the US Bureau of Reclamation initiated the Glen Canyon Environmental Studies (GCES). The objective of the GCES was to identify and predict the effects of variations in operating strategies on the riverine environment below Glen Canyon Dam within the physical and legal constraints under which the dam must operate. Critical elements for the development of GCES and other such projects include an ecosystem framework showing the causal connections among system components and potential management strategies that include humans as integral parts of the environment (National Research Council 1996b).

The GCES provided valuable information on sediment dynamics in the Colorado river between Glen Canyon Dam and Lake Mead. The GCES verified that the supply of sand reaching the Colorado River through tributaries below Glen Canyon Dam was sufficient to maintain beaches between Lee's Ferry and Lake Mead. GCES showed that the gradual loss of mass from beaches and gradual silting in of backwaters would occur unless occasional high discharges, or artificial floods, are part of the operating regime, even if daily operating regimes avoided drastic changes in flows and rapid changes in flow rates. GCES demonstrated that occasional flood flows are critical in moving coarse debris that accumulates at the mouths of the tributaries during storm flows (National Research Council 1996b).

In 1996, the US Department of Interior staged an artificial flood on the Colorado river in the Grand Canyon, primarily to restore beaches and habitat for native species of fish and wildlife. The artificial flood began on March 22 and released 1,274 m$^3$sec$^{-1}$ for eight consecutive days. This event constituted the first intentional flood ever released for environmental purposes. The Interior Department found that the flood was successful in creating more than 50 large beaches in the canyon, as well as numerous backwater channels that serve as habitat for the humpback chub and other endangered fish species. Non-native species were not significantly effected.

Partly as a result the GCES, the Bureau of Reclamation has committed itself to the concept of adaptive management, which will involve frequent consideration of adjustments in operations as a means of optimising the aggregate values of all resources below Glen Canyon Dam. In 1995, the Bureau proposed the establishment of an "Adaptive Management Programme" based on the need to maintain operational flexibility to respond to future monitoring and research findings and varying resource conditions (US Department of the Interior, Bureau of Reclamation 1995). To support the Adaptive Management programme, the Department of Interior established a monitoring and research centre in Arizona.

Various structural alterations to the dam are currently under consideration. These include the installation of a multiple-level outlet, slurry pipelines for augmenting the sediment supply, and a re-regulation dam that would allow more complete control of the flow for environmental purposes while also maintaining maximum power revenues (National Research Council 1996b). Scientists and resource managers are currently debating the range of management objectives for the river and the structural alterations that would be needed to achieve them. Alternatives being debated range from maximising power generation using existing structures to removing the dam and eliminating non-native fish and vegetation to achieve a fully restored ecosystem (Schmidt *et al.* 1998). In the case of the Colorado river, as with many other rivers throughout the world, enhanced understanding of the relationships between hydrology, geomorphology, and ecology of river systems has led to increasingly complex decisions for resource managers and the public to make.

### The dam decommissioning debate on the Snake river

One option for the restoration of natural flow regimes that has been implemented on some rivers and debated on others is the removal of dams. A number of relatively small dams are being removed or have already been removed from rivers in the US. Examples include the Edwards Dam on the Kennebec river in Maine (ordered to be removed by the US Federal Energy Regulatory Commission), and the Quaker Neck and Cherry Hospital Dams on the Neuse river in North Carolina (removed as an interagency co-operative project in 1997 and 1998). These dams have been or are being removed primarily to restore migratory pathways for fish. The small number of beneficiaries advocating their continued existence and relatively minor costs involved in their removal has limited controversy over the removal of these dams.

Now that successful precedents have been set, removal of larger dams on several major river systems is under consideration. One of the most controversial proposals is for the removal of four dams from the lower Snake river, a major tributary of the Columbia river, in the State of Washington. The dams in question include the Ice Harbor, Lower Monumental, Little Goose dams, and Lower Granite Dams which were completed in 1962, 1969, 1970, and 1975, respectively. The dams were part of the federal Lower Snake River Project, the purpose of which was to provide a navigable waterway from the confluence of the Snake and Columbia rivers to Lewiston, Idaho. Other project benefits included irrigation and hydroelectricity (Hunt 1988).

Since completion of the dams, salmon populations in the Snake and Columbia river basins have declined drastically (National Marine Fisheries Service 1995) Snake river Spring/Summer and Fall Chinook salmon were federally listed as threatened in 1992. Hydroelectric development in the mainstem Snake and Columbia rivers is widely recognised as the major factor causing the decline in the number of anadromous salmon returning to the Snake river (Figure 6) Loss of stock productivity and recruitment coincided directly with this development (Hassemer *et al* 1997).

The removal of the four dams on the lower Snake river (Figure 7) has been identified as a potential, partial solution to the dramatic decline in wild salmon populations in the Columbia river basin. While a wide range of factors, including overharvest from rivers and at sea, watershed alterations, riparian habitat destruction, water pollution, and changes in the ocean environment have contributed to these

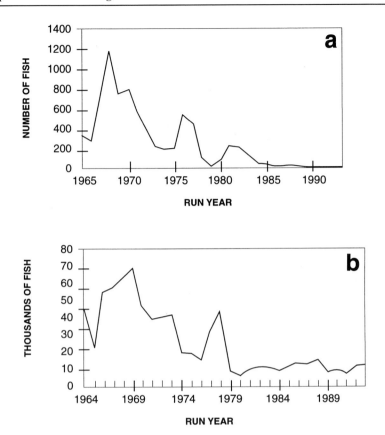

*Fig.* 6. Number of Sockeye salmon (a) and wild spring/summer Chinook salmon counted at the uppermost dam on the lower Snake river, 1965-1993. Uppermost dam is indicated by years: 1964-1968, Ice Harbor; 1969, Lower Monumental; 1970-1974, Little Goose dams; and 1975-1993, Lower Granite (From Hassemer *et al.* 1997).

declines, many scientists believe that the construction and operation of the dams is the largest contributing factor.

Salmon mortality as a result of dam construction occurs in a number of ways. Dams without fish passage facilities prohibit fish from migrating upstream, thus potentially cutting off large portions of their former ranges. Roughly one-third of the original habitat available to salmon in the Columbia river watershed has been cut off by dam construction. Fish passage facilities can result in delays in upstream migration of adults, increasing stress, pre-spawning mortality, and reduction in the success of late spawners (National Research Council 1996a). Smolts migrating downstream must either pass through spillways, bypass facilities, or turbines, each of which carries increased risks of injury or mortality above a natural river system. Reservoirs significantly slow down travel times for salmon migrating downstream, largely because they decrease the flow rates of large portions of the river. Delayed travel times increase the potential for disease or predation to deplete the cohort of smolt. The creation of reservoirs has also improved habitat for salmon predators,

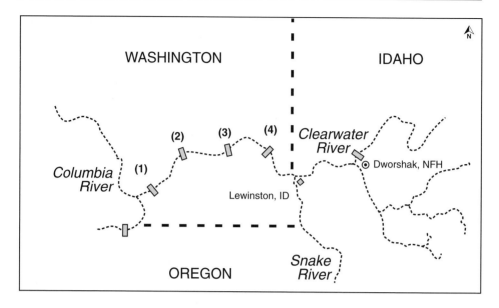

*Fig. 7.* Snake River showing locations of lower four dams (1: Ice Harbor; 2: Lower Monumental; 3: Little Goose; 4: Lower Granite).
Source: US Fish and Wildlife Service (http://www.r1.fws.gov/dworshak/projects).

both native and introduced, and thus has indirectly increased depredation of smolts (National Marine Fisheries Service 1995). Supersaturation of gas, primarily nitrogen, occurs when water spills over a dam. This gas is taken into the bloodstreams of fish during respiration and can then come out of solution as bubbles, resulting in a condition very similar to the bends experienced by deep sea divers (National Research Council 1996a). Reservoirs behind dams can inundate large areas of important spawning habitat.

The salmon fishery in the Pacific Northwest is extremely valuable from an economic perspective. The National Marine Fisheries Service (1995) estimates that over 8,000 full-time work years are employed in the west coast salmon industry. The combined employment value of the fishery, the direct regional economic value of the salmon catch (generally in the tens of millions of dollars), and all of the values that cannot be quantified in financial terms are of great regional significance. Thus, the decline of the salmon populations is of serious concern from both a regional and national perspective.

Debates about methods of recovering salmon populations have been ongoing for many years. Options evaluated have included transporting the fish around dams in barges and trucks, augmenting flows to move fish over the spillways, drawing down the levels of the reservoirs to reduce migratory travel times, using hatchery fish to further supplement natural population, and prohibiting anglers from keeping wild fish.

A feasibility study published by the Army Corps of Engineers in 1996 concluded that natural river drawdown, or dam decommissioning, is the only drawdown alternative that offered significant benefits for fish. The year 1999 is the final decision point for selecting between natural river drawdown and other options for salmon conservation. Information should be available at this time to determine whether the collection and upstream transport of adults in conjunction with improved in-river conditions or in conjunction with improved transportation of juveniles via barge will improve survivals sufficient to achieve recovery. Design of the natural river drawdown option should also be complete at this time. Congressional authorisation to implement natural river drawdown would be requested if the surface collection options proved insufficient (National Marine Fisheries Service 1995).

Dam decommissioning may be the most beneficial alternative for the salmon, but it is also an expensive and complex process for the region. The most difficult aspect of large dam removal may be management of the sediments that have accumulated behind the dam. These sediments, particularly if they are heavily polluted, can represent a significant source of pollution for the river ecosystem downstream. Other issues that present an engineering challenge include the maintenance of a river channel during the deconstruction process, the physical removal of the structure, and the recreation of a river channel through the bed of the former reservoir.

The prospect of dam decommissioning represents a complex political issue for the region and for the nation, as well. Various factions are lining up on either side of the dam decommissioning debate in the region. Perhaps predictably, environmental and sport fishing groups generally support the removal of dams from the lower Snake river and industrial groups, including aluminium manufacturers who use energy produced by the dams and farmers who pump irrigation water from their reservoirs oppose such an action. The proposition of dam decommissioning is frequently raised in Congressional hearings and has attracted considerable attention from both the regional and national press.

The fate of the dams on the lower Snake river remains uncertain. The option of dam removal will continue to surface as licenses for private dams come up for renewal, ageing infrastructure deteriorates, siltation depletes the useful lives of these structures, and society increases its valuation of ecological processes compared to power generation, navigation, irrigation, and other products produced by dams.

## 3. Conclusion

The US is clearly altering its approach to river management from one that is dependent on hardware to one that depends on information. While collecting and managing the information necessary to follow an integrated and information based approach is expensive and time-consuming, our country is learning that by investing up front in understanding the riverine ecosystem and the human aspirations for use of the river system costly mistakes and restoration measures may be avoided in the future.

There is no single solution to all of the resource management issues faced by various human communities and aquatic ecosystems. The key to successful integrated river management is gaining a thorough understanding of the people and ecological processes unique to each river system, and to use this understanding in the design and implementation of appropriate management strategies. All of the concepts focused on in this paper have the common characteristic of helping managers to adapt to the human and ecological elements of specific systems. Systemic thinking requires knowledge of the interconnections between various parts and functions of the river system. Public participation provides a pathway for local knowledge and priorities to be integrated into resource management. Adaptive management incorporates the social and economic responses of the system to management approaches, and adjusting the approaches to achieve a better fit with the system. Natural flow regimes provide a blueprint for river managers that allows management to be tailored to the specific rhythms of the river. By learning from the rivers and the communities that depend on them, we can create management approaches that maximise benefits to people and to river ecosystems.

# References

Anonymous. 1995. Alabama-Coosa-Tallapoosa/Apalachicola-Chatahoochee-Flint river basins comprehensive water resources study: Status report. US Army Corps of Engineers and the States of Alabama, Florida and Georgia, Mobile.

Ayers, B.D. 1993. What's left from the great flood of '93. The New York Times, August 10.

Belt, C.B. 1975. The 1973 flood and man's constriction of the Mississippi river. Science 189: 681-684.

Chagnon, S.A. & Kunkle, K.E. 1995. Climate-related fluctuations in Midwestern floods during 1921- 1985. Journal of Water Resources Planning and Management 121: 326-334.

Collier, M., Webb, R.H. & Schmidt, J.C. 1996. Dams and rivers: Primer on the downstream effects of dams. Circular 1126. US Geological Survey, Tucson.

Eiker, E. 1986. September 8 letter to Dr. D. Hey regarding capitol expenditures for flood control work by the US Army Corps of Engineers.

Governor's Commission on Sustainable South Florida. 1996. A conceptual plan for the C&SF Project restudy. Governor's Commission on Sustainable South Florida, Tallahasee.

Hassemer, P.F., Kiefer S.W. & Petrosky, C.E. 1997. Idaho's salmon: can we count every last one? In: Stouder, D.J., Bisson P.A. & Naiman R.J. (Eds.). Pacific salmon and their ecosystems: Status and future options. International Thomson Publishing, Florence. pp.113-126

Hunt, C.E. 1997. A natural approach for flood damage reduction and environmental enhancement. Long Term Resource Monitoring Program Special Report 97-S005. US Geological Survey Environmental Management Technical Center, Onalaska.

Hunt, C.E. 1998. Down by the river: The impact of federal water projects and policies on biological diversity. Island Press, Covelo.

Jacobson, S.M. 1999. Redwood river basin JD31 hydrologic modeling. Wetlands Journal 11/2: 3-6.

Lee, K.N. 1993. Compass and gyroscope: Integrating science and politics for the environment. Island Press, Covelo.

Leitman, S. & Starnes, J. undated. Preparing and using shared vision models for the Apalachicola-Chattahoochee-Flint watershed. http://www.ces/fau.edu/library/flms/39.html.

Meyers, C.J., Tarlock, A.D., Corbridge, J.N. Jr. & Getches D.H. 1988. Water resource management: A casebook in law and public policy. The Foundation Press Inc., Mineola.

Michener, W.K. & Haeuber, R.A. 1998. Flooding: Natural and managed disturbances. Bioscience 48/9: 677-680.

National Marine Fisheries Service. 1995. Proposed recovery plan for Snake river salmon. National Oceanic and Atmospheric Administration, National Marine Fisheries Service, Northwest Region.

National Research Council. 1996a. Upstream: Salmon and society in the Pacific Northwest. National Academy Press, Washington DC.

National Research Council. 1996b. River resource management in the Grand Canyon. National Academy Press, Washington DC.

National Research Council. 1997. Watershed research in the US Geological Survey. National Academy Press, Washington DC.

National Research Council. 1998. New directions in water resource planning for the US Army Corps of Engineers (Review Draft). National Academy Press, Washington DC.

Olson, D.M. & Dinerstein, E. 1998. The global 200: a representation approach to conserving the Earth's distinctive ecoregions. Draft manuscript. World Wildlife Fund, Washington DC.

Phillippi, N.S. 1995. Flooding and flood control in the Midwest, 1993: Three case studies. Wetlands Research Inc., Chicago.

Poff, N.L., Allan J.D., Bain M.B., Karr J.R., Prestegaard, K.L., Richter, B.D., Sparks, R.E. & Stromberg, J.C. 1997. The natural flow regime: A paradigm for river conservation and restoration. Bioscience 47/11: 769-784.

Richter, B.D., Baumgartner, J.V., Wigington, R. & Braun, D.P. 1997. How much water does a river need? Freshwater Biology 37: 231-249.

Schmidt, J.C., Webb, R.H., Valdez, R.A., Marzolf, G.R & Stevens, L.E. 1998. Science and values in river restoration in the Grand Canyon. Bioscience 48/9: 735-747.

Scientific Assessment and Strategy Team. 1994. Science for floodplain management into the Twenty-first Century. Preliminary report of the Scientific Assessment and Strategy Team to the Administration Floodplain Management Task Force. Washington DC.

South Florida Ecosystem Restoration Program. 1999. Cross-cut budget FY2000. http://www.sfrestore.org/documents.

US Army Corps of Engineers. 1994. Central and Southern Florida Project Reconnaissance Report: Comprehensive Review Study. US Army Corps of Engineers, Jacksonville District, Jacksonville.

US Army Corps of Engineers & South Florida Water Management District. 1999. Central and Southern Florida project comprehensive review study: final integrated feasibility report and programmatic environmental impact statement. US Army Corps of Engineers & South Florida Water Management District, Jacksonville.

US Department of the Interior, Bureau of Reclamation. 1995. Operation of Glen Canyon Dam. Final Environmental Impact Statement: Summary. US Department of the Interior, Bureau of Reclamation, Salt Lake City.

Wahl, K.L., Vining, K.C. & White, G.J. 1993. Precipitation in the upper Mississippi river basin, January 1 through July 31, 1993. US Geological Survey Circular 1120-B, Denver.

Winter, T.C. 1992. A physiographic and climatic framework for hydrologic studies of wetlands. In: Roberts, R.D. & Bothwell, M.L. (Eds.) Aquatic ecosystems in semi-arid regions: Implications for resource management. N.H.R.I. Symposium Series 7, Environment Canada, Saskatoon. pp. 127-148.

# PARTNERS IN WETLAND CONSERVATION AND DEVELOPMENT: STRATEGIC ENVIRONMENTAL ANALYSIS FOR THE UKRAINIAN DANUBE DELTA

J.C.J. van Wetten
*AIDEnvironment, Donker Curtiusstraat 7-523, NL-1051 JL Amsterdam,
The Netherlands; Present address: Dutch Society for Preservation of Nature
(Vereniging Natuurmonumenten), Noordereinde 60, NL-1243 JJ 's-Graveland,
The Netherlands*

## Abstract

This article describes a new approach to wetland management interventions. Instead of focusing solely on 'problems', more attention is given to 'opportunity identification' as a basis for modifying programmes and projects for wetland management. Assessing the basic causes of opportunities as well as constraints creates new options for innovative partnerships and coalition. The concepts of magnification and strategic communication are used to improve the outreach, outputs and sustainability of the interventions. The World Wildlife Fund (WWF) Partners for Wetlands project in the Ukraine has been designed and implemented along these lines and concepts, and is one of the testing grounds for Strategic Environmental ANalysis (SEAN) and magnification methodologies as described in this article.

## 1. Introduction

Wetlands and river systems are in great need of protection and restoration. Besides biodiversity wetland and river ecosystems provide a wealth of socio-economic values and functions. Hence support for conservation and restoration need not only be sought in the traditional nature conservation community. Based on experiences in the Netherlands and elsewhere in the world, World Wildlife Fund-Netherlands (WWF-Netherlands) has launched initiatives for improved wetland and river ecosystem protection (Helmer *et al.* 1993). Partnerships with other stakeholders and actors play a dominant role in the initiatives, whereas magnification of results and approaches is seen as an even higher goal than the direct project results. A good analysis of conditions, actors, stakeholders, interests etc. is a prerequisite for building a joint vision and strategy. Although environmental, ecological and socio-economic problems are often at the basis of the awareness that protection and restoration initiatives are needed, true partnership and enthusiasm is more effectively initiated on the basis of opportunity-driven initiatives rather than solely through problem-oriented approaches. Within the context of the WWF Programme 'Partners for Wetlands', AIDEnvironment was commissioned by WWF-Netherlands to support

*New approaches to river management, pp. 141–153*
*edited by A.J.M. Smits, P.H. Nienhuis and R.S.E.W. Leuven*
*© 2000 Backhuys Publishers, Leiden, The Netherlands*

the identification and formulation of four Model Wetland Projects world-wide. The Strategic Environmental ANalysis (SEAN) methodology (Kessler 1997) was used as a guiding tool to identify partnerships, magnification and opportunities and to render them operational.

## 2. Rationale and goal of partnerships

WWF will not be able to significantly change the trend of environmental destruction world-wide on its own. Important other actors are involved, such as governments, the private sector, consumers and multilateral agencies. Even modest changes in the behaviour of these actors and their investments can have major impacts on nature and environment. Therefore, WWF wishes to break the relative isolation of environmental advocacy and work with these actors to influence and inspire them to integrate environmental principles in decision making. The success of this co-operation should be recognisable and should result in enthusiasm, leading to the spontaneous continuation, expansion and replication of efforts, without WWF's assistance. Investments should become compatible with environmental principles and additional financial resources should become available to stimulate this process.

As a medium-term (3-5 year) goal, WWF will demonstrate practical solutions to wetland conservation through four selected model projects in the field, which are sufficiently credible to be adopted and applied by others, under the motto of 'Partners for Wetlands' (or Partnership Projects). This name reflects the central theme and challenge of fruitful participation of the actors involved. The main aspects of the approach are: magnification, partnerships, modular projects and communication. The following description of these four aspects is based on the framework of Kessler (1997).

### 2.1 Magnification

Magnification or scaling up is defined as the mobilisation of complementary stakeholders, from sectors not traditionally conservation oriented, in pursuit of an overall goal which cannot only be achieved with one's own resources.

Apart from the most important step of formulating an appealing vision that should generate a strong feeling of affiliation and involve partners, other important aspects to be considered for integration of the concept of magnification in the work of WWF are:
- a thorough strategic (environmental) analysis;
- a good strategic concept, and well defined expected results and specified targets;
- appropriate timing both for building up momentum and for phasing out;
- a strategic attitude towards target groups and partners, based on co-operation (formalised through a Memorandum of Understanding);
- a balanced, flexible, open and synergetic organisation;
- good internal and external communication;
- a well defined marketing strategy.

Magnification activities and their underlying mechanisms can have different dimensions (Figure 1). Some mechanisms help to magnify both at the project or programme level and on a wider scale. This applies to models which can be intro-

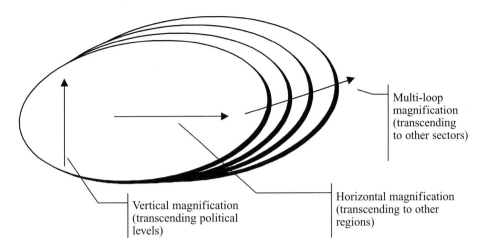

*Fig. 1.* Horizontal, vertical and multi-loop magnification (Kessler 1997).

duced in other areas and countries (horizontal magnification). An example of vertical magnification would be a project which shows the feasibility of integrated planning and participation and consequently triggers the adjustment of national policy or legislation. Double or multi-loop magnification is yet another form where magnification extends to other sectors. For example, the Forest Stewardship Council (FSC), by setting a standard for forest management and timber trade, has and will have an enormous positive influence on forest management all over the world, the first loop of spin-off (FSC 1999). The FSC has also served as a model for the Marine Stewardship Council, the second loop of magnification. Subsequent loops might well consist of similar approaches for other forms of exploitation of natural resources, potentially even including abiotic raw materials.

## 2.2 Partnerships

With regard to target groups, the choice is between confrontation and co-operation. Without necessarily always excluding the possibility of confrontation, WWF mostly, as a guiding principle, chooses co-operation and dialogue. Through dialogue, and where possible through co-operation, target groups become partners, and partners are the ultimate vehicle for magnification. The key questions are: who to involve and how to involve them strategically? The presentation of an appealing vision, which also addresses the opportunities, needs, problems and threats felt by (envisaged) partners, and which is disseminated through a clear message, plays a predominant role in attracting partners.

The strategic analysis of actors and stakeholders can help in many respects. It can identify their current and future needs, and constraints, trends, their evolution, vision, aims, means, capabilities and opportunities. As regards magnification, important questions for the identification of primary partners are:
- Are they part of the problem?
- Do they have the potential to significantly contribute to the objectives, either directly or indirectly, by influencing other groups or processes?

– Are they seen as market or opinion leaders, or can they positively influence the market, the respective target groups, or the general public's opinion?
– Have they expressed an interest in and willingness for innovation?
– How much or what is in it for them if they enter into the WWF Partnership or the activity proposed ('win-win'): *e.g.*, does it solve their constrains, does it help to 'green' their profile, either passively, through the publicity afforded by being associated with WWF, or actively, through concrete contributions to nature conservation, or by changing their conduct, by diversification of their products, or by entering or creating a new market?

Target groups and partners may be identified at all levels, local, national and international. They are also of all types: governments, multi-lateral agencies, Non Governmental Organisations (NGOs), the private (business) sector, the public at large (*i.e.*, consumers). WWF's role will be that of honest broker and facilitator, keeping track of the project's mandate on nature conservation. Again, the first and most important step on the path towards more effectiveness is the formulation of an appealing vision. A vision is both a precondition and a directive for magnification; it stands for what one ideally would like to achieve in the end, *i.e.*, the overall goal. The tension between the current situation and the overall goal provides the creative power both to WWF and to its partners.

In order to involve partners, a vision should generate a strong feeling of affiliation. Magnification without a vision is meaningless, and can even be counterproductive. Ensuring project 'ownership' and affiliation also means allowing for continued inputs in planning and implementation and verifying the outcome of planning and implementation with all partners at moments early enough in the process to allow for adjustments. Design of monitoring and evaluation during project implementation will have to be adjusted according to needs.

## 2.3 Modular projects

Partnership Projects will consist of one or two ready-to-be-implemented Core Modules (Box 1) which will relate to key conservation issues. The Partnership, including WWF, will be responsible for funding and implementing the Core Modules. These modules will focus on a major threat, problem or opportunity which is common in the region and which relates to wetland systems.

Box 1. Core and Non-core Modules of the portfolio of 'Partners for Wetlands' projects.

*Core Modules*
Core Modules address a problem, threat or opportunity in relation to the wetland, with partners engaged and committed to participate and collaborate, and with funding available. Therefore, the partnership should lead to results in wetland conservation within 3 to 5 years.

*Non-core Modules*
Non-core Modules address a problem or threat, but concrete opportunities and partners still need to be identified and a proposal needs to be formulated by the project. Non-core Modules are expected to become operational during the later life of the project.

Associated problems, solutions and opportunities will be described in one or two additional Non-core Modules, for which the project will merely finance the preparation of a fundable proposal as well as lobbying for financial assistance from additional partners from the government, the private sector, consumers, multilateral agencies and other important actors. Non-core Modules are considered important vehicles to involve these other partners in the wetland vision developed by WWF. After the end of the current project, *i.e.*, the Core Modules, the proposed Non-core Modules should be ready for implementation, thus guaranteeing a longer and wider involvement of WWF in the area.

*2.4 Communication*

Briefly, communication can be considered as the management of understanding, understanding by all WWF staff of the vision and strategies, as well as understanding between WWF and its target groups and partners. Without communication there is no understanding of vision. Without understanding there is no well-directed magnification. Both internal and external communication should be an integral part of all components and processes within the planning and implementation cycle, from vision to evaluation. The process of formulation of vision needs to be communicated, as well as the resulting vision itself, in order to focus all staff and potential partners involved.

The strategy to realise the vision needs to be communicated in its objectives and targets in order to provide timely direction and increase dedication. Results need to be communicated, including the lessons drawn, and targets groups have to be clearly defined. Regular communication is vital in order to involve staff, members, individuals, business, industry, governments and other organisations. As such, the eminent importance of communication for magnification is obvious. Therefore, there is a fully fledged communication component in every project and it is a central task in the management of the portfolio. Additionally, fund-raising for Core Modules (mainly from WWF and its Partners) and Non-core Modules (mainly from Partners) will also be supported by the project's communication component.

## 3. Strategic environmental analysis

SEAN is a planning framework for opportunity identification and the designing of sustainable development policies. This methodological framework includes practical tools and guidelines for analysing the environmental potentials for and constraints on human development. It is designed for use at the earliest possible stage of policy-making to allow the relevant environmental issues to be fully integrated into policy design (Figure 2). The methodology is based on experiences with Environmental Impact Assessment (EIA), Environmental Profiles, and environmental planning, monitoring and evaluation (Kessler 1997). SEAN is a process by which decision makers take account of environmental issues, opportunities and problems during the formulation or revision of strategies, programmes or policies. During this process, priorities are set and choices are made, mainly according to economic and social objectives. SEAN tries as much as possible to pursue an integrated analysis, with the aim to improve the design of sustainable development

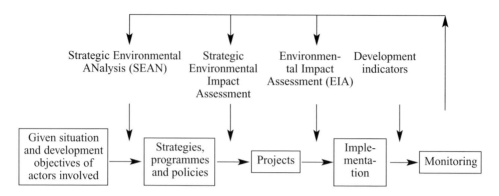

*Fig. 2.* Relevance of Strategic Environmental Analysis (SEAN) in the strategic planning process, in comparison to other environmental assessment tools.

policies by raising the level of environmental knowledge and understanding and enhancing integration.

SEAN is oriented towards human development. It takes the environmental and ecological dimension as its starting point, building upon the concept of sustainable development as a process of change geared to maintaining development potentials for future generations. This involves socio-cultural, economic, institutional and environmental/ecological dimensions (Figure 3). The interrelations between these dimensions are used to guide the analysis and so create maximum synergy. SEAN aims to support and influence the decision-making process by clarifying the importance and consequences of environmental issues in relation to the desired social and economic aspects.

The Life Support System is seen as a basic concept to clarify to which extent human actions do or do not hamper environmental and ecological functions and their outputs in terms of production, regulation and service capacities (De Groot 1992). Instead of just identifying critical norms and threshold levels, environmental trend identification is seen as an important tool to identify or understand threats. Loss of biodiversity and decreasing ecosystem functional properties should be understood in terms of increased obligations to compensate for these losses by management inputs and readjustment interventions in the system, often resulting in economic costs or damage.

Activities causing environmental and ecosystem degradation are further analysed in SEAN by identifying the primary and secondary actors (Figure 4). By investigating their motivations (why do they do what they do) and identifying their options (what can they choose from), the underlying causative factors (basic causes) are clarified. Understanding the basic causes allows new light to be shed on the strategic choices to be made, *e.g.*, should an environmental problem be mitigated or should a root cause be tackled by interventions on actor groups which at first sight may not have seemed related to the problem in the field. Perverse subsidies could, for example, be the basic cause of an environmental problem, whereas new investment subsidies could open the way for or stimulate more environmentally sound activities.

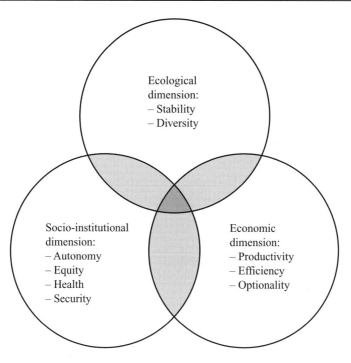

*Fig. 3.* Domains of sustainable development. The circles represent the limits for sustainability of each dimension. Such limits are set by norms (of society) and thresholds (of the ecological system). Sustainable development takes place only if the sustainability criteria of all three dimensions are met, which is represented by the darkest area. In all other cases (*e.g.*, lightly shaded areas) at least one dimension is not sufficiently addressed, and will be at risk.

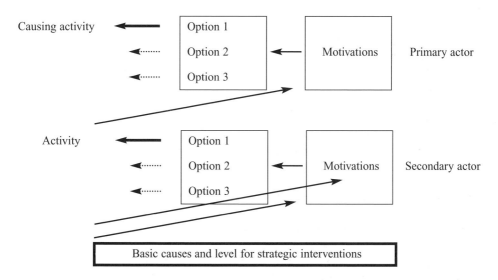

*Fig. 4.* Identification of the key factors and related actors causing the problem.

Ten methodological steps provide guidance to users of SEAN in clarifying the complex issues involved. As SEAN is a cyclic and iterative process, steps can be combined or repeated at different stages and at different levels of detail. The ten steps of SEAN are:

*Steps 1 – 4: Society-environment context analysis and impact assessment*
1. Identification of the main environmental functions (production and regulation); defining stakeholders dependent upon these functions.
2. Assessment of current trends in the functions revealed by environmental indicators.
3. Assessment of consequences (impacts) of trends on stakeholders, future generations and natural values, using environmental impact chains and a trend-impact matrix.
4. Defining the norms, standards and thresholds involved.

*Steps 5 – 6: Environmental problem analysis*
5. Definition of the main environmental problems, based on the impacts of trends and a risk analysis.
6. Identification of the key factors and related actors causing the problem, using the action-in-context approach (De Groot 1992); underlying factors could be mainly socio-cultural, economic and/or institutional.

*Steps 7 – 8: Environmental opportunity analysis, scenario development and win-win options*
7. Definition of the main environmental opportunities; identification of strategy and win-win options.
8. Synthesis of the key factors and actors related to the environmental problems and opportunities, and formulation of development scenarios; impact assessment of scenarios and priority setting.

*Steps 9 – 10: Formulation of a sustainable strategy and policy*
9. Definition of sustainable development action fields by integrating environmental action fields with priority issues from social and economic dimensions; formulation of a policy and coherent action plan for sustainable development based on the strengths and weaknesses of the relevant institutions and existing development policies.
10. Formulation of a follow-up strategy, including definition of co-ordination responsibilities, establishment of a monitoring system with relevant indicators, procedures for regular adjustments to policy using relevant SEAN steps, institutional strengthening and capacity building.

## 4. The Ukrainian project of 'Partners for Wetlands'

In the framework of WWF's Quality Programme and Wetland Programme, four projects have been supported that should serve the conservation of freshwater wetland ecosystems, such as rivers, river basins, catchment areas, underground aquifers, surface water bodies, lakes and all bio-regions associated with these wetland systems. The four projects selected by 'Partners for Wetlands' are situated in Zambia for the Africa and Madagascar Region, in Malaysia for the Asia and Pacific Region, in the Ukraine for the Europe and Near-East Region, and finally in Brazil for the Latin and Central America Region.

The core and non-core modules of the Model Wetland project in the Ukrainian Danube Delta and near-coastal Black Sea wetland are presented in box 2.

The Danube Delta and Black Sea coastal area (Figure 5) is an area with tremendous biodiversity values (WWF 1998a,b). It is an important breeding ground for fish, a filter for nutrients entering the Black Sea from the Danube River, and a major bird breeding and migration stop-over point. Because of the importance of the region and existing institutional difficulties in protecting and restoring this resource, major opportunities exist for investment in nature conservation. These opportunities may range from support for the operational budgets of highly underfunded nature conservation agencies to investment in nature conservation infrastructure, such as mapping and park facilities, and support for NGOs, who are beginning to play a pivotal role in changing societal values towards nature and wetland protection.

All of the existing nature conservation needs of the region can clearly not be met by funding and initiatives by WWF alone. The strategy adopted for this project is therefore to use the funds and activities carried out under the project as a catalyst and framework for attracting other initiatives in support of nature conservation

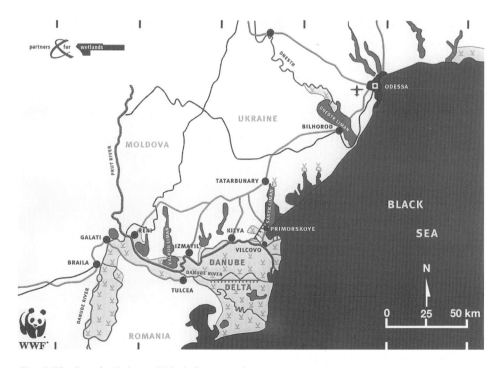

*Fig. 5.* The Danube Delta and Black Sea coastal area.

*Box 2.* Core and non-core modules of the Model Wetland project in the Ukrainian Danube Delta.

Core module A: Wetland restoration and engineering at Stensovsko Zhiebrianski Plavni (SZP).

*Threat, problem or challenge*
Large parts of the water, navigation and land-use/irrigation works established by the previous political regime are no longer functional. They are disrupting the natural flooding regime and related ecological processes, directly affecting the living environment of adjacent communities. The project will result in restoration of SZP and a rehabilitation of natural resource-based economic activities.

| *Core module* | *Main partners* | *Likely benefit for partners* |
| --- | --- | --- |
| – restoration of natural flooding at Stensovsko Zhiebrianski Plavni (12,000 ha) | – government<br>– World Bank (Global Environment Facility)<br>– Dutch Ministry of Transport, Public Works and Water Management<br>– local communities | – restoration of wetland functions (biodiversity, water purification, hunting, fisheries, ranching and tourism) |

Core Module B: Natural resource use development in buffer zones.

*Threat, problem or challenge*
Due to the economic crisis, agriculture in large parts of the Ukraine is receiving low inputs and is actually moving towards organic farming. With support from the project, this type of agriculture could be promoted in areas surrounding wetlands, and markets for these products could be explored inside and outside the Ukraine.

| *Core module* | *Main partners* | *Likely benefit for partners* |
| --- | --- | --- |
| – capital for transformation to eco-agriculture<br>– local and foreign trade and companies, markets explored<br>– pilot of organic farming<br>– magnification | – foreign investors<br>– national and international food companies<br>– national and local authorities<br>– farmers' associations | – opportunities for investors, with additional (tax) incentives put in place by Western Governments<br>– income from buffer zones |

Core module C: Recreation and wildlife tourism development.

*Threat, problem or challenge*
There is a growing recognition of the potential of and interest in the coastal wetlands in Odessa Oblast, for both local recreation and national and international tourism. Linkages and coalitions between the recreation and tourism sector and nature conservation agencies are underdeveloped, however.

| *Core module* | *Main partners* | *Likely benefit for partners* |
| --- | --- | --- |
| – tourism development (pilots)<br>– investment capital available<br>– tourism policy | – cruise-ship companies<br>– local tour operators<br>– foreign green investors<br>– government<br>– nature conservation agencies | – income from tourism<br>– improved conservation<br>– financing mechanism for habitat management |

Non-core modules
– Development of a Black Sea coastal wetland restoration policy and programme portfolio
– Development of a masterplan for Sasyk Liman (over 200,000 ha)

goals. In this strategy, a clear choice has been made not to invest in all kinds of investment opportunities but to organise the investments into a frame through which magnification and maximum outreach will be attained. This implies that rather obvious investment opportunities, such as the traditional nature conservation allies and organisations, are not included in this project but investments are directed towards potential partners and targets in relation to magnification and outreach.

The wetland restoration engineering (Core Module A) of Stensovsko Zhiebrianskie Plavni (12,000 ha) or a part of the Dnjester Delta (6,000 ha) will be an initial example of directing investments to solve and 'clean up' the remains of unsound wetland management approaches and policies. It also is expected that this module will clarify the benefits for multi-user interest wetland ecosystem restoration and convince decision makers of the need and potential for wetland restoration and new wetland management approaches.

A Master Plan for Sasyk Liman (200,000 ha, Figure 6) will be developed (Non-core Module), from which a number of construction and engineering solutions to the ecological problems of Limans are expected to evolve. Funding to implement such solutions can then be identified. In addition to Sasyk Liman, two other areas with high potential for wetland restoration have been identified. One is the river isle of Yermakow, where breaching of dikes can rather easily be implemented, based on the WWF's and Danube Delta Institute's experience with the restoration of the nearby island of Babina in Romania. The other opportunity has been found at Lake Kugerlug (former Liman; 10,000 ha), where a 1.5 km wide reclaimed former floodplain can be reversed into river-fringing wetland. This will then allow re-development of the open connection between the Danube River and Lake Kugerlug.

The Policy and Portfolio Development activities (Non-core Module) are expected to yield new opportunities for investments in wetland restoration. By the time a new policy on wetland restoration will materialise, these opportunities will have become more detailed and defined. The identification and formulation of new wetland restoration opportunities within this WWF project and the additional opportunities emerging from other partners could all be submitted as projects in the Black Sea Coastal Wetland Restoration Programme.

WWF's communication and lobbying capacity will play a pivotal role in attracting donors and partners to fund and implement an anticipated Euro 9,100,000 worth of wetland conservation and restoration initiatives under the Wetland Restoration Programme Portfolio. First of all, the WWF project would provide means and opportunities to use allocated wetland restoration budgets of Euro 136,000 – 181,000 under the Global Environment Facility (GEF) Danube Delta Biodiversity projects for this purpose during the lifetime of this GEF project. In addition to support for wetland restoration, preparation work for this WWF project has already resulted in an Euro 36,000 contract being awarded to WWF by the World Bank for NGO training in the Ukraine. A second contract for this work is currently under preparation. Secondly, a Memorandum of Understanding between the Ukrainian Republic and the Netherlands includes commitments by which Dutch water engineering expertise and institutes can implement their supportive role in wetland restoration and wetland management. The involvement of these Dutch institutes further paves the way for extension of institutional and financial support from the Netherlands and the European Union. Foreign private capital, especially capital

*Fig. 6.* The Danube Delta and Sasyk Liman.

invested in so-called Green Funds, is intended to become an important source to facilitate and initiate land use reforms (Core Modules B and C). An amount of Euro 450,000 from such green funds has been targeted for the investment in the project area within the lifetime of this WWF project.

Apart from partners such as the government and its agencies, donor agencies such as World Bank, GEF and EU, Green Fund Investors and the Ukrainian tourist sector, other important partners for this project are local people, user groups and NGOs. Their involvement will allow for a greater political impact of the project, especially since these actors are in the process of emancipation. The commercial sector and the emerging class of innovative and creative businessmen are also seen as a high-potential partner group. Their support will be engaged especially in the context of common interests between wetland conservation and the recreation and tourism sector. The emerging urban middle class, with its growing awareness of environmental and nature conservation issues, is seen as a strong political influence in the future. Secondly, the transformation of the agricultural sector is believed to provide an opportunity to implement sustainable land utilisation within the buffer zones and edges of the major wetlands.

Odessa has been chosen as the home base for the WWF project. First of all, the City of Odessa is experiencing a speedily economic development and is rapidly outgrowing its former Soviet-system setbacks. Secondly, the political and institutional position of the Odessa Oblast is one of rather advanced independence from the central government in Kiev. On the one hand, it may be contented that not aiming beyond the Odessa Oblast's geographical area and policy level provides too modest a scope. On the other hand, overstretching the expectation, as would be the case with a national scope, creates the risk of diluting resources and getting bogged down in reduced momentum and achievements.

## References

De Groot, W.T. 1992. Environmental science theory. Concepts and methods in a one world, problem-oriented paradigm. Elsevier Science Publishers, Amsterdam.

FSC. 1999. FSC Principles and criteria for forest stewardships. Forest Stewardship Council A.C. (FSC), Oaxaca.

Kessler, J.J. 1997. Strategic Environmental Analysis (SEAN). A framework for planning and integration of environmental care in development policies and interventions. AIDEnvironment/ SNV, Amsterdam.

Romijn, B. & Wakker, E. 1997. In search for magnification. Lessons drawn from the international WWF network. AIDEnvironment, Amsterdam.

Helmer, W., Litjens, G., Overmars, W., Barneveld, H., Klink, A., Sterrenburg, A. & Janssen, B. 1993. Living rivers. World Wide Fund for Nature, Zeist, Bureau Stroming voor natuur- en landschapsontwikkeling b.v., Laag Keppel.

WWF. 1998a. Partners for Wetlands, a portfolio of WWF freshwater projects (1998-2002), Ukraine Danube Delta. World Wildlife Fund – Green Danube Programme, Vienna/AIDEnvironment, Amsterdam.

WWF. 1998b. Green Danube. A European lifeline. World Wildlife Fund Journal, Vienna.

# BRIDGING THE COMMUNICATION GAP IN RIVER MANAGEMENT

G.J. Matthews[1] & M. Horner[2]
[1] World Bank, 1818 H St., NW Washington DC 20433, The United States of America;
[2] World Press Centre, 20 Route de Pre Bois, CP 1829, CH-1215 Geneva, Switzerland

## Abstract

Finding new approaches for bridging the communication gap between communities within river basins to improve decision making for sustainable development, has become very urgent in these days of water resources pressures. A new and evolving communication service called the World Hydrological Cycle Observing System (WHYCOS), combined with knowledge services on the Internet, Hydroinformatics, training and learning, collaborative decision making and conflict resolution, offers the opportunity for communities to bridge this gap, and furthermore to develop a harmonious relationship with their rivers and the natural resources upon which they depend. As a consequence the development process of the communities within river basins would be more equitable and sustainable.

## 1. Introduction

The Dutch Foundation for Extraordinary Chairs of Nature Conservation feel that it is important for researchers, policy makers and commissioners involved in water management, to evolve new approaches to aquatic ecosystem management. We agree with this statement knowing that (1) the growing pressure on water resources in many regions of the world is provoking the need for water related dialogue between communities within river basins; (2) credible and reliable scientific data, information and knowledge are prerequisites for fruitful dialogue in terms of fair and economic allocation; and (3) there is a communication gap between the hydrologists, water resource managers, environmentalists, commercial interests, investors, stakeholders and decision makers which must be bridged.

The World Hydrological Cycle Observing System (WHYCOS) is proposed to be one of the networks to provide this communication "bridging" service, because it:
- provides a scientific basis for monitoring and assessing water resources for development and integrated management at community, river basin, national, regional, continental and global levels;
- aspires to contribute to the better understanding of the interaction of hydrological processes with, the climate, the environment, natural resource capital, investment and national, regional and global markets through managed open discussion.

*New approaches to river management, pp. 155–165*
*edited by A.J.M. Smits, P.H. Nienhuis and R.S.E.W. Leuven*
*© 2000 Backhuys Publishers, Leiden, The Netherlands*

This paper describes the background, the communication gap and the evolution of WHYCOS from its conception as a real time hydrological monitoring network for Sub-Saharan Africa, to a world-wide knowledge system for hydrology and water resources management with the potential for providing a discussion forum for communities which are concerned with the sustainability of the social, economic, environmental and disaster management services which their "Working Rivers" and river basins provide.

## 2. Background

During the latter half of the 20th century, the pressure on natural water resources in many regions of the world has been increasing dramatically. This can be attributed to the rapid growth in population and the ensuing urban sprawl, and the increased pace of industrialisation, agricultural development and polluting. As a consequence a growing number of regions are facing increasing water stresses and suffering from scarcities caused by failure to adapt to the renewable but finite amount of water which is regularly made available by rain and snowfall. Water availability is now estimated to be 7,500 cubic meters per person per year, while it was 12,900 cubic meters as recently as 1970 (United Nations 1997). Considering that freshwater is one of the vital elements that supports life and the functioning of the environment upon which society is built, it is critical that society manages its available freshwater resources in a manner that shows that it understands that its very survival depends on it. Today's global stress dates from around the late 1970's, a mere 30 years ago, so for many governments and their people this will be a very new experience. For the first time in their history they will have to learn to manage water co-operatively and comprehensively to ensure that allocation is socially, economically and environmentally equitable. For decision makers the question is no longer, "What can we do to develop?" but rather, "What can we do with what we have?" This situation raises the spectre of some strong institutions, or commercial sectors, within a river basin, influencing water management without integrating communities' broader perspectives of water resources management into their operational objectives and without respecting the demands of the aquatic environment so that it can continue to provide those services upon which the sustainability of the socio-economic activities within the river basin depend. This will create tension that could prejudice fair and economic water resource allocation for the common good. Although legislation would be of some assistance, this management issue has been correctly perceived as a serious communication gap between different approaches to, and perspectives of, the problem. The challenge is to bridge this communication gap to generate the necessary interaction between all parties, which would eventually persuade humankind to change attitudes lifestyles, and behaviour to those which are conducive to the creation of a fair and equitable and sustainable water resource allocation process.

## 3. Communication Gap

The key to fair and equitable water resource allocation is the promotion of a dialogue between decision-makers and all water users and the aquatic environment as

a whole. However for the dialogue to be fruitful, the following four conditions must be fulfilled (Matthews 1997):
1. There must be an agreement of the importance of sharing water resource data, information and knowledge.
2. All water users must have the possibility to join in the dialogue, including those who speak for the environment and in particular the rivers and the aquatic ecology.
3. The dialogue must be carried out in a non-threatening environment.
4. Each stakeholder in this process must be able to perceive its own water management behaviour, its community, its economy and its ecology, in a hydrological context.

The first condition is probably the most contentious, because it is about power. Knowledge is power and water knowledge is all-powerful. In water stressed regions it is essential that raw hydrological data and water resource information be in the public domain.

The second condition also poses a difficult dilemma for many communities world-wide. Many water stressed regions are densely populated with people having modest incomes and so the provision of communications services is a daunting task. Table 1 confirms the historical evolution of transparency and participation in water resources development and illustrates the scale of the communication challenge.

In the past when decision making was the responsibility of a few, a workshop or seminar sufficed. This communication technique is still a valuable tool but as a stand alone operation it can neither accommodate all the decision makers, nor continuity of discussion for contentious, sensitive and complex issues which require a long gestation period for reaching consensus. This is particularly important when social, cultural, spiritual, aesthetic, health and ecological concerns are some of the ingredients of the discussion. Experience has shown that when the process is shortened and insufficient facts are available the result is very stressful, emotional and expensive public hearings that can lead to a mutual loss of benefits.

The third condition is about an environment of intimidation. This can result from perceived uncertainties such as loss of existing employment, loss of new employment, loss of property, legal wrangling about compensation, loss of competitive advantage. Fear and/or the risk of violence can distort the discussion resulting in a loss of benefits to the community.

The fourth condition, the provision of sufficient information and knowledge to all stakeholders to enable them to perceive their behaviour and their community in their hydrological context, is really a question of education and awareness. It can be taught in institutions of education, but the problem is that the hydrological context is a dynamic one in which everything is in a constant state of flux. Everything seems to be included: the seasonal hydrological cycles, local and international trade, markets, culture, politics, fashion, health, irrigation, agriculture, aquatic ecology, industry, rural and urban development, and natural disasters. To complicate matters the local or regional hydrological context may be influenced by natural phenomena on the other side of the planet, such as El Nino and La Nina.

Only when the four conditions are met can a communication system between all stakeholders be created. What follows is an account of the experience of the World

Table 1. Broadening the constituency of water resources development (from Goodland 2000).

| Design team | Approximate Era |
|---|---|
| Engineers | Pre 1945s<br>Mainly dams |
| Engineers + Economists | Post 1950s<br>Mainly dams |
| Engineers + Economists + then add-on Environmental Impact Statement to end of complete design | Late 1970s |
| Engineers + Economists + Environmentalists + Sociologists | Late 1980s |
| Engineers + Economists + Environmentalists + Sociologists + Affected People | Early 1990s |
| Engineers + Economists + Environmentalists + Sociologists + Affected People + Non Governmental Organisations | Mid 1990s |
| Engineers + Economists + Environmentalists + Sociologists + Affected People + Non Governmental Organisations + Public Acceptance | Early 2000s? |

Bank, United Nations Development Programme (UNDP), African Development Bank (ADB), French Ministry of Co-operation, European Union (EU), World Meteorological Organisation (WMO), United Nations Education, Science and Culture Organisation (UNESCO), United Nations Department of Economic and Social Development (UNDESD), the countries of Sub-Saharan Africa (SSA), the Aral Sea region, and the Mediterranean Sea basins. These entities contributed to the creation of a communication concept called the World Hydrological Cycle Observing System (WHYCOS; WMO 1998). WHYCOS is designed for participatory water resources development and management that satisfies the conditions noted.

## 4. WHYCOS – Creation and evolution

WHYCOS evolved in three stages, each one driven by the need to provide more comprehensive data, information and knowledge services to hydrologists, water resources managers and decision makers in different regions of the world.

*Stage 1 – The Sub-Saharan Africa hydrological assessment*

From 1988 to 1996, the World Bank, UNDP, ADB, French Ministry of Co-operation, EU, WMO, UNESCO and UNDESD carried out a hydrological assessment of nearly all the countries of SSA. The conclusion of the assessment was that hydrometric networks and the quality of the data gathered have generally declined over the past two decades, and that this decline is attributable to two major causes. The first was the severe economic difficulties prevalent throughout that region, which has led to cuts in general public funding. The second was the lack of awareness of the economic value of hydrological information by the policy and decision-makers of SSA. This causes hydrological services to be perceived as a low priority within the development process and further exacerbating under-funding in the region. Using the World Bank water resources policy criteria for sustainable water resources development and management as a guide, the *SSA hydrological assessment report* recommended that the conventional hydrometric data systems be reinforced with modern technology (World Bank 1993). The purpose was to install infrastructure and people that would be capable of delivering timely high quality data for inclusion in economic and financial analyses of the Ministries of Economy, Finance and Planning for encouraging local and foreign investment in their countries. It was this economic imperative that led to the concept of the Hydrological Cycle Observing System (HYCOS).

The vision was (and is) that the first stage of the proposed HYCOS would interlink the conventional hydrological networks with existing telemetry and satellite systems already operating in various sub-regions and river basins in SSA. This will provide the SSA hydrologists with about 100 strategic bench mark hydrological stations. The demand from individual countries or regions for hydrologic data for the analysis of the economic value of water was expected to drive the implementation of the total system and make it financially sustainable. It was immediately obvious to the SSA Hydrological Assessment Steering Committee that this concept was generic, and could be replicated anywhere. It was also realised that by promoting the dissemination of this data and information via the Internet, the national and international scientific and economic communities and the global hydrological cycle could be drawn together for the purposes of integrated water resources management. So with the encouragement and blessings of the President of the World Bank and the Secretaries General of the WMO and UNESCO, the concept of the WHYCOS was born. It would be therefore the sum total of regional components called HYCOS, which are created at the demand of the sovereign states within natural hydro-geological boundaries, or political regions such as the Southern Africa Development Community (SADC). The SADC HYCOS was the first network to be requested and this is now being implemented with funds from the European Community.

The Mediterranean HYCOS (MED HYCOS) came next with funding from the World Bank and the French Government. At various stages of preparation are the West and Central African HYCOS, Intergovernmental Authority on Drought and Development HYCOS in East Africa (IGADD HYCOS), Caribbean HYCOS, Pacific Islands HYCOS, and the Aral Sea HYCOS. The Black, Caspian and Baltic Seas are other potential candidates. Although WHYCOS was perceived as having the potential for becoming a communication network for facilitating comprehensive river basin development and management, embracing all social, economic and environmental activities, this did not evolve until the World Bank became involved in the Central Asian Aral Sea programme.

*Stage 2 – The Central Asian Aral Sea Programme Experience*

During 1993/94 the Heads of State of Kyrgistan, Tadjikistan, Uzbekistan, Kazakstan and Turkmenistan requested the World Bank, UNDP and UNEP to assist them in their efforts to address the water management issues within the Aral Sea basin. The main components of the scenario were, two rivers flowing from Kyrgistan and Tadjikistan, across Uzbekistan and Kazakstan to supply Turmenistan and the Aral Sea, 35 million well educated people of several cultures, a deteriorating water and natural resources capital base, and a command economy making its first steps in the direction of a market economy. Unlike Sub-Saharan Africa the information infrastructure was very well developed, as the region was the centre of intense scientific activity. The water resources were very well monitored from the snow and ice fields in the Pamir Mountains, through cascades of hydropower reservoirs, across the Central Asian plains with their 7 million hectares of irrigated farmland, to the Aral Sea, from where the water resources evaporated. The task was not to set up a completely new hydrometeorological monitoring system therefore, but to evolve the way information was disseminated and managed, from a solely command information environment, to a combination of formal and informal information sharing. As informal information sharing was an undeveloped management tool in that region, the challenge was to find an acceptable non-threatening mechanism for creating it, both nationally and regionally. The Aral Sea Programme was seen as the vehicle for facilitating this exercise as it was an officially recognised regional activity whose participants included the five heads of State, Ministries, Municipalities, Academies of Science, UN Agencies, the international donor community and Non Governmental Organisations (NGOs). It was self evident that a river basin development with eight complex simultaneous sector sub programmes, needed to improve programme information. Full Internet was in its infancy at that time, but electronic mail was very common, so this was proposed as the preferred communication medium for the programme.

Unfortunately the general programme circumstances which prevailed at that time were not conducive to a rapid implementation of this idea. Nevertheless the idea prevailed in its generic form and it was incorporated into the WHYCOS concept and included in the project design of all other HYCOS'. This paved the way for WHYCOS to create opportunities, using electronic mail and the World Wide Web, for informal discussions and information exchanges allowing communication related to new approaches to water resources management. The Home Page of WHYCOS on the World Wide Web therefore announced that a HYCOS would provide communities living in river, lake and aquifer basins with:

—   Scientific hydrological data for determining the boundary and behaviour of the hydrological envelope within which they live;
—   A non-threatening information sharing environment for enabling decision makers to discuss how water resources should be managed and allocated within that envelope to ensure fair and economic water resource allocation for the common good.

MED HYCOS was the first to operate with these objectives. After about two years it became evident that the scientific hydrological component was beginning to function, but the communication forum opportunity, based on an e-mail register, was being used by very few people within the Mediterranean Basin. This situation led to Stage 3 and knowledge management.

## Stage 3 – WHYCOS and knowledge management

To improve the capacity of WHYCOS to develop and energise discussion on water related issues within and between HYCOS regions, the WHYCOS International Co-ordination Group at its first meeting in 1998, endorsed the following two proposals:
1. That the objectives of WHYCOS should be broadened to encompass the dissemination of water and aquatic environmental information and knowledge for social, economic, and environmental development as well as hydrological data and information.
2. That the WMO Secretariat review the limitations of WHYCOS as a means of promoting regional discussion and dialogue among HYCOS professionals and the user community, and develop a clear concept for WHYCOS in the area of information infrastructure.

The implementation of the first proposal consists of creating a space on the home pages of WHYCOS and its HYCOS' for Unique Reference Locations (URLs) of World Wide Web sites with information and knowledge related to the role of water and the natural aquatic economy in social, economic and environment activities. Examples of these can be found on the MED HYCOS home page at "EXCHANGE", which stands for knowledge exchange. There are links to the:
- World Bank's Internet Based Training Programme on Water Resources and Comprehensive River Basin Management.
- Global Land and Water Management Network, managed by the Centre for International Earth Sciences Information Network (CIESIN).
- Global Run-off Data Centre (GRDC) with information about the world's rivers.
- Other sites include, GIS, climate, socio-economic and environmental information related to this region, and the management of natural capital.

In effect MED HYCOS is becoming a "knowledge portal" and it provides a vast number of services to its riparian countries of the Mediterranean. MED HYCOS can be considered a "Working Sea" and as such must be cared for in the same way as a "Working River". Therefore communities with working rivers within their bioregional boundaries which have a HYCOS will have the opportunity to create a knowledge portal which could be used as a resource for managing them.

The second proposal is to encourage stakeholders within river basins to adopt and develop collaborative decision making and dispute resolution skills. This could be catalysed by WHYCOS using new knowledge management services developments via the Internet. These services would link HYCOS' Regional Centres, social, economic and environmental water users with hydrologists and water resource decision-makers making up a distinct community. Discussion and dialogue will be designed, set-up, facilitated and moderated by a steering committee of well known and respected water users, decision makers, hydrologists and academicians from the HYCOS regions. For those who do not have access to the Internet, such as people in remote rural villages, the HYCOS information infrastructure could interact seamlessly with other communications media, *e.g.*, print, radio, television, video and CD ROM.

## 5. Knowledge management services

Knowledge management is a discipline that promotes an integrated approach to identifying, capturing, retrieving, sharing and evaluating the information assets of an enterprise. The information assets may include databases, documents, policies and procedures as well as the uncaptured, tacit expertise and experience resident in individual people.

Knowledge management is a new discipline gradually gaining respectability and is now taught in business schools, used in industry as a major change programme category and most of all, seen as a totally new sector of the economy. The World Bank itself has a major effort to transform itself into a "Knowledge Bank". In this context the WHYCOS can benefit from the latest thinking and hopefully improve river basin management. Such a strategy is in harmony with the long-term trends in management. Over a 200-year period the trend in management has been to focus on the management of tangible assets. Over the long haul this has been successful and what has emerged is the need for effective ways to manage intangible assets. This is the root driver for the work in valuing and managing knowledge since knowledge is part of the intangible asset base.

### 5.1 Internet and the World Wide Web

The revolution in communications and computer technology have combined together to create a global infrastructure allowing easy flow of digitised information. As of 1998 roughly 400 million people are connected to this infrastructure and the rate of connection increases every month. On top of this basic structure known as "The Net" is a capability known as "The Web". This can be conceived as a repository of information organised as "Web Sites". There is a huge amount of information published on these sites and many new business models, products and services are the focus of creative efforts and occasional business successes, taking advantage of this intangible asset. Most of these efforts can be viewed as transitional forms and using the automotive evolution as an analogy they are horseless carriages. What is needed is of course an example of a car.

The conceptual base for existing information services on the Net and the Web is two models. Firstly there is a push model corresponding to e-mail types of services. The source of a message pushes information to users. This approach often results in information overload, as users have no say in the communication process. This model can be classified as one to many communications. Secondly there is a model where a reader visits Web Sites and pulls information. This approach increasingly results in waste of time and the source has no involvement in the communication process. This model can be classified as many to one communications. A third model has been conceptualised and exists only in the latest types of services. In this model the communication system itself is more active and the result is a many to many class of communication. The third model has been the centre of the design of a new service referred to in this document as "Update". The company introducing the service has decided to focus initially on public policy organisations as these organisations have a great need to send and receive organised information. Indeed that is often their primary modus operandi.

What follows is a brief description of the "Update" service as an example of a specific aspect of knowledge management. In this case rapidly changing freely available information is an unusable community asset and by organising this asset, a community is empowered and can be effective. Such a service is a necessary condition for successful river basin management by the people who belong to a number of communities simultaneously and yet need to collaborate while taking the hydrological view.

## 5.2 Update

As a service "Update" assumes a community exists or can be created. Messages known as "items" are sent by sources to a clearinghouse and tagged so they can be positioned (organised) along three axes by lists of three types of terms. These terms are the agreed vocabulary of the community and are used both by sources and readers. In this way readers accessing the clearinghouse use the same terms to define their "space" of interest and so receive only the items sent to their space. This model avoids both data overload and ensures no omission. In addition delivery is under control of readers and is as good as the technology permits in terms of speed. Essentially the focus is on information quality, not technology. Sources could be, intergovernmental, ministries, parliaments, pressure groups, professionals, locals, researchers, finance and industry. The users could be reporters, specialists, media freelancers, policy networks, executives, education and libraries.

## 5.3 Training and learning, collaborative decision-making and dispute resolution

The knowledge which can be delivered to the inhabitants of a river basin can only be effective if they can understand it in a systemic fashion and have the interpersonal communication skills to use it effectively. In the absence of this understanding and these skills, solutions to the current problems of working rivers, such as pollution, navigation in very sinuous rivers, and floods and droughts and the maintenance of the services provided by the aquatic ecology, will not be forthcoming and at best the river basin economy will steadily decline and at worst civil unrest and conflict could accelerate the demise of whole communities. It is imperative therefore that communities be educated and made aware of their hydrological context through training and learning programmes and be encouraged to enhance their interpersonal communication skills so they may practice collaborative decision making and conflict resolution. A HYCOS can deliver these training programmes in the form of distance learning and/or, provide the materials for trainers in the traditional classroom environment. This service is particularly useful when dealing with transboundary water issues. Transboundary in the sense of working rivers which flow through several sovereign states or culturally, or economically distinctive regions within a country.

## 5.4 WHYCOS and Hydroinformatics

Through WHYCOS and appropriate decision aiding tools and skills, it would be possible to bring together all the social, technological, ecological and scientific aspects of river basin development. By observing the interaction between the hydrological cycle and all social, economic and environmental activities WHYCOS can provide data and information for generating knowledge. In turn this knowledge can be managed by the communities within the river basin for decision making with the objective of discovering the "truth" about the sustainable development potential of the river basin. This knowledge management process, as discussed by McGinnis *et al.* (1999), Abbott (1999) and Cunge & Erlich (1999), is known as Hydroinformatics. In essence it is a knowledge management technique which uses water as the communication medium between all activities. The water resources management communication gap is therefore being bridged via the water itself and the behaviour of the hydrological cycle. Perhaps more important than the ability of water to assist better understanding between the inhabitants of a river basin, is the potential that Hydroinformatics presents for communities to develop a harmonious relationship with the working rivers and all the other natural resources upon which they depend for their survival.

## 6. Conclusion

All river basins "naturally" provide social, economic, environmental and disaster management services to humankind. However, in recent history some rivers, like the Rhine, Mississippi and Danube, have been modified artificially to increase some services "unnaturally", with serious consequences to the communities within their basins. Serious as described in the "communication gap", *i.e.*, strong institutions and their commercial and political interests. In sum these consequences have prevented economically fair and equitable allocation of water resources to some stakeholders, including the river and the aquatic ecosystems, and thereby have restricted, or reduced their ability to reach their full productive and service potentials. The challenge is to redesign, and, or tailor community activities within the river basins to match the river's natural service capacity. To do this the four conditions for fruitful dialogue must first be satisfied.
1.  There must be an agreement of the importance of sharing water resource data, information and knowledge.
2.  All water users must have the possibility to join in the dialogue, including those who speak for the environment and in particular the aquatic ecology.
3.  The dialogue must be carried out in a non-threatening environment.
4.  Each stakeholder in this process must be able to perceive its own water management behaviour, its community, its economy and its ecology, in a hydrological context.

Stage 3 WHYCOS with the use of knowledge services, collaborative decision making and dispute resolution, can satisfy these conditions. The conjunctive use of WHYCOS, knowledge management services, Hydroinformatics and persuasion through collaborative decision making and dispute resolution would enable hydrologists, water resource managers, environmentalists, commercial interests, investors, stakeholders and decision makers to bridge their communication gap for the purpose of crafting agreements and resolving conflicts about the allocation of water resources related to the management of working rivers and the aquatic ecology. As a consequence the development process of the communities within these river basins would be more equitable and sustainable.

## Disclaimer

The findings, interpretations, opinions and conclusions expressed in this paper are entirely those of the authors and should neither be attributed in any manner to the World Bank, to its affiliated organisations, or to members of its Boards of Executive Directors or the countries they represent.

## References

United Nations. 1997. Comprehensive assessment of the freshwater resources of the world. United Nations, New York.

Matthews, G.J. 1997. Communication for bridging different water perspectives. In: Safeguarding water resources for tomorrow, new solutions to old problems. Proceedings sixth Stockholm Water Symposium. Stockholm Vatten AB, Stockholm. pp. 249-256.

Goodland, R.J.A. 2000. Is there a future for big dams? In: Smits A.J.M., Nienhuis P.H. & Leuven R.S.E.W. (Eds.), New Approaches to River Management. Backhuys Publishers, Leiden. pp. 187-207.

WMO. 1998. World Hydrological Cycle Observing System WHYCOS). Publication 876, World Meteorological Organisation (WMO), Switzerland. (WHYCOS on the Web: http://www.wmo.ch).

World Bank. 1993. Sub Saharan Africa hydrological assessment report. World Bank, Washington.

McGinnis, M.V., Wooley, J.T. & Gamman, J. 1999. Bioregional conflict resolution: rebuilding community in watershed planning and organizing. Environmental Management Journal 24/1: 1-12.

Abbott, M.V. 1999. Introducing Hydroinformatics. Journal of Hydroinformatics 1/1: 3-19.

Cunge, J.A. & Erlich, M. 1999. Hydroinformatics in 1999. Journal of Hydroinformatics 1/1: 21-31.

# ECO-CENTRIC COST-BENEFIT ANALYSIS FOR HYDRAULIC ENGINEERING IN RIVER BASINS

J.J. Bouma & H.L.F. Saeijs
*Erasmus Centre for Environmental Studies, Erasmus University,*
*Burgemeester Oudlaan 50, 3062 PA Rotterdam, The Netherlands*

## Abstract

Research into the relationship between environment and economy, focusing on the assessment of hydraulic engineering projects is producing interesting results. The present study identified the causes underlying decisions for which *ex post* assessments show that they failed to deliver the expected societal benefits. Stimulation of sustainable development stresses the interrelationships between economy and environment. The present paper addresses some major problems of incorporating the, often non-market, economic value of aquatic ecosystems into decision-making, using the example of large hydraulic engineering projects in a sea inlet. The cost-benefit analysis (CBA) is evaluated for a group of engineering projects. Recommendations are given for incorporating environmental values into the CBA. The need for an eco-centric CBA is discussed and illustrated with a case study of lake Grevelingen, situated in the delta of the rivers Rhine and Meuse. An eco-centric CBA incorporates the costs and benefits relating to the status of the ecosystems. It prevents decision-makers from perceiving improvements in environmental quality merely as a rise of costs. Performing an eco-centric CBA requires a method to determine the economic value of ecosystems.

## 1. Introduction

Research into the relationship between environment and economy, focusing on the assessment of hydraulic engineering projects is producing interesting results. The present study identified the causes underlying decisions for which *ex post* assessments show that they failed to deliver the expected societal benefits. The purpose of a research programme at the Erasmus Centre for Environmental Studies (ECES) of the Erasmus University is to improve the decision making process for hydraulic engineering projects by designing approaches and methods for economic and environmental evaluation. Stimulation of sustainable development stresses the interrelationships between environment and economy. This has resulted in improved better monitoring and assessment of environmental and economic performance. For example, governmental agencies and international organisations such as the Organisation for Economic Co-operation and Development (OECD) and Development Banks have furthered the aim of sustainable development through the design of a set of indices (Asian Development Bank 1997). Such indices are representative of the way the environmental impact and economic performance of engineering projects are being assessed. The environmental impact is reflected by indicators such as water quality and numbers of species. On the other hand, the eco-

*New approaches to river management, pp. 167–178*
*edited by A.J.M. Smits, P.H. Nienhuis and R.S.E.W. Leuven*
*© 2000 Backhuys Publishers, Leiden, The Netherlands*

nomic performance in relationship with the environmental impact focuses mainly on the costs of achieving certain levels of environmental quality. The Costs Of Remediation (COR) are a widely used parameter for this purpose. COR assesses the costs of modifying the environment from its present condition to a more desirable state. However, the economic benefits of a good environmental quality are often not expressed by indicators. The present paper assesses the need for an eco-centric cost-benefit analysis (CBA), illustrated by a case study of lake Grevelingen, situated in the delta of the rivers Rhine and Meuse. An eco-centric CBA incorporates the costs and benefits relating to the status of the ecosystems. It prevents decision-makers from perceiving an improvement in environmental quality merely as a rise in costs (*e.g.*, COR). Performing an eco-centric CBA requires a method to determine the economic value of ecosystems.

Section 2 describes the theoretical background and the context for the development of a CBA. This context for the design of a tool to support decision-making is analysed in section 3 by focusing on the role of a CBA. The use of CBAs in the decision-making process for hydraulic engineering projects at the Grevelingen sea inlet is mapped. The shortcomings of a partial inclusion of environmental costs and benefits are identified and an improved approach to assessing hydraulic projects is suggested. This improved approach to CBAs, called eco-centric CBA, is presented and illustrated in section 4.

## 2. Theoretical background of cost-benefit analysis

An ecosystem is the basic unit of interactions between organisms and their environment, the result of the complex combined interaction between living and non-living elements in a particular area (Saeijs 1995). The decision-making process that procedes hydraulic engineering projects only partly takes the effects on ecosystems into consideration. The positive and negative effects on a ecosystem are only considered in sofar as they have a short-term impact on human beings. This is the logical consequence of an anthropocentric approach to ecosytem assessment. The long-term effects on ecosystems (25-50 years) are often not taken into consideration, despite the existence of economic methods such as multi-criteria analysis and CBA which can be used to evaluate projects with environmental impacts (Nijkamp 1979). It may be expected that different decisions would be taken if the long-term impact on ecosystems were to be taken into account.

The Netherlands has a great deal of experience with decision-making about hydraulic engineering projects, for instance the closure of a number of North Sea inlets as part of the so-called Delta Plan. The Delta Act (1958) included far-reaching projects to protect parts of the Netherlands against floods. The need for a CBA that would properly include the environmental effects has led to the development of an approach to deal with these effects in an economic assessment methodology. This approach was built upon the solid foundation of an economic theory of CBA and is still playing an important role in the assessment of hydraulic engineering projects listed in the Delta Act. In economic theory there is consensus about the procedure for performing a CBA and about the significance of the results of a CBA. The standard procedure for conducting a CBA consists of five stages (Common 1996):

1. *Project definition and identification.* The project for which the costs and benefits are to be calculated must be clearly defined. Closely related projects should be combined, allowing their costs and benefits to be calculated together. There are several reasons, however, why combined assessment of related projects may not be possible. For example, budgetary reasons or legal constraints (Vertonghen & Van Rompuy 1994) may result in impediments for a CBA which would take into account linkages between projects.

2. *Establishment of an overview of the physical effects of the project over its total life time.* The consequences of a project have to be identified and described in physical terms. Examples include more efficient travel routes for ships that transport goods or reduced fishery revenues.

3. *Attributing a monetary value to the physical effects of the project over its total life time.* The consequences of the project or set of combined projects should be expressed in a monetary value. This requires listing all costs and benefits.

4. *Discounting the costs and benefits of the project.* The present value of the costs and benefits is to be calculated. This is done by discounting the cost and benefits. The discount rate that is used is of significant influence on the outcome of the discounting procedure. The present values of the listed costs and benefits can be summed and the outcome of the CBA shows whether the projects result in a net loss or benefit to society as a whole.

5. *Conducting a sensitivity analysis.* Because of the uncertainties in the costs and benefits of a project, a sensitivity analysis can be used to reveal the effects on the outcome of a CBA of changes in the assumptions made in that CBA.

Environmental effects deserve special attention in the phase in which a monetary value is attributed to the effects of a project. A problem with these effects is that they are often not directly linked with cash flows. Nevertheless, the value of the quality of the environment or of specific ecosystems is a generally accepted factor in the CBA of projects. Pearce & Turner (1990) distinguished three categories of environmental values, *viz.*, use, option and existence values. The use value of the environment is the result of direct use (for example, hunting, fishery and recreational use). The option value is the value that people attribute to natural amenities because of the potential of the environment to be of use to society in the future. The option value includes the possible use the environment has for other parties and future generations. The existence value is the value of the environment that exists without any direct (or optional) economic use. As Pearce & Turner (1990) note, "Existence value is a value placed on an environmental good and which is unrelated to any potential or actual use of a good". Existence value arises from the knowledge that a particular area will continue to exist in its present state, and is independent of any actual or prospective use of the area (Common 1996). The debate about the existence value is difficult and complex. One of the reasons for this complexity is that the basis of existence value is constituted by fundamental and ethical considerations. One of the points of discussion is the applicability of the economic model of utilities (Pearce & Turner 1990, Perman *et al.* 1996).

Together, the 'use value', 'option value' and 'existence value' constitute the total (economic) value of nature (Common 1996, Pearce & Turner 1990, Perman *et al.* 1996). A number of methods, have been designed to calculate the three value categories for nature:

1. Methods to determine environmental values according to the demand (preferences) for changes in the environment (demand-side-oriented).
2. Methods that determine the costs of modifying the environment (supply-side-oriented). The widely used costs of remediation result from these methods.
3. Methods that determine environmental values by combining the demand for environmental change with the supply of such change (supply-demand approach).

Three well-known examples of methods that belong to demand-side-oriented category of methods (Constanza *et al.* 1989, Barde & Pearce 1991, Pearce 1993, Dixon & Sherman 1990) are:
1. Hedonic Pricing Method (HPM). HPM determines the environmental value by identifying the part of market prices that reflects the environmental aspects (attributes) of a marketable good. For example, price differences in properties are explained by differences in environmental quality. HPM only calculates the value of use.
2. Contingent Valuation Method (CVM). In CVM individuals are asked (in surveys) for their willingness to pay for environmental changes (Pearce & Turner 1990, OECD 1993, Mitchell & Carson 1989). CVM is the only method that calculates all the categories (Common 1996) of environmental value (use, option and existence values).
3. Travel Cost Method (TCM): this method uses the cost of travelling necessary to enjoy a particular aspect of environmental quality as an indicator of the value of this environmental quality. Only the value of use is reflected in this method (Pearce & Turner 1990).

CVM is increasingly used because it incorporates the use, option and existence values. This has been stimulated by developments in the USA (Tietenberg 1992) where CVM is used to assess the scope of costs for which polluters can be made liable (far-reaching legal liabilities for environmental damage). However, a fundamental problem remains to be dealt with, namely, how the individuals who are to be interviewed can be fully informed about the ecological and economic consequences of a certain state of environmental quality.

An example of a method belonging to the supply-side-oriented methods is the Elimination Cost Method (ECM), which estimates the minimum costs of achieving an environmental improvement. Another example is the Shadow Price Method (SPM), which determines the cost of compensation of environmental losses.

Finally, examples of the third category of methods (supply-demand approach) include those methods that use shadow prices in such a way that the costs of environmental improvement equal the price society is willing to pay to achieve a certain environmental quality.

## 3. Case study: Lake Grevelingen

The hydraulic works in the Grevelingen sea inlet have been the subject of three CBAs over the period 1954 – 1980. These hydraulic projects are part of the Delta project and are works further referred to below as the Grevelingen project. The

*Table 1.* Morphological characteristics of lake Grevelingen (Wattel 1996).

| Lake characteristics | |
| --- | --- |
| Surface area (ha) | 10,800 |
| Volume (m³) | 557,000,000 |
| Length (km) | 23 |
| Width (km) | 4 -10 |
| Average depth (m) | 5.4 |
| Maximum depth (m) | 48 |

hydraulic works changed a sea inlet into a lake that is separated from the North Sea by barriers. Table 1 and figure 1 characterise lake Grevelingen.

The first CBA was performed in 1954 and assessed the Delta project as a whole, including, the Grevelingen project (Delta Act 1958). The second CBA was performed in 1972 and assessed the Grevelingen project with respect to the costs and benefits of developing the Grevelingen as a conservation and recreation area (Van Alderwegen 1972). The third CBA was performed in 1974 and was a restricted version of the second which can be regarded as a cost-effectiveness analysis (IWKBAG 1974).

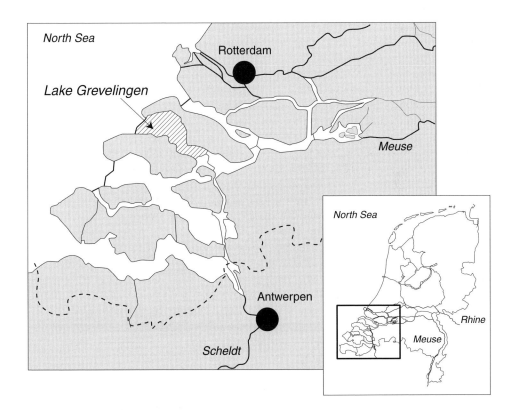

*Fig. 1.* Geographical location of lake Grevelingen.

The three CBAs differed from each other in several respects. The most complete one is the 1954 CBA, which assessed all projects of the Delta Plan in an integrated study. Several cost and benefit items were included, but environmental values were not given a great deal of attention. A more complete identification of the environmental costs and benefits was made in 1972 and 1974 CBAs. On the other hand, these CBAs were less complete in that they focused only on those projects relevant to developing the Grevelingen as a recreation and conservation area within the constraints set by the Delta projects that had already been completed by then. Table 2 compares the three CBAs. All three CBAs identify the recreational benefits of hydraulic projects, but two of them (1954 and 1974) provide only partial analyses of these benefits. The 1974 CBA calculated the value of recreation in the Grevelingen by determining the consumer surplus. The consumer surplus is the difference between the price that consumers are willing to pay for a product or service and the actual price they pay in the market. The 1954 and 1974 CBAs calculated the recreational value only by estimating the potential cash flows (for example, from rent) resulting from the recreational use of lake Grevelingen. Environmental values (referred to as natural values) were identified in the 1972 and 1974 CBAs but were not quantified.

A comparison between the various CBAs shows that environmental values were taken into consideration, but in different ways. The impact of the hydraulic projects on the existence value of natural amenities was identified in the CBAs, but was not quantified as a cost or benefit. Furthermore, the 1954 CBA did not calculate the costs and benefits in great detail, because of technical and other uncertainties (*e.g.*, impacts on eco-systems and market developments). With regard to the cost specifications of the Delta Plan the Dutch Delta Act states: "a more extended specification of the amounts listed in this balance with respect to the general and preliminary characteristics of the CBA seems inappropriate ...". However, for large hydraulic works (including some of the works related to lake Grevelingen) cost estimates were made.

The uncertainties involved in the Grevelingen project can result in considerable differences between *ex ante* and *ex post* CBAs. Therefore, an *ex ante* CBA for the Grevelingen project alone was performed, using the same methods as the 1954 CBA. The result is shown in table 3. Several techniques were used to calculate the cost and benefit items. A number of assumptions had to be made about the physical effects of the Grevelingen project on the environment. The most likely assumptions were used in the CBA. The CBA used a 4% discount rate to calculate the present value of future costs and benefits.

One problem of calculating the costs of the Grevelingen project was that the hydraulic projects were considered as projects with joint costs. These projects are

*Table 2.* A comparison of three cost-benefit analyses assessing the hydraulic works in the Grevelingen sea inlet.

|  | 1954 | 1954 | 1972 | 1972 | 1974 | 1974 |
|---|---|---|---|---|---|---|
|  | Identified | Quantified | Identified | Quantified | Identified | Quantified |
| Recreational value | Yes | Partly | Yes | Yes | Yes | Partly |
| Environmental value | No | No | Yes | No | Yes | No |

linked with other projects of the Delta Plan. Consequently, arbitrary rules had to be formulated to allocate joint costs to those projects that are part of the Grevelingen project. The following rules were used.

– The construction costs of the Grevelingen barrier were allocated as a fixed proportion of total Delta Plan construction costs (16.5% of total construction costs for Grevelingen; 83.5% allocated to the other Delta projects). The same proportion of the joint costs of the Brouwer-barrier was allocated to the Grevelingen project.

– The maintenance costs were calculated as a fixed percentage of the total usage costs of the Grevelingen project (this percentage was derived from the CBA for the Delta Plan as a whole);

– The 'other costs' item equals the costs not included in the other listed cost items, minus 'other revenues'. The 'other costs' item was determined by using the surface area as a cost driver. Lake Grevelingen represents about 20% of the total surface area directly related to the Delta Plan. Therefore, 20% of the other costs of the Delta works were allocated to the Grevelingen project.

Several assumptions also had to be made for the benefits:

– The benefits of reduced dyke maintenance costs (as a consequence of the protection from the open sea afforded by the barriers) were determined according to the length of dykes affected by the Grevelingen project.

– The effects of the Grevelingen project on the total revenues of fishery were determined by allocating a particular proportion of the total Delta Plan surface area (Koopman 1955). The net effects of the Delta works on fishery are negative, and 20% of these negative benefits were allocated to the Grevelingen project. The same allocation rule was used to calculate the recreational benefits of the Grevelingen project (20% of the total recreational benefits of the Delta Plan).

– The benefits of increased agricultural revenues were calculated by determining the effect of the Grevelingen project on the influx of saline water into agricultural land. The Grevelingen-barriers reduce the influx of saline water and hence increase agricultural revenues. This required an arbitrary estimation of the proportion of the total agricultural benefits achieved by the Grevelingen-barriers (NLG 15 million).

– The transport benefits were calculated by allocating 10% of the total benefits of increased mobility as a consequence of the Delta Plan to the Grevelingen project (estimation based on the surface area affected by the Grevelingen project and the population size).

*Table 3. Ex ante* cost-benifit analysis for the Grevelingen project (in millions of Dutch guilders). Cost-benefit data were derived from the Delta Act (1958) and NMNH (1954).

| Costs | | Benefits | |
|---|---|---|---|
| Construction costs: | | Reduction of dike maintenance | 11 |
|   Grevelingen-barrier | 20 | Revenues of fishery | -5 |
|   Brouwer-barrier | 180 | Revenues of recreation | 20 |
| Maintenance and capital costs | 33 | Increase of revenues of agriculture | 15 |
| Desiccation prevention | 2 | Improvement of mobility | 21 |
| Other costs | 10 | Increase of safety | p.m. |
| Total | **245** | Total | **62** |

– The 1954 CBA regarded the benefits of increased safety for the entire Delta Plan as a closing entry amounting to NLG 500 million). The Grevelingen project's increased safety benefits were estimated on the basis of the percentage of the total Delta population who live in the area affected by the Grevelingen project (13%). This led to an estimated benefit of NLG 65 million.

In addition to this *ex ante* CBA, an *ex post* CBA for the Grevelingen project (Table 4) was performed on the basis of *ex post* data provided by Bouma & Nijssen (1998).

A comparison between the *ex ante* and *ex post* CBAs shows significant differences, for which several causes can be indicated. The most important cause is the lack of data on the technological details of the constructions and hence on its costs. This is a difficulty inherent to the assessment of hydraulic projects that involve new technological developments with unique effects on the environment. Another problem is that these environmental effects can occur over a longer period of time. Although a hydraulic project may have immediate effects on ecosystems, these are only identified when they become visible to society (for example, by a reduction in the revenues of fishery).

A more complete assessment of hydraulic projects than that offered by the 1954, 1972 and 1974 CBAs should identify and value all direct and indirect effects of the Grevelingen project on the ecosystems. In other words, the effects of a project on the relevant ecosystems should be identified, and direct and indirect consequences of these impacts should be assessed. Direct consequences are related to the area where the projects are executed (for example fisheries within the Grevelingen sea inlet). Indirect consequences are related to other areas than those in which the projects are executed (for example North Sea fisheries). The assessment should also look at a project's long-term effects. The 1954, 1972 and 1974 CBAs did not take the indirect consequences fully into consideration. An approach that would extend the scope of cost and benefit items by identifying the impacts of a project on an ecosystem and its repercussions for other ecosystems is referred to as an eco-centric CBA. This approach to CBAs systematically determines the value of an ecosystem, and changes in this value due to hydraulic works are allocated as costs or benefits in the relevant CBA. In line with the CBA methodology, this ecosystem value should be assigned a monetary value.

*Table 4. Ex post* cost-benifit analysis for the Grevelingen project (in millions of Dutch guilders).

| Costs | | Benefits | |
|---|---|---|---|
| Construction costs: | | Reduction of dike maintenance | 1 |
|   Grevelingen barrier | 16 | Revenues of fishery | -4.6 |
|   Brouwer barrier | 110 | Revenues of recreation | 83 |
| Maintenance and capital costs | 21 | Increase of revenues of agriculture | 0 |
| Desiccation prevention | 0 | Improvementof mobility | 63 |
| Other costs | 10 | Increase of safety | p.m. |
| Total | **157** | Total | **142.4** |

## 4. An eco-centric cost-benefit analysis

Eco-centric CBAs are based on the same approach as traditional CBAs, but a more complete inventory of environmental costs and benefits is achieved by adding indirect eco-revenues. Traditional CBAs reflect mostly the direct revenues of an ecosystem, i.e., those benefits (revenues of fishery, recreation and agriculture) that are achieved within the area where the project is executed. Indirect eco-benefits are those benefits that can only be achieved through the continued existence of the ecosystems of the area where the project is executed, for example, the revenues from North Sea fish that used to propagate in the Grevelingen sea inlet. A reduction in these revenues is a negative indirect eco-revenue of the Grevelingen barrier that closes off the sea inlet.

Before the Grevelingen hydraulic projects were executed, this area was a sea inlet with regular tidal movements. The sea inlet was regarded as a high ecological value estuary. The barriers ended the tidal movements and changed the water quality from saline to a much lower salt content and also made the water clearer. The hydraulic works changed the Grevelingen inlet into a lake, and the flora and fauna changed accordingly. This affected the ecological value of the Grevelingen area.

Changes in an ecosystem can be quantified by estimating net carbon production per square metre over a certain period (for example a year). The carbon production is the lowest level of the food chain in an ecosystem, so changes in the carbon production have repercussions for the ecosystem's revenues (*e.g.*, fisheries and supply of drinking water). The carbon production is referred to as the primary production of the ecosystem (*pp*). The production of an ecosystem is reflected in those goods with a market value (fish, water supplies, etc.) and this is reflected in the secondary production function (*P(sp)*) which is partly explained by the *pp*. In addition to *pp*, water temperature and clarity are examples of other important factors *(a, b, ..m)* that determine the secondary production of an ecosystem. The total production of an ecosystem includes those values that are not related to the *pp*, (*P(eco)*), for example, part of the recreational revenues (*P(r)*), flood prevention (*P(u)*) and existence value (*P(x)*). Thus, it can be argued that an eco-centric CBA requires the following functions to be determined for the ecosystem in which the project is executed:

$$P(sp) = f(pp, a, b, c, ..., m)$$

$$P(eco) = P(sp) + P(u) + P(r) + ... + P(x)$$

Performing an eco-centric CBA using these production functions means that the *pp* has to be determined and that its relationship with the secondary production has to be mapped. When this approach was applied to the Grevelingen project it was found that it was impossible to determine the secondary production function, because of a lack of insight into the relationships between the ecosystems in, or related to the Grevelingen project. This problem could be overcome by estimating the total production of the ecosystem (*P(eco)*) by calculating or estimating the outcomes of a set of functions that reflect the production of ecosystems situated in lake Grevelingen. The following estimates or calculations were made of changes in the outcomes of functions that occurred as a consequence of the Grevelingen project.

– The production of economically valuable items realised within the Grevelingen area (fisheries, direct effects on agriculture near the Grevelingen project, recreation).
– The production of economically valuable items realised outside the area of the Grevelingen project (North Sea fisheries).
– The value of natural amenities (existence value due to characteristics such as biodiversity and rare flora and fauna).
– Drinking water production.
– Flood prevention along the rivers.

So far, no monetary value has been attributed to the changes in the production functions relating to lake Grevelingen. The CBAs that have been conducted up to now have not fully integrated the changes in these ecological revenues of ecosystems. Some idea of the monetary value of these changes can be derived using the approach presented by Constanza et al. (1997). These authors estimated changes in ecosystem value to show the human impact on terrestrial and aquatic ecosystems. Such changes include the benefits and costs that impact on human welfare either through established markets or through non-market activities. Constanza et al. (1997) provide monetary values for the following ecosystem functions: gas regulation, climate regulation, disturbance regulation, water regulation, water supply, erosion control and sediment retention, soil formation, nutrient cycling, waste treatment, pollination, biological control, habitat for resident and transient populations, food production, raw materials, genetic resources, recreation and cultural aspects (providing opportunities for non-commercial uses). In order to attribute a value to these functions, Constanza et al. (1997) conducted a thorough literature review and made a number of original calculations. By combining existing valuation estimates, they determined crude value estimates for various ecosystems. These value estimates are based on various methods such as those described in section 2. Constanza et al. (1997) stress the crude character of the valuation estimates and point at limitations and assumptions underlying the valuation methods. The Grevelingen hydraulic works have meant a change from an open sea inlet that can be characterised as an estuary to a biome that can be characterised as a lake. The total value of an estuary has been estimated by Constanza et al. (1997) as $22,832 per ha per year, while the value for a lake is $8,498 per ha per year. This implies a significant reduction in lake Grevelingen's economic value ($14,334 per ha per year). This value reduction can be included as a cost in the eco-centric CBA. However, the CBA should not include the values of ecosystem functions twice. Therefore, table 5 presents the outcome of an eco-centric CBA for the Grevelingen project including the following benefits: reduction of dike maintenance, improved mobility, increased safety and ecological revenues.

Table 5 illustrates that the outcome of an *ex ante* CBA for the Grevelingen project can be significantly different from that of an *ex post* CBA because it includes ecological revenues (*cf* table 4). The ecological revenues for Lake Grevelingen (10,800 ha) declined by at least NLG 325 million ($14,334 per ha per year).

Using values incorporated in the ecological revenues introduces potential biases, however, as these values are based on crude value estimations. Nevertheless, the total value of these ecological revenues appears to be very significant for the out-

*Table 5.* Outcome of an *ex post* eco-centric cost-benefit analysis for the Grevelingen project (in millions of Dutch guilders).

| Costs | | Benefits | |
|---|---|---|---|
| Construction costs: | | Reduction of dike maintenance | 1 |
| Grevelingen barrier | 16 | Improvementof mobility | 63 |
| Brouwer barrier | 110 | Revenues of recreation | 20 |
| Maintenance and capital costs | 21 | Ecological revenues | -325 |
| Desiccation prevention | 0 | Increase of safety | p.m. |
| Other costs | 10 | | |
| Total | **157** | Total | **-261** |

come of the CBA. Therefore it seems worthwhile to include them in the CBAs used in decisions on hydraulic works in rivers with such ecological values. At the same time, one should take care not to include these benefits or costs twice. For example, the value of flood prevention along rivers may be incorporated in the changes in the existence value of an ecosystem (estimated by using CVM).

Even if this danger of biased cost and benefit figures as a result of the introduction of ecological values can be dealt with accurately, it may be questioned whether the introduction of these ecological revenues into the decision-making process is only possible by integrating these values into a CBA. The decision-makers responsible for hydraulic works often use the outcome of CBAs as only one of several criteria.

If the outcome of a CBA is used, it is important to what extent ecological revenues are accounted for. The CBA that uses the figures on ecological revenues provided by Constanza *et al.* (1997) shows that these revenues can be significant. Nevertheless, the further exploration of an eco-centric CBA and a more consistent valuing of ecological revenues may improve the decision-making process by allowing the weighing of loss of ecosystem services against the benefits of specific projects.

## 5. Concluding remarks

CBA has its foundations in welfare economics. The outcome of a CBA indicates to what extent a society is better off with the implementation of a project (change in welfare).The *ex ante* CBAs performed to assess the Delta Plan projects in general and the Grevelingen hydraulic engineering projects in particular have only partly taken the environment into consideration. Environmental benefits of an ecosystem, like the purification of surface water and flood prevention, are typical benefits not included in the traditional CBAs performed for hydraulic engineering projects. This does not imply that the decisions taken at the time when these CBAs were conducted (1954, 1972 and 1974) were incorrect. At that time, such ecosystems benefits were unknown. The future assessment of hydraulic engineering projects, however, will require a more complete inventory of the environmental effects of projects. The present paper has discussed one approach to this, *viz.* that of an eco-centric CBA. Experience with this new approach has shown that more research will be needed to determine the economic value of ecosystems. The availability of such data is a necessary precondition for an eco-centric CBA to map the impact of a project on the economic value of an ecosystem. If the decision-making process on hydraulic engineering projects is to be improved by designing new assessment methods, it should be understood what role such methods have in that process. The outcomes of the assessment methods need to be understood and accepted by the decision-makers, which means that decision-makers will have to be receptive to the outcomes of the assessment tools.

## References

Asian Development Bank. 1997. Measuring environmental performance in Asia. ADB Environment Paper 13. Asian Development Bank (ADB), Manila.

Barde, J.P. & Pearce, D.W. 1991. Valuing the environment: six case studies. Earthscan, London.

Bouma, J.J. & Nijssen, R. 1998. De kosten en baten van de deltawerken: een aanzet voor een ecosysteem georiënteerde kosten-batenanalyse op het niveau van een watersysteem. Erasmus University, Erasmus Centre for Environmental Studies, Rotterdam. (in Dutch).

Common, M. 1996. Environmental and resource economics, an introduction. Longman, London.

Constanza, R., Faber, S.C. & Maxwell, J. 1989. Valuation and management of wetlands ecosystems. Ecol. Econ. 1: 335-361.

Costanza, R., Déarge, R., De Groot, R..S., De Farber, S., Grasso, M., Hannon, B., Limburg, K., Naeem, S., O'Neill, R., Paruelo, J., Raskin, R.G., Sutton, P. & Van den Belt, M. 1997. The value of the world's ecosystem services and natural capital. Nature 387: 253-260.

Delta Act. 1958. Wet van 8 mei 1958, houdende de afsluiting van de zeearmen tussen de Westerschelde en de Rotterdamsche Waterweg en de versterking van de hoogwaterkering ter beveiliging van het land tegen stormvloeden. Staatsblad 8-5-1958. Sdu Uitgevers, Den Haag. (in Dutch).

Dixon, J.A. & Sherman, P.B. 1990. Economics of protected areas. Island, Washington.

IWKBAG. 1974. Kosten-effectiviteitsanalyse van de inrichting van het Grevelingenbekken. Interdepartementale Werkgroep Kosten Baten Aanalyse Grevelingenbekken (IWKBAG), Den Haag. (in Dutch).

Koopman J. 1955. Benaderende berekening van het kapitaalverlies en de inkomensderving voor de visserij ontstaan door de uitvoering van het Deltaplan. [S.N.], [S.L.] (in Dutch).

Mitchel, R.C. & Carson, R.T. 1989. Using surveys to value public goods: the contingent valuation method. Resources for the future, Washington.

NMNH. 1954. Het Deltaplan, afdamming zee-armen. Nederlandse Maatschappij voor Nijverheid en Handel (NMNH), [S.L.] (in Dutch).

Nijkamp, P. 1979. Naar een prijzenswaardig Milieu? Van Gorcum, Assen. (in Dutch).

OECD. 1993. Project and policy appraisal. Organisation for Economic Co-operation and Development (OECD), Paris.

Pearce, D. 1993, Economic values and the natural world. Earthscan, London.

Pearce D.W. & Turner, R.K. 1990. Economics of natural resources and the environment. Harvester Wheatsheaf, Hemel Hempstead.

Perman, R.W., Yue, M. & McGilvray, J. 1996. Natural resource and environmental economics. Longman, Harlow.

Saeijs, H.L.F. 1995. Levend water en een wereldstad, ecologie als economische factor in het waterbeheer. Erasmus University, Erasmus Centre for Environmental Studies, Rotterdam. (in Dutch).

Tietenberg, T.H. 1992. Innovation in environmental policy: economic and legal aspects of recent developments in environmental enforcement and liability. Edward Elgar Publishing Limited, London.

Van Alderwegen, H. 1972. Proeve van een KBA van de inrichting van het Grevelingenbekken als recreatie- en natuurgebied. Landbouwhogeschool Wageningen, Wageningen. (in Dutch).

Vertonghen, R. & Van Rompuy, V. 1994. Sociaal-economische KBA, evaluatie van investeringsprojecten in de publieke sector. Acco, Leuven/Amersfoort. (in Dutch).

Wattel, G., 1996. Grevelingenmeer, uniek maar kwetsbaar, RIKZ-nota 96.014. Rijksinstituut voor Kust en Zee (RIKZ), Middelburg. (in Dutch).

# "FISQUALITY": A NEW TAX BONUS TO IMPROVE THE HYDRO-ECOLOGICAL RESILIENCE OF RIVER CATCHMENTS

A. Corporaal

*Department of Nature Management of Stream Corridors, University of Nijmegen, P.O. Box 9010, NL-6500 GL Nijmegen, The Netherlands*

## Abstract

Deteriorated flow regimes of large rivers are related to land use changes which decrease the hydro-ecological resilience of their catchment. Therefore, a new spatial policy concept is proposed, aiming at improvement of the water retaining capacity (spongity) of river catchments by rural entrepreneurs. This paper briefly describes the main pillars of the concept: (1) the development of a hydro-ecological mainframe (HEM) and (2) the introduction of a new tax bonus for rural entrepreneurs in order to stimulate spongity improving measures in the HEM. Based on a case study in a Dutch part of the Rhine river catchment, further elaboration and opportunities for implementation of the concept are discussed.

## 1. Introduction

In the course of thousands of years, many landscapes have gradually changed from their pristine forms to a state transformed and dominated by man (Ellenberg 1978, Ozenda, 1988, Zonneveld 1980). After establishing permanent settlements, man started to influence his environment. Nomadic hunters became small-scale farmers and deforested small areas. Later on, large-scale deforestation followed, along with expansion and intensification of agriculture, open mining and excavations for sand, gravel and peat. Man degraded natural water systems, normalised and regulated streams and rivers, urbanised large areas, homogenised the soil, paved the surface, compacted the sediment and minimised the porosity of the soil. Human interventions in the landscape have ultimately led to a decrease in the hydro-ecological resilience of many river basins and have contributed to a water crisis on a global scale (Gleick 1993).

In many developed river basins, man-made changes to landscapes and the over-exploitation of natural resources have led to a succession of drops in water tables and increased water discharges (Blab 1986, Bouma 1993, Havinga *et al.* 2000, Petts & Amoros 1996, Picard 1973, Smits *et al.* 2000, Van den Brink 1994). For several centuries, the answer to flooding problems was to raise the dikes and to straighten and deepen the river so that the water could be discharged as rapidly as possible. Gradually, however, the idea began to take form that such an ongoing process of harnessing the river was not a sustainable solution. The preferred management strat-

*New approaches to river management, pp. 179–186*
*edited by A.J.M. Smits, P.H. Nienhuis and R.S.E.W. Leuven*
© *2000 Backhuys Publishers, Leiden, The Netherlands*

egy is now the restoration of natural processes, and especially opportunities to create more space for rivers and their tributaries. This means that the floodplains
should only be used for necessary, river-related activities, while measures should be
taken to give the river more room to expand. Such measures may include deepening and widening the main channel, lowering the winter bed, and digging side and
flood channels in the floodplains (Havinga & Smits 2000, Smits *et al.* 2000, Van
Leussen *et al.* 2000). In addition, a more fundamental, long-term strategy to solve
the problem is a recovery of the hydro-ecological resilience of river systems. This
strategy should involve the water being retained in the catchment areas for a longer
period of time, so that discharges become spread over a longer time and discharge
peaks are reduced.

The present paper explores opportunities for the participation of new stakeholders, *i.e.*, the rural entrepreneurs, in the recovery of the hydro-ecological resilience
of river systems. A new spatial concept to improve the sponge function of river
catchments is proposed. This concept has two pillars: (1) the development of a
hydro-ecological mainframe (HEM) and (2) the introduction of a new tax bonus to
stimulate rural entrepreneurs (private land users in rural areas) to improve the
hydro-ecological quality of the HEM. The concept is called 'fisquality'. This term
originated from a play upon the words 'fiscus' and 'quality', representing the
means (tax bonus for rural entrepreneurs) and the goal (improvement of hydro-ecological quality of rural areas in river catchments) of the concept.

## 2. Towards a hydro-ecological mainframe

The main pillar of the fisquality concept is development of a hydro-ecological
mainframe (HEM) in river catchments. Because of the large impact of land use on
the water discharge of rivers, a HEM is proposed in which the physical relation
between the river and its catchment is qualified and quantified and all kinds of measures can be taken to improve the sponge function of the river catchment (Figure 1).
In the HEM two categories of environmental effects can be identified: 1) improvement of the hydrological resilience of the river catchment by hydrological and
hydraulic measures on a regional scale and 2) improvement of the ecological
resilience of the water system by ecological and environmental measures. The first
category of effects contributes to a decrease in the risks of extremely high as well
as extremely low discharges of tributaries, both of which are important goals of
water management related to safety and navigation. The ecological effects of the
HEM fit in rather well with national and international plans for nature conservation
and ecological rehabilitation. Large rivers, their tributaries and riverine ecosystems
are the backbone of the Dutch and European ecological networks (Jongman 1998).

The measures to improve the water retaining capacity of river catchments are
called spongity improving measures (SIMs), and include afforestation, rehabilitation of woodland and reticulate landscape elements, termination of drainage of farm
land and restoration of regulated streams and rivulets. In addition, areas with controlled inundation are used to prevent the inundation of areas with greater potential
damage. All of these measures raise water tables and retard water discharges in the
river catchment.

In addition to SIMs, national or regional governments may develop additional policies with effects on rural enterprises (*e.g.*, recreation, sport fishing or regional artisanal production) within the HEM, which may improve the overall prosperity and societal role of rural entrepreneurs.

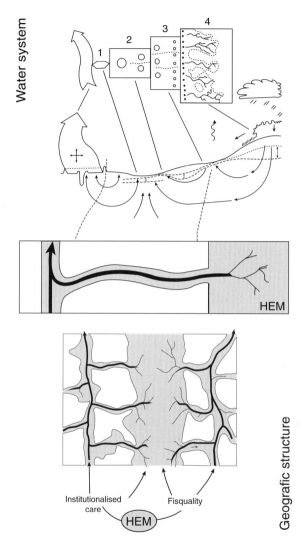

*Fig. 1.* A schematic representation of various spatial relations between the water systems in a regulated, lowland river basin and the geographic structure of the proposed hydro-ecological mainframe (HEM). The upper panel of the figure visualises a cross-section of the river system, the water flows of various streams and the geographic structure of the HEM. In the upland areas, many small streams (4) converge via rivulets (3) into tributaries (2) of rivers (1). The HEM consists of landscape elements relevant to the hydro-ecological resilience of river catchments (*e.g.*, forests, woodlands, estates, fringes, inundation areas along water courses, wetlands and reticulate elements). Improvement of the sponge function of the HEM can be stimulated by a tax bonus for rural entrepreneurs as well as by institutional care of governmental and non-governmental organisations (lower panel).

## 3. Participation of new stakeholders

In principle one may question if care for the HEM and  SIMs should be the exclusive domain of institutionalised (governmental) care or the rural entrepreneurs, or a combination of both. However, the fisquality concept intends to optimise the contribution of rural entrepreneurs (mostly farmers, foresters and estate owners) to the HEM and SIMs by a tax bonus (see section 4). In the past, the rural entrepreneurs were encouraged by governmental subsidies to produce as many resources (wood, agricultural products) as possible, provided they acted within the environmental directives related to emissions of nutrients, pesticides, etc. (Lenders *et al.*1997, Schreur *et al.* 1994, Sijtsma & Strijker 1994). This mainly resulted in a maximum food production with minimum care for nature, the environment and water systems. At present, several national and regional governments and the European Union are searching for new regulations to optimise production as well as environmental quality. However, these regulations often lack explicit contributions to improve the sponge function of the river catchments (Baldock & Beaufoy 1993, Baldock & Mitchell 1995). Rural entrepreneurs who are interested in regulations aiming at an optimisation of production and environmental quality would like to expand their incomes, using financially interesting instruments (high bonus for long periods). In the Netherlands, the debate is moving towards instruments, stressing the role of private stakeholders in managing our landscapes (Davidson 1995, De Hoo 1998, RIZA 1999, Sijtsma & Strijker 1995).

## 4. Preliminary desk study on fisquality for farm land

A preliminary estimation of fisquality at company level included 21 farm enterprises, situated in the eastern, sand covered area of the Netherlands (Corporaal 1995). The study site is situated in the lower parts of the Rhine basin. The area is characterised by farmland with reticulate landscape elements and is drained by predominantly normalised and regulated streams and rivulets. Their catchments still show an original relief of low hills. The average surface area of the farms is 30 ha. In 1995, the average economic value of the farmland was about 22,700 Euro per ha. However, there is a tendency in the Netherlands for the economic value of farmland to rapidly increase due to the scarcity of land. Table 1 shows the land use in the present situation and according to two scenarios for SIMs. These measures include land use changes (*i.e.*, creation of reticulate elements, woodland and forest) in order to increase the hydro-ecological quality of the landscape and the occasional inundation of farmland along the streams and rivulets. In scenarios 1 and 2 the production area is reduced, in favour of woodland, forest and reticulate elements, by  4% and 16%, respectively. Due to occasional inundation, the crop productivity may be decreased in 8% and 16% of the farmland, respectively.

*Table 1.* Comparison of the present land use on farms in the sand covered part of the Netherlands with two scenarios for spongity improving measures.

| Land use | Percentage of surface area | | |
|---|---|---|---|
| | **Present situation** | **Scenario 1** | **Scenario 2** |
| Infrastructure | 4 | 4 | 4 |
| Reticulate elements | 2 | 4 | 8 |
| Forest and woodland | 2 | 4 | 12 |
| Production area | 92 | 80 | 60 |
| Occasionally inundated production area | - | 8 | 16 |
| Total | 100 | 100 | 100 |

The potential loss of production capacity as a result of spongity improving measures will be compensated according to the proposed tax bonus system (Table 2). The estimated average decrease in the production capacity of inundated farmland would be 35%. However, due to occasional inundation, the production capacity would vary greatly varies over the years. The change in the production volume by afforestation, and the creation of woodland and reticulate landscape elements out of farmland is valued as 100%, because it is considered a permanent land use change. In addition, a 5% rate is proposed to maintain existing forest, woodland and reticulate elements.

The estimated tax bonuses are based on the loss of economic value of the production area (Table 2). The difference in economic value between the present and future situation is divided by the length of a fictitious marked-down period of 25 years. The farmers receive the fisquality bonus as a net taxation bonus. If fisquality should exceed tax, the farmer would be reimbursed for the difference by the government.

*Table 2.* Tax bonus after implementation of spongity improving measures.

| | **Present situation** | **Scenario 1** | **Scenario 2** |
|---|---|---|---|
| *Average surface area (in ha)* | | | |
| Occasionally inundated production area | - | 2.4 | 4.8 |
| Existing, forest, woodland and reticulate landscape elements | 1.2 | 1.2 | 1.2 |
| New forest, woodland and reticulate landscape elements | - | 1.2 | 4.8 |
| *Tax bonus per year (in Euro)* | | | |
| Fisquality bonus[1] | - | 1,900 | 10,365 |
| Average fisquality bonus[2] per ha | - | 350 | 960 |

1: net, tax-free; 2: for the actually changed surface area.

What do the results of the case study mean? Until 1995, an average Dutch farmer received a total annual subsidy of 1,700 Euro per ha (Corporaal 1995), including subsidies from the European Union and national and regional subsidies. Meanwhile, this amount has already been reduced to 1,200 Euro per ha. International negotiations (*e.g.*, European agricultural policy, GATT agreements) are expected to mean that the subsidies for farmers will be terminated around the year 2010. In view of this perspective, many farmers are searching for more sustainable forms of income, including allowances to care for high quality rural landscapes. The preliminary estimations show that fisquality should be considered as a serious alternative.

## 5. Discussion and conclusions

This paper focuses on the relations between land use driven by economic aims, the hydro-ecological resilience of river catchments and extremely high and low discharges of large rivers. The proposed fisquality concept aims to improve the hydro-ecological resilience of river basins. At present, the political momentum for implementation of this concept seems to be optimal. On the one hand, river managers are asking for more structural and less expensive measures to decrease peak discharges by integrated catchment management (Havinga & Smits 2000, Smits *et al.* 2000, Van Leussen *et al.* 2000). On the other hand, the incomes of farmers are gradually decreasing owing to the agricultural policy of the European Union and GATT. In addition, it is underlined that the fisquality concept fits in well with the general trend towards greening the tax systems and in particular the proposals for complementary policies to achieve sustainable development of agricultural areas by environmental taxes (OECD 1992, 1993, 1996) and prosperity of rural entrepreneurs (Matthews 1993). Moreover, the Dutch government is already performing small-scale experiments in several river catchments, in which farmers combine agricultural production with landscape care and nature management. Along the Dinkel rivulet (Province Overijssel), for instance, hydrological problems are not solved by enlarging or improving the drainage capacity, but by paying farmers the economic damage caused by periodical inundations and high water tables. The province of Limburg has developed a policy to restore the natural behaviour of the tributaries of the Meuse, aiming at a reduction of the maximum discharges by 20% (Provincie Limburg 1999, Van Leussen *et al.* 2000). With this measure the province tries to anticipate on the expected increase in river discharges over the coming century as a result of climate change. Additionally, these tributaries are being reconstructed as important linking zones in the ecological network. However, these are isolated examples and there is not yet a tendency towards a structural policy on mutual attenuation of land use and water management. Recently, the Dutch institutes Alterra and WLDelft Hydraulics have presented a map of areas which offer opportunities for water storage during extreme meteorological circumstances (> 75 mm rain per day; Aarden 2000). This map is a good starting point for discussions on the geographical boundaries of the HEM.

Meanwhile, various Dutch stakeholders support the societal and hydro-ecological relevance of the fisquality concept. Therefore, a feasibility study is recommended to consider implementation of the concept. Important issues for further research are identifying the boundaries of the HEM, assessment of the quantitative effects of spongity improving measures on the hydro-ecological quality of the river basin (*e.g.*, effects on peak discharges of streams, fluctuations in water tables, crop productivity and ecosystem succession), rating of the tax bonus for various measures, elaboration of a transparent and verifiable fiscal system, and implementation in farm management.

## References

Aarden, M. 2000. Ruimte voor water. Kansenkaart voor waterberging. De Volkskrant – Wetenschap, 12 februari 2000. (in Dutch).
Baldock, D. & Beaufoy, G. 1993. Nature conservation and new directions in the EC common agricultural policy. Ministerie van Landbouw, Natuurbeheer en Visserij, Den Haag.
Baldock, D. & Mitchell, K. 1995. Cross-compliance within the common agricultural policy. A review for options for landscape and nature conservation. Institute for European Environmental Policy, London.
Blab, J. 1986. Grundlagen des Biotopschutzes für Tiere. Schriftenreihe für Landschaftsphlege und Naturschutz 24, ein Leitfaden zum praktischem Schutz der Lebensraume. 2$^e$ Auflage. Kilda-Verlag, Bonn-Bad Godesberg. (in German).
Bouma, J. & Hack - Ten Broeke, M.J.D. 1993. Simulation modelling as a method tot study land qualities and crop productivity related to soil structure differences. Geoderma 57: 167-182.
Corporaal, A. 1995. Fiskwaliteit. Ecologisch en fiscaal verantwoord economiseren van belangrijke kwaliteitskenmerken van onze groene ruimte. Ministerie van Landbouw, Natuurbeheer en Visserij, Deventer. (in Dutch).
Davidson, M. 1995. Liberalen en ecologisering. Milieuplatform, Amsterdam. (in Dutch).
De Hoo, S. (Ed.). 1998. Sustainability. Choices and challenges for future development. RABObank International, Amsterdam.
Ellenberg, H. 1978. Vegetation Mitteleuropas mit den Alpen. Verlag Eugen Ulmer, Stuttgart.
Gleick, P.H. (Ed.). 1993. Water in crisis. A guide tot the world's fresh water resources. Oxford University Press, New York.
Havinga, H. & Smits, A.M.J. 2000. River management along the Rhine: a retrospective view. In: Smits, A.J.M., Nienhuis, P.H. & Leuven, R.S.E.W. (Eds.). New approaches to river management. Backhuys Publishers, Leiden. pp. 15-32.
Jongman, R.H.G. 1998. Rivers: key elements in European ecological networks. In: Nienhuis, P.H., Leuven, R.S.E.W. & Ragas, A.M.J. (Eds.). New concepts for sustainable management of river basins. Backhuys Publishers, Leiden. pp. 53-66.
Lenders, H.J.R., Leuven, R.S.E.W., Nienhuis, P.H. & Schoof, D.J.W. 1997. Natuurbeheer en -ontwikkeling. Handboeken Milieukunde 2. Boom, Amsterdam. (in Dutch).
Matthews, G.J. 1993. Overall credit worthiness as a tool for sustainable development. UNESCO, Montevideo.
OECD. 1992. Environmental taxes in OECD countries. Organisation for Economic Co-operation and Development (OECD), Paris.
OECD. 1993. Taxation and the environment: complementary policies. Organisation for Economic Co-operation and Development (OECD), Paris.
OECD. 1996. Implementation strategies for environmental taxes. Committee on fiscal affairs, Environment Policy Committee. Organisation for Economic Co-operation and Development (OECD), Paris.
Ozenda, P. 1988. Die Vegetation der Alpen im Europaischen Gebirgsraum. Gustav Fisher Verlag, New York.
Petts, G.E. & Amoros, C. (Ed.). 1996. Fluvial hydrosystems. Chapman & Hall, London.
Picard, M.D. & High, L.R. 1973. Sedimentary structures of ephemeral streams. Developments in sedimentology 17. Elsevier, Amsterdam.
Provincie Limburg. 1999. Investeren in kwaliteit. Schets van het omgevingsbeleid voor Limburg. Provincie Limburg, Maastricht. (in Dutch).

RIZA. 1999. De toekomst van de natte natuur. Eindrapport Nationaal Onderzoek Verdroging (NOV). Rijksinstituut voor Integraal Zoetwaterbeheer en Afvalwaterbehandeling (RIZA) en NOV, Lelystad en Den Haag.

Schreur, J., Kuper, M., Weultjes, C. & Ter Woord, R. 1994. Basisboek milieurecht; milieuhygiene, water, natuur en landschap. Coutinho, Bussum. (in Dutch).

Sijtsma, F. & Strijker, D. 1994. Financiele steun aan de Nederlandse landbouw. Stichting Natuur en Milieu, Utrecht. (in Dutch).

Sijtsma, F. & Strijker, D. 1995. Effect-analyse Ecologische Hoofdstruktuur. Deel I (Reg-8) en Deel II (Reg-9). Stichting Ruimtelijke Economie Groningen, Groningen. (in Dutch).

Smits, A.J.M., Havinga, H. & Marteijn, E.C.L. New concepts in river and water management in the river basin: how to live with the unexpected? In: Smits, A.J.M., Nienhuis, P.H & Leuven, R.S.E.W. (Eds.). New appraoches to river management. Backhuys Publishers, Leiden. pp. 267-286.

Van den Brink, F.W.B. 1994. Impact of hydrology on floodplain lake ecosystems along the lower Rhine and Meuse. Thesis. University of Nijmegen, Nijmegen.

Van Leussen, W., Kater, G. & Van Meel, P. 2000. Multi-level approach to flood control in the Dutch part of the river Meuse. In: Smits, A.J.M., Nienhuis, P.H. & Leuven, R.S.E.W. (Eds.). New approaches to river management. Backhuys Publishers, Leiden. pp. 287-305.

Zonneveld, J.I.S. 1980. Tussen de bergen en de zee. Bohn, Scheltema & Holkema, Utrecht. (in Dutch).

# IS THERE A FUTURE FOR BIG DAMS?

R.J.A. Goodland
*Environment Department, World Bank, Washington DC 20433, The United States of America*

## Abstract

This paper proposes that there could be a future for dams, but only if they are made to be sustainable. It specifies ways to make hydropower and irrigation dams environmentally and socially sustainable. The main message is that while hydropower is far from perfect, its impacts are mitigable. The impacts of alternatives to hydropower, namely nuclear energy and coal, cannot be mitigated. The main means to approach sustainability is to integrate environmental and social criteria into traditional economic least-cost sequencing, which makes it Sectoral Environmental Assessment (SEA). Select more sustainable generation modes (*e.g.*, demand-side management, hydro and other renewable resources) before less sustainable generation modes (*e.g.*, coal, and nuclear energy). When the best mode and the best site (*e.g.*, a hydro dam) have been selected, then the normal project-level Environmental Assessment (EA) should be used to mitigate residual impacts, such as by lowering the dam or moving it upstream. While project-level EA is essential and needs to be strengthened, SEA to select the better projects is far more powerful. In addition, the energy sector needs to foster transparency and participation, substantially strengthen implementive capacity, show that conservation is well in hand and that electricity pricing is adequate before new capacity is contemplated. The biggest impact of dams, involuntary resettlement, needs the most attention. Oustees must be better off promptly after their move. Finally, the energy sector should play by the same economic rules; all sectoral subsidies should be revoked, and all power projects should internalise external environmental damage costs, including those of greenhouse gas emissions. To do less means the sectoral playing field is not level. This promotes coal and penalises hydro and other renewable resources: an environmentally retrogressive course.

## 1. Introduction

This paper shows how to achieve sustainability of big dams (Box 1). The paper focuses on hydroelectricity dams. Irrigation dams are mentioned, although much of what is proposed for hydroelectricity dams applies to all dams, such as for flood control, water supply and navigation. The raging international controversy for and against big dams has led to a decline in big dam building, to an increase in coal-fired electricity, and to a decrease in irrigation per capita. Developing countries are the main places dams are contemplated and are the focus of this paper.

Proponents of dams and other renewable energy sources are losing the fight to promote them. Sustainability will be strongly promoted by phasing out of the big impact forms of energy production, and phasing into the lower impact forms of energy, such as renewables. This means essentially phasing out of coal and into hydro and other renewables. Hydro is on the cusp between fully renewable and clearly non-renewable. Hydro dams have not yet become fully environmentally sustainable.

*New approaches to river management, pp. 187–207*
*edited by A.J.M. Smits, P.H. Nienhuis and R.S.E.W. Leuven*
*© 2000 Backhuys Publishers, Leiden, The Netherlands*

*Box 1.* Environmental sustainability in hydro dams.

The starting point is the solar-powered hydrological cycle, which is the quintessence of sustainability. Water flow is a renewable resource. The cycle must be harnessed so that the project continues to generate benefits (such as power and fish; in multipurpose dams irrigation, flood control, navigation and water supply) for a long period, certainly decades, preferably a hundred years or more. In the narrow sense, sustainability means the hydro's lifetime should be as long as possible. In the broad sense, sustainability means environmental and social damage has been prevented or offset such that net residual impacts are insignificant. In addition, sustainability requires that the environmental and social costs (*e.g.*, costs of climate change) are low and do not increase, especially not for future generations, such as climate change (the intergenerational equity component of sustainability). Sustainability is not only a continuation of power output. A modest fraction of power sales allocated to social and environmental needs ensures their acceptability. The concept of environmental sustainability in general is amplified in Goodland (1995) and Goodland & Daly (1996). From this point of view some aspects related to hydro dams can specifically be addressed.

*Involuntary resettlement (includes affected people)*
The number of oustees is zero or low (*e.g.*, Nepal's Arun reservoir); those relocated are promptly better off after their move. To be no worse off means stagnation, so cannot be called development. Of course, "no worse off" would be much better than historic achievements. Diseases cannot be allowed to increase. Brazil and China call for fractions of power sales to be allocated to oustees. The policy of China and of the International Commission on Large Dams is to ensure oustees are better off, not "no worse off". Impact on affected people should be made acceptable.

*Sedimentation*
The reservoir electricity generation capacity will not be curtailed; certainly for longer than the amortisation of the loan. Opponents claim that 50 years of power is too brief a benefit to outweigh the environmental costs. Early designs need to calculate the ratio of live to dead storage to aid in dam selection. Catchment protection should be an integral component to all relevant hydro projects. Current sediment loading; expected life of reservoir before sediment starts to curtail generation. Thereafter, if the plant operates as run-of-river, what are the implications? Potential (*e.g.*, by bottom gates) for de-silting; downstream effects of de-silting. Calculate and monitor erosion processes upstream.

*Fish*
Fish contribution to nutrition and especially protein must not decline. Unless fish catch increases substantially and permanently, the big new opportunity of the reservoir will have been wasted. Need to ascertain how many people currently depend for what part of their livelihoods on fish (self-consumption or barter or commercial sales). Non-marketed fish value usually exceeds marketed fish value. Much so-called weekend or recreational fishing forms part of poor household budgets, so must be included. The potential for fish cultivation in the new reservoir or elsewhere should be realised, including the high initial off take, but then to decrease harvests as productivity stabilises. Dam operating rules for optimising fisheries need to be implemented, and costs internalised. Reduction in all fishing, especially subsistence, in downstream areas must be permanently compensated for.

*Biodiversity*
Species or genetic diversity should not decline due to the project. Sustainability means the project does not cause the extinction of any species. Moreover, migrations (*e.g.*, seasonal, anadromy, catadromy and potadromy) should not be so impeded as to harm populations. For example, fish breeding or fish passage facilities should be proven in advance. Will wildlife habitat be lost? Are equivalent (or better) compensatory tracts purchasable nearby? Improvements in net biodiversity are not difficult, and should be sought.

*Box 1. Continued.* Environmental sustainability in hydro dams.

*Land pre-empted*
Agricultural production lost; clarify that the net power benefits clearly exceed the net value of lost agricultural production; equivalent areas need to be made available for oustees.

*Water quality*
Can acceptable water quality be maintained? Ensure that the reservoir does not impair quality. It does not mean cleaning up dirty water filling the reservoir (*e.g.*, Zimapan fills from Mexico city's effluent). Can water weeds and decaying vegetation be controlled so that water of acceptable quality will occur downstream? Phosphorus is important, as is organic mercury releases from rotting biomass. Mercury contamination in reservoirs is a relatively recently discovered impact. Mercury seems to arise from its use in recovering gold in the Amazon, from coal-fired thermal generating plants, and traffic in Organisation for Economic Co-operation and Development (OECD) and elsewhere, but is in some soils without such sources. It is accumulated in the organic (methyl mercury) form from sediment, especially in anoxic humus and peat, through algae and insects to fish. Poisonous methyl mercury accumulates up the food chain to such an extent that carnivorous fish consumption can harm vulnerable humans, such as children and pregnant women. The United States Food and Drug Administration (US FDA) limit of 1.0 $\mu$g g$^{-1}$ wet wt is commonly exceeded.

*Downstream hydrology*
Harm must be prevented to downstream uses by people (e.g., irrigation, soil fertility restoration, recession agriculture, washing and cattle watering; Collier *et al.* 1996) and ecosystems (e.g., mangroves, deltaic fish, wetlands and floodplains; Horowitz 1991, 1994). The benefits of water regulation downstream: flood control, urban and industrial water supply, multiple use, can be substantial. Temperature control of releases needs to be controlled.

*Regional integration and aesthetics*
The project is more sustainable if well integrated into the activities and future of the region; cultural property lost and aesthetics marred (Goodland & Webb 1989).

*Greenhouse gas production*
Total greenhouse gas (from biomass, cement, steel etc.) should not exceed a gas-fired equivalent. Rotting biomass remaining in the reservoir after filling produces estimable amounts of $CO_2$ and $CH_4$.

*Institutional capacity strengthening*
Achieving sustainability needs more trained people dedicated to implementing the above priorities. All dams seeking sustainability should invest substantially in capacity strengthening.

Opponents of big dams have been so successful in pointing out inadequacies that hydro development is slowing and coal is burgeoning, precisely the retrogressive course. Hydro proponents have not been totally successful in persuading opponents that the benefits of big dams clearly outweigh the costs. Hence the controversy over many water development projects (Boxes 3 and 4). By far the best documented and thorough sources on the inadequacies of hydro projects are those of McCully (1996, 1997). This is the starkest warning for the hydro industry to become environmentally sustainable. Further details are available in Goldsmith & Hildyard (1984-1991), Pearce (1992) and Sklar & McCully (1994).

This paper begins with emphasising the most recent progress with big dams, namely transparency and participation. The paper then outlines how to select the next least-bad dam by Environmental Least-Cost Ranking (ELCR). Then the worst impact of big dams, involuntary resettlement, is outlined. The paper concludes with sections on Irrigation Dams, Greenhouse Gas, and speculation on the Future of Dams.

## 2. Transparency and participation

Dam proponents scarcely fostered transparency and participation of stakeholders in the past. Planning behind closed doors by expert hydro planners who know best was the order of the day. Secrecy often reigned. Now dam proponents see that secrecy is no longer possible. In the last very few years, especially since about 1995, transparency and participation can no longer be avoided, that is why they top the rank of the ten commandments for dam sustainability (Box 2; Goodland 1997c,d). Proponents are nervous about exposing their schemes to public scrutiny; Governments are concerned about risks to sovereignty. The Mekong River Commission is widely reported in the press not to have fully embraced transparency and participation on several occasions in the mid-1990s, which differs with the United Nation's Development Programme's promotion of transparency (Rothert 1995). But participation is here to stay and is slowly spreading world-wide.

Participation is essential for democracy, and greatly improves project selection and design. As EA is performed by the proponents, external scrutiny and participation in the whole process is essential to reduce any possible conflict of interest. The World Bank (1998) now insists that EA reports become publicly available, and this is helping to raise EA quality. Now that civil society or non-governmental organisations are burgeoning, national governments and governance are weakening, and privatisation is sweeping the globe, it is increasingly difficult to impose major investments covertly on taxpayers, so new big proposals are increasingly subject to transparency and full participation from the earliest stages. Most importantly, participation and transparency foster early agreement and builds consensus thus

*Box 2.* Ten commandments for sustainability of hydro dams.

1. Increase transparency and participation.
2. Achieve demand side management before adding new capacity.
3. Follow least-cost ranking.
4. Improve involuntary resettlement.
5. Internalise greenhouse gas emission damage costs.
6. Promote capacity strengthening to implement mitigation.
7. Balance rural *versus* urban supply.
8. Balance small, medium and big projects.
9. Balance storage dams *versus* run-of-river.
10. Balance hydro with other renewables.

reducing controversy and opposition later on. This expedites implementation. These two relatively new aspects are mandated by an increasing number of governments and development agencies.

As transparency and participation are here to stay, dam planning can no longer be restricted to experts (Narayan 1995). Although they are here to stay, they are not yet at all the norm; the 'big dams' debate (Box 3) still rages, and there are still too many dam controversies (Box 4). Laos, on the other hand, was until recently an almost closed society. It held its first public three day participation meeting in 1997 on its biggest proposed hydro project, Nam Theun 2; now they are held regularly. Nam Theun Hydro proponents are receiving many useful proposals from non-traditional stakeholders because of such participation.

Stakeholder analysis has become a useful tool in promoting participation (Boxes 5 and 6). Major dam projects are improving in this regard. In an increasing number of countries, a major dam is likely to go ahead without massive opposition only if civil society has been fully involved and broadly agrees that the proposed project is the best alternative. That is the least objectionable, the least environmentally and socially costly. The project has to meet goals that have been agreed upon in advance by civil society and government, supported by financiers and development agencies. Society as a whole bears the financial debts and the environmental and social costs, so society as a whole needs to be meaningfully consulted before such costs are incurred (Narayan 1995, World Bank 1994b, 1996c).

Transparency and participation mean that civil society exercise a role in the selection of criteria to be subsequently used for decision-making and in identifying stakeholders. These normally include affected people (eventually all tax payers), or their advocates, government, academia, syndicates, consumer and safety organisations, as well as project proponents. Civil society assists in the selection and design of studies needed before decisions can be made, in the interpretation of the findings of such studies, in the burden sharing or relative weights given to demand side management, pricing, conservation, efficiency on the one hand, and new generation capacity on the other.

## 3. Environmental least-cost ranking

Dam opponents are very keen to start environmental prudence before the next individual project is selected. Once a project is selected there is only modest scope for reducing impacts such as by lowering dam height. The biggest opportunity to reduce impacts is by integrating social and environmental criteria into project analysis. In practice this means expanding traditional least cost sequencing in a sector to include social and environmental criteria in order to find the true least cost path. Sectoral environmental assessments (SEA), a relatively new tool, is starting to be applied to the hydro-subsectors by means of coarse and fine screening so that the lowest impact projects are taken up first (Goodland & Mercier 1999). The world's best example is Nepal's superb SEA based on coarse and fine screening and ranking of an inventory of 132 potential projects, now narrowed down to the seven economically and financially feasible projects with low or the least environmental and social impacts.

*Box 3.* Claims of proponents and opponents in the general 'big dams' debate (Goodland 1997a).

| Proponents | Opponents |
|---|---|
| It is possible to mitigate hydro's impacts significantly, given political will | Historically, hydro's known impacts have not always been mitigated in practice, even when well known, such as involuntary resettlement |
| Developing countries need large power projects; many small power projects (deforestation, old diesels) can be environmentally and economically worse than the best hydro | Developing countries are better served by less lumpy power investments than big hydro |
| The impacts of hydro's alternatives (coal, nuclear) cannot be mitigated | Lumpy power projects demote demand-side management (DSM), so small coal and gas turbines make DSM more likely |
| Hydro generates much less greenhouse gas (GHG) compared with coal alternatives | GHG reduction by hydro is unlikely to be the least cost; transport sector improvements are more likely to be less cost |
| Gas is best reserved for transport fuels or for chemical feedstock; costly for base load | Use natural gas for the next decade or so or until other renewables become competitive |
| Many countries still have good hydro sites left; the best hydro sites should promote local development, to export electricity to neighbors, to postpone coal or nuclear alternatives, to benefit the country by attracting energy intensive industries | Practically all good hydro sites have already been developed, especially in Europe and USA |
| The worst hydro sites should not be built: tropical, many oustees and species, large reservoir areas, shallow, etc. | The main really good hydro sites are non-tropical (that is, mountainous), no biomass or resettlement, no fish or no endemics, high head, deep reservoirs |
| Government regulation is needed; enforcement possible | Government regulation unlikely and enforcement may be weakening |
| Privatisation needs government regulation | Private sector less regulable by government |
| Public and private power projects should follow least cost | Private sector less likely to follow least cost; prefers to externalise all it can |
| Electricity sales help the country irrespective of the use to which the power is put, such as exports or for the already electrified elites | More electricity for elites not needed. Electricity for basic needs, health, education and for the poor is not best met from big hydro feeding the national grid |
| Must not let water "waste to sea" unharnessed | Water to sea not wasted, but used by ecosystems |
| Need large scale for urban, industries and surpluses, especially as their capability to pay is greater | Poor and rural benefit less, if at all, from large scale. Priorities should be poor before industries |

*Box 3. Continued.* Claims of proponents and opponents in the general 'big dams' debate (Goodland 1997a).

| Proponents | Opponents |
|---|---|
| Subsidies to rich can be cut; pricing can help poor | Subsidises the rich; decreases equity |
| Foreign contractors create jobs and transfer technology | Too dependent on foreign exchange and contractors |
| Poor countries lack capacity to build large dams; low maintenance cost and simplification of operations suitable for low developed countries (LDCs) | Indigenous, smaller often more appropriate for LDCs to begin with; big hydro has huge capital costs |
| Big/small not substitutable | Small/medium hydro dam can partly substitute for big ones, and with more equitable goals |

Dam proponents normally invest in the single project that meets their own criteria of what type of dam, the timing of its implementation, the size of investment they have experience in, and which project is likely to have the higher returns on capital. Proponents, particularly private investors, cannot get involved with the whole sector; that is clearly the government's role.

Pre-construction planning and investigation time is often less generous with a private investor than with government. The private sector would like the government to accept as much as possible of the sectoral needs, feasibility studies, preconstruction planning and risks. Development agencies can indeed help with sectoral planning and feasibility costs.

*Box 4.* Examples of controversial dams.

1. Thailand's 576 MW ($352 M) Nam Choan was indefinitely postponed by the Royal Thai cabinet in 1982 because the 140 square km reservoir would flood 4% of the 4,800 square km Thung Hai Wildlife Sanctuary. This sanctuary was (and is even more since) being actively logged and poached which the project could have halted. This is an example of many, that hydro projects are indeed dropped on environmental grounds.
2. Sweden has banned further hydro projects on half of its rivers; New government may rescind this decision partly because of availability of Finland's nuclear energy.
3. Norway until recently was 100% hydro-based, which was then considered good and sustainable. Norway has now postponed all new hydro projects because of excess capacity and opposition.
4. Slovakia is defying the EC and the EC-appointed tribunal looking into the Danube's Gabcikovo Dam which is alleged to have lowered the water table in Hungary's prime agricultural area (yields dropped 30%) by 6 m in the lower central part of Hungary's Szigetkoz wetland. Most Danube fish are reported to have since declined; work was halted for a period in mid-construction (Leentvaar & Glas 2000). International Court of Justice found both parties guilty in 1997.

*Box 4. Continued.* Examples of controversial dams.

5.  USA: New York State (NY Power Authority) cancelled their 20-year $12.6 bn contract to buy 1000 MW of Quebec's James Bay power, reportedly for environmental (and social) reasons, in 1992. Demand reduction in New York played a role too, but is now much more exploited than previously, so there will be decreasing scope for more demand side management. HydroQuebec indefinitely postponed Great Whale hydro 1994.
6.  India requested the World Bank on March 31, 1993 to cancel the outstanding $170 M Sardar Sarovar (Narmada) loan, partly because contractual agreement schedule was unlikely to be met on time. This was the world's most intense dam controversy for years on environmental and social impacts as amplified by Morse & Berger (1992).
7.  Nepal's 401 MW Arun hydro (43 ha reservoir; little resettlement), twice entered Nepal's Supreme Court in 1994 because of opposition related to the 122 km access road, and transparency; petition lodged with World Bank's Inspection Panel in 1994; project dropped in 1995 largely because of financial risk although environment was criticised by opponents.
8.  China's 18,200 MW Three Gorges, the largest in the world, had US support withdrawn in 1993 and US Ex-Im Bank withdrew 1994. Contracts signed in 1977 with Asea Brown Boveri, General Electric/Alsthom, Kvaerner, Voith, Siemens); Japan and Germany (Hermes-Buergschaften Ex-Im Bank) involved as of 1997.
9.  Chile's 400 MW, Pangue hydrodam, the first of five (see below) planned for the Biobio river ($150 million, approved 1992, completed 1997), litigated in Chile's Supreme Court in 1993, partly because the EA failed to address downstream impacts. An independent review commissioned by IFC, led by Jay Hair former President of IUCN-World Conservation Union, is said to damn both the project process and IFC; World Bank Group President Wolfensohn (February 6, 1997) threatens to declare default to Finance Minister Aninat. March 11, 1997: Chile severs ties with IFC by prepaying IFC's loan and obtaining cheaper money from the Dresdner Bank, with fewer environmental conditions.
10. Chile's 570 MW Ralco dam on the Biobio river has become a test of Amerindian rights, as well as divergent views between those vulnerable ethnic minorities preferring traditional living, and those preferring economic development at the risk of assimilation. The 1000 acre, $500 million reservoir planned by Spanish private corporation ENDESA would displace 500 Pehuenche Amerindians, a sub-group of the Mapuche ethnicity who have been beleaguered since the Spanish conquistadors. The Government claims that the Electric Service Law takes precedence over the 1992 Indian Rights Law that prohibits sale of Indian lands without unanimous consent of the community involved. The director of the National Environmental Commission was fired in 1997 after a report finding against the project. In 1998 President Frei dismissed three members of the National Indigenous Peoples Board when it appeared they would vote against the project. The fired director, Domingo Namuncura, pointed out that the lands offered to the Amerindians are too infertile to support their traditional wheat and potato crops. Demonstrations, country-wide road blockades, and a 3 day Indian protest march could halt the project. Will oustees be penalised for the greater good of the nation?
11. Malaysia's 2,400 MW Bakun dam was cancelled in 1997 breaking ABB's $5 bn. contract when agreement on financial risk allocation (cost over-runs) could not be reached. Vulnerable ethnic minority oustees (9,000) rejected resettlement arrangements; the EA was declared illegal (and secret).

*Box 5.* Historic evolution of transparency and participation; broadening the constituency of the dam design team.

| Design Team | Approximate Era |
|---|---|
| 1.  Engineers | Pre-1945 |
| 2.  Engineers + Economists | Post-1950 |
| 3.  Engineers + Economists + then add-on EIS to end of complete design | 1970s |
| 4.  Engineers + Economists + Environmentalists & Sociologists | 1980s |
| 5.  Engineers + Economists + Environmentalists & Sociologists + Affected People | 1990s |
| 6.  Engineers + Economists + Environmentalists & Sociologists + Affected People + NGOs | 1995 |
| 7.  Engineers + Economists + Environmentalists & Sociologists + Affected People + NGOs + Freely-given, fully-informed, prior consent of affected people | Early 2000s? |

Note: These dates hold more for industrial nations than for developing ones, although meaningful consultations with affected people or their advocates and local non-governmental organisations, and the involvement of environmentalists in project design are now mandatory for all World Bank-assisted projects. The World Bank's mandatory environmental assessment procedures are outlined in World Bank (1991). Environmental Impact Statements (EIS) were added on to the end of a completely designed project – a certain recipe for confrontation and waste. "Environmentalists and sociologists" should routinely include public health specialists, planners and management specialists.

*Box 6.* Treatment of stakeholders: trends from warning, through consultation and participation to partnership.

| | |
|---|---|
| **Pre-1950s:** | Warning: One-way information flow: oustees were warned that they would be flooded or otherwise affected in a few weeks or months time and had to get out of the way for the greater good of distant citizens. |
| **1960s:** | Information: Primitive consultation in selection of resettlement sites: Oustees were informed that they would be flooded out, and were asked where they would like to move to among a few sites selected by the proponent; compensation often inadequate. |
| **1970s:** | Consultation: Participation in resettlement site selection: oustees were consulted about their impending move, and invited to assist in finding sites to which they would like to move. |
| **1980s:** | Meaningful consultation: Resettlement participation evolves into consultation: Oustees are meaningfully consulted in advance and can influence dam height, or its position on the river; oustees views on mitigation of resettlement are addressed. |
| **1991:** | Mandatory consultation: World Bank's "EA Sourcebook" mandates meaningful consultation in all EAs. The EA is unacceptable without such consultation (World Bank 1991). |
| **1990s:** | Stakeholder consultation: Resettlement consultation evolves into stakeholder consultation: Stakeholders views are sought on all impacts, not just involuntary resettlement. |
| **1992:** | Participation: The World Bank's EA Policy mandates participation. This means stakeholders are fully informed and they participate in decisions affecting them (World Bank 1996a,b). |
| **1996:** | "Participation Sourcebook" published (World Bank 1996c). |

Environmental Assessment (EA) historically focused on individual projects. Indeed, in the past, EAs used to be performed after the project had been designed. In the last few decades, EAs have moved "upstream" so that they now start more or less at the same time as project design. By the time the project has been designed, environmental and social concerns would be fully internalised. While this is a huge improvement over the add-on of the EA to a previously designed project, it is now clear that project-level EAs are inherently weak. Project-level EAs have to focus on the project identified and being designed. For example, if an EA of a highway proposal is requested, that precludes the more important modal choice between highway and rail. Similarly, the EA of one proposed atomic energy reactor may be able to improve site selection, design of the containment vessel, and safety of radioactive transport and disposal. However, it cannot do much if the preferred choice would not have been atomic energy, but natural gas imports, for example.

The EA of a proposed dam may be able to site the dam on another river then what was originally proposed, may even reduce impacts by lowering dam height, or moving it upstream, as was done in the case of Thailand's Pak Mun hydro. But to do this, one needs to be able to distinguish between better dams and worse dams (Box 7). Indonesia's Saguling dam was lowered by 5 m to halve oustee numbers. 'Oustee' is a term meaning ousted people, such as people ousted by a reservoir. The term is used here because OED lists it (personal communication G. Goodland, 1994), it is readily understood and widely used, and there seems no better choice. The synonyms 'displaced person', displacee, and 'resettler' are less precise. 'Affected person' is a non-synonymous euphemism. The number of potential oustees is often the most important distinction between a better and a worse dam (Table 1; Goodland 1994).

But the project-specific EA could not make the case that alternatives to the proposed hydro (*e.g.*, gas, wind or solar) could possibly be less costly overall. These consideration have led governments and development agencies to adopt "Sectoral EA" (Goodland & Tillman 1995). SEA environmentally scrutinises the whole sector as part of the least cost analysis. Least cost sequencing now should integrate the conventional economic least cost criteria with social and environmental criteria (Oud & Muir 1997). This is easy to do reliably at the first approximation (Box 7 and Table 1). All rehabilitation and expansion of existing dams should be substantially completed before new dams are started. As this is almost always achieved at much less environmental and economic cost than construction of new dams, it should routinely be part of the least cost analysis. SEA, related to analysis of alternatives, ensures that the subsequent project-level EA is quick, cheap and reliable.

## 4. Involuntary resettlement

Opponents and proponents agree that involuntary resettlement must and can be improved. Because resettlement is such an inescapable companion of infrastructure development, and as the world has changed from being relatively empty of people at World War II to one full or overfull but still filling fast, involuntary resettlement and its impacts on people in general have become the most contentious of all socio-environmental issues of dams. Adverse social impacts of big dams have been seri-

*Box 7.* How to distinguish better dams from worse.

The first approximation coarse environmental/social screening and ranking of potential hydro dam sites: This is the first step of the Sectoral Environmental Assessment (SEA). SEA integrates environmental and social impacts into conventional least-cost sequencing.

Opponents and those seeking to improve dams claim that a reliable first approximation to distinguish between 'better' dams and 'worse' are two simple and robust proxies. First, the number of oustees, and second, the size (area) lost, filling the reservoir. These two figures suffice to rank, crudely but reliably, most sites. A second approximation disaggregates these two numbers on further criteria. After these two, the next ranking should include downstream impacts, including the number of affected families, length of river dewatered (or altered regime), fish migrations, and minimum dry season release regime (Gillilan & Brown 1997).

**1. Social Rank**

*Number of oustees*
Oustees per MW produced electricity ranking (Table 1). There is huge scope for taking up projects with zero or very few oustees. Disaggregate type of oustee by proportion with land and dwelling lost, land lost but not dwelling, and partial losses. Rural oustees weigh more than urban. Is replacement land readily or scarcely available? The World Bank endorses the notion that it should be possible to resettle oustees successfully (World Bank 1994a). As this has rarely been the historical experience, this number needs to be stringently minimized in all future projects

*Vulnerable ethnic minorities*
Proportion of affected people in this category as they are extremely difficult to relocate adequately. There is a case that involuntary resettlement of such people has never been successful, so the project should not go ahead. The recent extension of the Bank's policy on vulnerable ethnic minorities to less vulnerable minorities may not best serve truly vulnerable societies.

**2. Environmental Rank**

*Intact habitat lost*
The size of the flooded area is the single most relevant proxy for environmental impact, yet proponents of dams rarely calculate it in advance and is difficult or impossible to ascertain from dam publications. Historically, reservoir area has not been accorded great importance by dam proponents. Area flooded per MW ratio (Table 1) shows how much scope there is for selecting projects with little or no reservoir (those in uninhabited rocky canyons), run-of-river, or outstream diversions to reduce impacts. Generally, moist forest contains more biodiversity than dry ecosystems. Intact ecosystems are more valuable than agriculturally modified agro-ecosystems or barren landscapes. Largely captured in the kilowatts per hectare ranking. If part of the 'land lost' is a National Park or other conservation unit, that would weigh much heavier in the ranking.

**3. Conclusion**

If projects are ranked on such social, environmental and downstream criteria, and if only projects with good scores are considered further, impacts will be significantly less than in the past when Environmental Assessment started after a project was identified.

*Table 1.* Rank of hydropower generated: Following the two proxies of number of oustees and area of reservoir.

| Country | Project Name | Mega Watt (MW) | Reservoir area (ha) | Oustees | Reservoir area per MW | Oustees per MW |
|---|---|---|---|---|---|---|
| China | Three Gorges | 18,200 | 110,000 | 1,300,000 | 6 | 71 |
| Brazil/Paraguay | Itaipu | 12,600 | 135,000 | 59,000 | 11 | 5 |
| Venezuela | Guri Complex | 10,300 | 426,000 | 1,500 | 41 | 0 |
| Brazil | Tucurui | 7,600 | 243,000 | 30,000 | 32 | 4 |
| US | Grand Coulee | 6,494 | 33,306 | 10,000 | 5 | 2 |
| Canada | Churchill Falls | 5,225 | 665,000 | 0 | 127 | 0 |
| Pakistan | Tarbela | 3,478 | 24,280 | 96,000 | 7 | 28 |
| China | Ertan | 3,300 | 10,100 | 30,000 | 3 | 9 |
| Brazil | Ilha Solteira | 3,200 | 125,700 | 6,150 | 39 | 2 |
| Argentina/Paraguay | Yacyreta | 2,700 | 172,000 | 50,000 | 64 | 19 |
| Turkey | Ataturk | 2,400 | 81,700 | 55,000 | 34 | 23 |
| Malaysia | Bakun | 2,400 | 70,000 | 9,000 | 29 | 4 |
| India | Tehri | 2,400 | 4,200 | 100,000 | 2 | 42 |
| Egypt | Aswan High | 2,100 | 400,000 | 100,000 | 191 | 48 |
| Mozambique | Cabora Bassa | 2,075 | 380,000 | 250,000 | 183 | 120 |
| Pakistan | Ghazi Barotha | 1,450 | 2,640 | 899 | 2 | 1 |
| Brazil | Sobradinho | 1,050 | 415,000 | 65,000 | 395 | 62 |
| India | Narmada Sagar | 1,000 | 90,820 | 80,500 | 91 | 81 |
| Pakistan | Mangla | 1,000 | 25,300 | 90,000 | 25 | 90 |
| Ghana | Akosombo/Volta | 833 | 848,200 | 80,000 | 1,018 | 96 |
| Nigeria | Kainji | 760 | 126,000 | 50,000 | 166 | 66 |
| Laos | Nam Theun 2 | 600 | 34,000 | 4,500 | 57 | 8 |
| Chile | Pehuenche | 500 | 400 | 10 | 1 | 0 |
| Nepal | Arun III | 402 | 43 | 775 | 0 | 2 |
| Thailand | Khao Laem | 300 | 38,800 | 10,800 | 129 | 36 |
| Brazil | Balbina | 250 | 236,000 | 1,000 | 944 | 4 |
| Sri Lanka | Victoria | 210 | 2,270 | 45,000 | 11 | 214 |
| Laos | Nam Theun-Hinboun | 210 | 630 | 0 | 3 | 0 |
| Laos | Nam Ngum | 150 | 37,000 | 3,000 | 247 | 20 |
| Thailand | Pak Mun | 102 | 6,000 | 4,945 | 176 | 60 |
| Indonesia | Kedung Ombo | 29 | 4,600 | 29,000 | 159 | 1,000 |
| Burkina Faso | Kompienga | 14 | 20,000 | 1,842 | 1,426 | 132 |

ously underestimated (Scudder 1990, 1993, 1994, 1997), and this is nearly always the case, not the exception. Open-cast coal mines, ash disposal sites, and mine drainage ponds also displace thousands of people, and displace more as the project operates through the years. Reservoirs displace millions of people, but only before operation, so the number of affected people does not increase with time. Reduction of downstream agricultural productivity, or harm to recession agriculture (*e.g.,* Zambezi) also increases displacement of people.

Until recently, many social costs of dams were externalised. Violence, bloodshed and murders are reported in many controversial dams, which are deplored by proponents and opponents alike. But human rights violations bolster the case of dam opponents. Violence is socially regressive as it penalises the poor more than the rich, as noted earlier. The world-wide, sad record of involuntary resettlement, since it was started on any scale after World War II, is well documented by the World Bank (1994a). Recent years have seen a world-wide struggle to internalise the environmental and social costs of power development; numbers of people involved are staggering and increasing. Involuntary resettlement must be perceived as a grand opportunity to help the poor, not as a constraint, to providing more power (Goodland 1994).

Thus there are at least four important goals for that resettlement that cannot be avoided: (1) Oustees must be no worse off during the move; (2) Promptness of the move itself; (3) Immediately better off in a material sense after the move; (4) Opportunities to develop as well as non-moved neighbours. This has recently become official policy in, for instance, China Laos, and Brazil, but not yet in development agencies. The International Commission Of Large Dams (ICOLD), the world's main dam proponent, has recently adopted an improved policy: *"Resettlement must result in a clear improvement of their living standards because people directly affected by a project should always be the first to benefit instead of suffering for the benefit of others"* (ICOLD 1997). ICOLD thus wants oustees to be better off ('clear improvement in living standards') and this goal shall be extended to direct project-affected people.

Proponents and opponents agree that involuntary resettlement can be avoided. Wherever possible, project sites should be selected such that involuntary resettlement is not needed. This emphasises the paramountcy of sectoral EAs to select the best projects, the ones with no or very little involuntary resettlement. Oustees should be the foremost beneficiaries of any project that forces their involuntary resettlement. Projects should be designed with resettlers' needs in mind, especially jobs.

## 5. Irrigation dams

Food consumption is more important than electricity consumption. Food production has much less choice than does power supply. Electricity supply is improving; food consumption is unsatisfactory and worsening. Irrigation dams are far more problematic environmentally than hydroelectricity dams. Irrigation is usually in flat, highly populated and fertile plains. Thus such dams displace many people, lose valuable topsoil, are shallow, large in surface area and sluggish in water renewal. Hydro is almost the opposite: the best are small, deep reservoirs in unpopulated mountain canyons with high hydraulic head and fast turnover or less retention time. As the surface area of the reservoir is the main surrogate for impacts, irrigation reservoirs *a priori* usually cause more impacts than hydro-reservoirs, although with much overlap. Multipurpose reservoirs are in between those two poles, but are still ill-defined. Usually, they are mainly single purpose, but with one or more firmly subsidiary purposes as add-ons. It is rare for a reservoir to be equally for electricity, irrigation and flood control. As mentioned, there are many exceptions. Some irrigation reservoirs are in canyons above the irrigated plains below. For example, Pakistan's giant Bakhra dam on the Sutlej is in a mountainous gorge, but feeds irrigation water to the Indus plains below. It has been unexpectedly difficult to obtain 'area flooded' by reservoirs as it is not commonly provided in the literature. This suggests that area flooded has not been important to proponents. Similarly with oustees, their numbers just are not known for earlier projects. Proponents should be required to count oustees well in advance and to provide reasonable estimates of area lost to flooding also well in advance.

Hydro has problems admittedly, but clear alternatives are already available. There are few alternatives to providing more water to crop roots. In addition, although both are essential, hydroelectricity is arguably less important than food production for poverty alleviation and to feed burgeoning world populations. Water is often the limiting factor in crop yield, so there is no alternative, short of increasing rainfall, except to supply more water to the crop. Irrigation is essential. Already it produces 36% of the world's food from 16% of the world's surface area. Because irrigation has such problems, irrigated area per capita has stagnated over the last 40 years. The most significant criterion from the environmental impact point of view is the choice of how to get the water to the crop roots. The conventional choice, big irrigation dams, can impose the highest impact. Most alternatives to big storage dams are lower in impact.

Just as for electricity, increases in food supply should always be accompanied by demand-side management. In this context, demand-management means: (a) reduction in water use per unit of output, or improving efficiency of water use; (b) improving the efficiency of food use, eating efficient, low impact foods, and decreasing the use of inefficient, high impact foods. This translates first into pricing. Water already is scarce world wide, and getting scarcer. Not paying the long run marginal cost of producing the water encourages waste. This aspect has garnered political support in the last few years. Water is not an economic commodity like any other. Although it has been a struggle to price water, political will is changing in the right direction.

World population exceeded 6 bn in 1999. Demand side management for food must include population control. Just as prudent developers would not invest in increased electricity supply until electricity demand side management is well in hand, so with food production. Without population control, there is no way the world can keep up with food demand. Population is stabilising in industrial countries, where the average growth has fallen to 0.3% per year. About 30 nations have achieved population stability. However, as developing countries grow at 1.7% per year, 80 million new consumers need feeding every year.

The world's population is expected reach 9.4 bn within 50 years according to UN projections. Developers are not yet in the position to refuse support to countries where population growth is very high, nor should they. However, the prudent course might be to link development assistance for food production with progress on maternal health and family planning in high population growth countries.

As a result, the world is in a race between environmental conservation and population stabilisation. How much environmental function will the world retain when the population finally stabilises? How much of the world will be pre-empted by the single human species, and how much should be left for the millions of non-human species? Historically, most environmental costs of food production have been created by rich overconsuming nations. In the future, increased food demand is expected to come from underconsuming developing countries.

After water pricing and population stability, the other main areas of food demand management are production efficiency and intensification. Can foods be produced which have low impacts, high equity, needing less water and agricultural chemicals, and which yield more from smaller areas? Conversely, can high impact, inefficient low-yielding foods, which consume much water, be taxed to internalise the environmental costs they create? The key here is to move down the food-chain, from mammalian meat and poultry, to less resource consumptive foods (Goodland, 1997e). If the full costs of grain-fed livestock were incorporated into the price, much less meat would be consumed. Continuing to externalise such costs means that the poor are subsidising the rich. Efficiency and equity mean emphasising grains/legumes, while reducing livestock promotion. The International Nutrition "Wheat vs. Meat" Congress and China's "Pork vs. Soy" debate (Geissler 1999) attest that food efficiency is being taken seriously. Overconsumption of food in rich nations already has caused degenerative diseases (*e.g.*, heart disease and cancers) to overtake communicable diseases as the major cause of death and disability. Promoting efficiency in food production tends to decrease both overconsumption by the affluent, as well as malnutrition of the poor.

Environmental sustainability mandates intensification of food production, rather than extensification. Extensification means appropriating even more of the world's dwindling natural capital (environmental function or habitat) to human use. There are compelling reasons why marginal lands have been left uncultivated until now (Goodland 1998e). In addition, the scope of extensification is small. Most new land is so erosion-prone, infertile, or arid that yields will be smaller on new lands.

The most important source of food by a long way is rainfed agriculture. Before resorting to high impact irrigation dams, rainfed agriculture could be improved at lower environmental cost. Growing water-efficient crops, mulching, drought-proofing, terracing, contour bunding, inter-cropping, agroforestry, home-gardens and similar improvements in rain-fed agriculture can increase yields at lower environmental cost (Postel 1998). This is not to say that rainfed agriculture can boost yields as much as irrigation can. But in view of rising environmental and social costs of irrigation, rainfed productivity becomes more important.

With all its problems (*e.g.*, eutrophication, fertilizer residue build-up, need for pest control, nitrate pollution, mono-cropping and soil compaction), intensification is the only opportunity humanity has not yet foreclosed. All forms of intensification should be addressed, not only provision of more water. However, the main aspect of intensification of deep concern to food production and centrally relevant here is the future role of irrigation dams. As emphasised for hydro, the rehabilitation of existing irrigation schemes is the priority, long before new irrigation dams are contemplated.

Next, all forms of removing water constraints should be addressed. Big irrigation dams must not be the automatic response to food demand. As a full 80% of all fresh water is allocated to the agriculture sector, this is one of the most severe global issues of our times. The first focus of irrigation is best diverted away from large storage reservoirs, and onto annually replenished groundwater. Fossil groundwater abstraction in excess of replenishment clearly cannot meet any sustainability test. Evaluation of water mining projects should be subjected to El Serafy's rule of quasi-sustainability for non-renewable resources (Goodland & El Serafy 1998). Fossil water is being mined world-wide. Water tables are falling fast in many areas; in India by 1-3 m annually and in China by 1.5 m. An increasing number of rivers have ceased flowing into the ocean for much of the dry season as so much is abstracted. Essentially no fresh water is released to the sea during a large portion of the dry season by the Ganges, most rivers in India, the Yellow river, the Chao Phraya, the Nile and the Colorado rivers. Sea water extends further up rivers hampering yields. Industrial and domestic water demands usually outcompete agricultural use.

Measures to foster annual replenishment of aquifers are feasible, but are not implemented widely. Watershed conservation works. Measures to recharge aquifers are feasible in many areas. Tubewell irrigation (circa $1000 per ha) is often one third the cost of surface gravity irrigation and twice as productive.

There are vast efficiency gains to be obtained in irrigation. "Doing more with less" is usually the most cost effective approach to irrigation, rather than building new dams. The new low-energy precision application by sprinklers can achieve 95% efficiency when well managed. With efficiency gains well in hand, the scope for major expansion of irrigated area at acceptable environmental and social cost could next be considered. However, the best projections are for continued stagnation in irrigated area/capita into the middle of the next century. Can many small check dams in rivers prolong dry season water to postpone the need for a big storage reservoir? What is the potential for farm ponds, "tanks" such as used in Sri Lanka for millennia? Just as in hydro, the potential for small-scale irrigation holds much promise which should be evaluated before recourse to large reservoirs. The conjunctive use of water (groundwater and reservoir water) to prevent salination and water logging are well known but not effectively implemented. If, having exploited all possible alternatives, a big irrigation dam is felt needed, the problems will probably exceed those of a comparable hydro dam. If dams in general are under threat, irrigation dams *a priori* result in greater environmental impacts than hydro dams. The environmental rank of irrigation methods can be summarised as:

**Lowest impact**: Seepage *vs.* Drip or Trickle *vs.* Spray *vs.* Flood: **Greatest impact**

### 6. Greenhouse gas emission damage costs

Why is greenhouse gas (GHG) important in economic development and the energy sector? There is general agreement that the main GHG, carbon dioxide ($CO_2$) has been accumulating in the atmosphere. It's now more than 30% higher than it was a century ago. GHG traps solar heat; the world is getting hotter and the climate is changing, mainly in damaging and expensive ways. 1998 broke the global temperature record by almost half a degree Fahrenheit, which in climate terms is a huge leap. 1997 was the next hottest year on record. The six hottest years since record keeping began in 1866 were all in the 1990s. The 15 hottest years have all been since 1979. Glaciers and icecaps are melting; Antarctica's sea ice is shrinking; sea levels are rising. Insurance premia for climate-related damage are at an all-time high. Forest fires in Indonesia, Amazonia and Central America were at an all time high in 1998. Limiting global warming to 2°C will require a 50% cut in GHG emissions. Total compliance with the December 1997 Kyoto Protocol, for industrial countries to cut collective GHG emissions to at least 5.2% below 1990 levels during the 2008-2012 period, will slow the rate of climate change only slightly. Full compliance with the Kyoto treaty would go less than 10% of the way needed to achieve a stabilised climate.

GHG emissions are very important for dam proponents, but until very recently have been totally ignored. Some dams generate significant amounts of GHG; most dams generate trivial amounts of GHG compared with a coal-fired alternative. Therefore, dam generated GHG analysis should make dams look much more attractive. Dam GHG analysis should become standard operating procedure in all dam feasibility work.

There are about 437 nuclear power plants operating in 1997, and an additional 36 under construction. As closure of nuclear energy plants vastly exceeds new plants, this increases GHG production. When oil topped $40 per bbl in the late 1970s, the future of the nuclear industry looked brighter. The last order for a US nuclear plant was in 1978, and three were shut down in 1998. Deregulation throughout many power sectors lowers the price of electricity; this makes nuclear electricity even less competitive. Oil is now $12 per bbl and may fall further. The GHG case for promoting atomic energy is weak. New gas-fired cogeneration/combined cycle plants are financially loss costly, environmentally and socially less risky, and roughly comparable on GHG balance, depending on how much cost is permitted to be externalised.

Most GHG production from water projects is generated from decay of flooded biomass (soil organic matter, peat, roots and vegetation). This biomass varies greatly from grassland to forest, so the amount which will eventually rot when inundated differs markedly from project to project. The usually very minor source of dam generated GHG comes from the cement and steel used in construction. GHGs emitted from the manufacture of the dam's cement and steel, plus the construction energy, are less than 10% of the $CO_2$ avoidance achieved in the first year of generation, compared with a fossil-fuelled equivalent (Oud 1993, Rosa & Schaeffer 1994, 1995, Rudd *et al.* 1993).

The world derives about two thirds of its commercial energy from fossil fuels, of which two thirds is from coal. About half of GHG is $CO_2$; most $CO_2$ (80%) is energy related, and emissions now reach 22 bn tonnes of $CO_2$ annually. Electric power generation world-wide contributes 25% of GHG, mainly from coal. Because there is so much coal available world-wide, possibly 236 years at current consumption levels, there is scant prospect for an impending fuel scarcity that would send the kind of price signal needed to phase down coal. And because developing countries persistently experience capital shortages, they are less likely to opt for higher cost technologies (*e.g.*, solar) on their own. While natural gas produces much more energy with less GHG during generation, leakage from pipelines make gas almost as polluting as coal in some countries. As there are only about 40 years of oil and 56 years of gas left at current depletion rates, coal is by far the most important fossil fuel to control. Modernisation of captive fossil fuel plant can reduce GHG by a huge 30%, so is a substantial part of the solution. Proponents claim there is about five times as much proven potential hydro still available as is used today, about the equivalent of today's annual oil production. The need is to accelerate the transition away from GHG production, mainly coal, and towards hydro and other renewables. GHG emissions of developing countries is now (1999) overtaking GHG emissions from industrialised countries. Agonising trade-offs are being faced in many countries between massive increases in coal burning on the one hand, and the world's biggest dams, China's Three Gorges and India's Narmada dams, on the other.

China's Three Gorges multipurpose project is projected to generate 84,000 GWh, which is the equivalent of annually burning 40 million tons of local coal (based on 1 tonne = about 2100 kWh). The health and environmental effects of burning that amount of coal can be estimated. If the expected deaths from the next 100-year flood are regrettably allowed to occur, presumably Three Gorges will sail ahead. One has to balance the tradeoffs. If over 1 million oustees can be made better off in that overpopulated nation, given China's political will, surely avoiding the burning of 40 million tons of coal annually is preferable? Such comparisons need to be made systematically and transparently by proponents and opponents alike.

Proponents and opponents alike have big stakes in the rate at which GHG is internalised in cost benefit analysis throughout the energy sector. If the hydro industry insists on a level playing field and on good economics, GHG will be internalised sooner and the transition to hydro and other renewable recourses will accelerate. Ironic reluctance to internalise dam externalities (*e.g.*, involuntary resettlement) has led, in part, to a decline in dams. On the other hand, because there is less pressure to internalise coal's even more severe externalities (*e.g.*, involuntary resettlement and $CO_2$), coal use is increasing, still with many costs externalised.

## 7. The future of dams

Fossil fuelled competitors to hydroelectricity are winning, both in political image and in price. Coal's average price has dropped from $40 per tonne to $16 per tonne between 1980 and 1996 due to cheap strip-mined coal from Wyoming selling for $6 per tonne, and similarly-priced strip-mined Australian and Sumatran coal. The relatively stable price of oil does not seem to signal impending scarcity. Weakening economies in Japan, China and the former Soviet Union, as well as the Asian, and Latin American economic recessions, suggests demand for energy may remain low for some years. This tends to postpone capital intensive energy (nuclear, hydro) and promote low capital intensive plant (combined cycle gas). Thus the outlook for much new hydro does not look promising at least for the next few years, and possibly longer. Of course, all that will change the moment we have an expensive GHG-related catastrophe, and decide to get serious about GHG emissions.

Non-fossil technologies proceed apace, such as the hypercars now being introduced by many major automakers, which achieve >60 miles per gallon (mpg) (Hawken *et al*. 1999, http://www.rmi.org). At least five automakers plan to be mass-producing 80 mpg cars by the end of 1999. Transportation improvements are imperative because the fuel efficiency of the US fleet has declined since 1987 as people buy vans and utility vehicles for personal use. US transportation GHG emissions in 1997 were 10% higher than in 1990 and still rising. Gasoline taxes equivalent to $1000 per tonne of carbon still have not reduced Parisian congestion. American's reject gas tax, and one theory has it that the US went to war in 1991 to prevent Iraq from cornering Persian Gulf oil. Hydrogen-battery combinations seem a good bet for future transportation. This will boost solar hydrogen generation, and to a less extent hydroelectricity. Much of the uncertainty devolves on the rate of political internalisation of GHG risks.

Japanese, European and American solar roofing tiles, and solar windows mean many dwellings can cease being net users of grid electricity within two years or so (Hawken *et al*. 1999). Accelerating advances in both demand- and supply-side technologies will inexorably curb the demand for fossil-fuels. While it is becoming generally accepted that the world cannot afford to burn the 300 years of coal left in the ground, now it looks as if we may not even need to run dry the world's 60 years of oil. Getting serious about climate change would accelerate these encouraging trends towards renewables.

Technological pessimists note that water consumption per person is rising twice as fast as population growth, and today's 6 bn population will double in the next 50-90 years. Eight billion people will face water shortages by 2025. The world's impending water crisis demands population control, water conservation, less pollution into to water courses, and prudent management of supply and demand. Recent sources are Postel (1998), UNESCO (1998) and "Solutions for a watershort world" in: http://www.jhuccp.org/popreport/m14edsum.stm and http://www.lboro.ac.uk/departments/cv/wedc/dl.htm.

How will the Subcontinent share water when water tables are falling fast? The Middle East's shared and shrinking water supply already heightens tensions. What happens to Egypt, dependant for 85% of its water from the Nile, when Ethiopia's population doubles? How will China react now that 300 major cities face grave water shortages? By 2050 half of the world will have insufficient water. More than 40% or the world could face either water stress (< 1700 cubic meter per capita), or scarcity (<1000 cubic meter per capita).

The prospects for irrigation, by far the biggest water consumer, are not encouraging. Aquifer depletion especially in India and China, many rivers running dry before they reach the ocean, losses from soil erosion, compaction, salination and water logging mean land is removed from irrigation at a rate approaching that at which new irrigation land is developed. While there are good prospects for boosting efficiencies and decreasing irrigation losses, most food must come from rain-fed lands without big storage dams.

The most encouraging achievement is the creation of the World Commission on Dams (WCD) following the broad stakeholder consensus reached in Gland, Switzerland in 1997 (Goodland 1997b, www.dams.org). This Commission is devising guidelines, criteria and polices to choose the best option among alternatives, whether that includes a dam or not. Where a dam is seen as the best option, WCDs work will help ensure that it becomes sustainable. Much hinges on their deliberations. Worsening climate changes intensified by fossil-fuelled greenhouse gas emissions will also make their findings politically palatable and promptly implemented. If the climate for food production worsens, water supplies for agriculture will become much more important.

## 8. Conclusion

The vision for dams is that they should support economic and social progress, as well as becoming environmentally sustainable just as soon as possible. The vision is for the best and sustainable dams to become an interim stopgap measure on the transition to other renewables. The phase down of coal to oil to gas and hydro with other renewables needs to be accelerated. The transition to sustainability is urgent. The needed 50% cut in greenhouse emissions is impossible without a prompt and major shift to hydro and other renewables. Making dams sustainable, the goal of this paper, will not be easy; sustainable dams will be fewer in number than at the apogee of dam building, and possibly smaller in size. But they will be much less costly socially and environmentally in the short and long runs.

## Acknowledgements

For their helpful comments on earlier drafts, I offer warm thanks to E. Oud, S. Postel, T. Scudder and J. Veltrop.

## References

Collier, M., Webb, R. and Schmidt, J. 1996. Dams and rivers: primer on downstream effects of dams. Circular 1126, US Geological Survey, Washington DC.

Geissler, C. 1999. China: the soya-pork dilemma. Proc. Int. Nutrition Soc. Congress Wheat or Meat for the Next Millennium? CAB Press, London.

Gillilan, D.M. & Brown, T.C. 1997. Instream flow protection. Island Press, Washington DC.

Goldsmith, E. & Hildyard, N. 1984-1991. Social and environmental effects of large dams. Volumes 1, 2 and 3. Ecological Centre, Wadebridge.

Goodland, R.J.A. 1994. Ethical priorities in environmentally sustainable energy systems. Env. WP 67. World Bank, Washington DC.

Goodland, R.J.A. 1995a. The environmental sustainability challenge for the hydro industry. Hydropower and Dams 1: 37-42.

Goodland, R.J.A. 1995b. The concept of environmental sustainability. Ann. Rev. Ecology 26: 1-24.

Goodland, R.J.A. 1997a. The big dams debate: the environmental sustainability challenge for dam engineers. The 1996 Freeman Lecture Boston. J. Society Civil Engineers/ASCE 12/2: 11-32.

Goodland, R.J.A. 1997b. Environmental sustainability in the hydro industry: Disaggregating the debates. In: Dorcey, T. (Ed.). Large Dams: Learning from the past, looking at the future. IUCN/World Bank, Washington DC. pp. 69-102.

Goodland, R.J.A. 1997c. Environmental sustainability in water projects: recent trends. House of Representatives, Diet Members Association for Public Works Review, Tokyo.

Goodland, R.J.A. 1997d. Environmental sustainability for civil engineering. Mexico. Nat. Civ. .Eng. Congress.

Goodland, R.J.A. 1997e. Agricultural sustainability: diet matters. Ecological Economics 23: 198-200.

Goodland, R.J.A. & Daly, H.E. 1996. Environmental sustainability: universal and non-negotiable. Ecological Applications 6/4: 1002-1017.

Goodland, R.J.A. & El Serafy, S. 1998. The urgent need to internalize $CO_2$ emission costs. Ecological Economics 27: 79-90.

Goodland, R.J.A. & Mercier J-R. 1999. The evolution of environmental assessment in the World Bank: from "approval" to results. Environment Department Papers 67. World Bank, Washington DC.

Goodland, R.J.A. & Tillman, G. 1995. Strategic environmental assessment. Shell International Environment Paper, The Hague.

Goodland, R.J.A. & Webb. M. 1989. The management of cultural property. TP 62. World Bank, Washington DC.

Hawken, P., Lovins, A, & Lovins, H. 1999. Natural capitalism: creating the next industrial revolution. Little Brown, New York.

Horowitz, M.M. 1994. The management of an African river basin: alternative scenarios for environmentally sustainable economic development and poverty alleviation. Inst. for Dev. Anthropology: IV73-IV82. Proc. Int. Conf. Water Resources Planning in a Changing World.

Horowitz, M.M. 1991. Victims upstream and down. J. Refugee Studies 4/2: 164-181.

Hunter, J., Rey, L., Chu, K., Adekolu-John, E. & Mott, K. 1993. Parasitic diseases in water resources development: the need for intersectoral negotiation. World Health Organization, Geneva. .

ICOLD, 1997. Position paper on dams and environment. International Committee on Large Dams.

Leentvaar, J, & Glas, P.C.G. 2000. A policy analysis for the upper Danube river section in Hungary. In: Smits, A.J.M., Nienhuis, P.H. & Leuven, R.S.E.W. (Eds). New approaches to river management. Backhuys Publishers, Leiden. pp. 249-266.

McCully, P. 1996. Silenced rivers: the ecology and politics of large dams. Zed Books, London.

McCully, P. 1997. The corrupt alliance between dam builders and the overseas development industry. International Rivers Network, Berkeley CA.

Morse, B. & Berger, T. 1992. Sardar Sarovar: Report to the Independent Commission. Resource Futures Int., Ottawa..

Narayan, D. 1995. The contribution of people's participation. Env. O.P. 1. The World Bank, Washington, D.C.

Oud, E. 1993. Global warming: a changing climate for hydro. Water Power and Dam Construction 45: 20-23.

Oud, E. & Muir, T. 1997. Engineering and economic aspects of planning, design, operation and construction of large dam projects. In: Dorcey (Ed.). Large Dams. IUCN/World Bank, Gland. pp. 17-40.

Pearce, F. 1992. The dammed: rivers, dams, and the coming world water crisis. Bodley Head, London.

Postel, S. 1998. Water for food production: will there be enough in 2025? BioScience 48/8: 629-637.

Rosa, L.P. & Schaeffer, R. 1994. Greenhouse gas emissions from hydroelectric reservoirs. Ambio 22/3: 164-165.

Rosa, L.P. & Schaeffer, R. 1995. Global warming potentials: the case of emissions from dams. Energy Policy 23/2: 149-159.

Rothert, S. 1995. Lessons unlearned: Damming the Mekong river. IRN Working Paper 6. International Rivers Network (IRN), Berkeley CA.

Rudd, J.W.M., Harris, R., Kelly, C.A. & Hecky, R.E. 1993. Are hydroelectric reservoirs significant sources of greenhouse gases? Ambio 22/4: 246-248.

Scudder, T. 1990. Victims of development revisited: the political costs of river basin development. Dev. Anthr. Network 8/1: 1-5.

Scudder, T.1993. Development-induced relocation: 37 years of change among Zambia's Gwembe Tonga. Journal of Refugee Studies 6/5: 123-152.

Scudder, T. 1994. Recent experiences with river basin development in the tropics and subtropics. Nat. Res. Forum 18/2: 101-113.

Scudder, T. 1997. The social impacts of big dams. In: Dorcey, T. (Ed.). Large Dams. IUCN/World Bank, Gland. pp. 41-68.

Sklar, L. and McCully, P. 1994. Damming the rivers: the World Bank's lending for large dams. WP 5. International Rivers Network, Berkeley CA.

UNESCO. 1998. The real price of water. Sources 101: 4-8.

World Bank. 1991. Environmental Assessment Sourcebook Volumes 1, 2 and 3. Technical Paper. World Bank, Washington D.C.

World Bank. 1994a. Resettlement and development: a Bankwide review of projects involving involuntary resettlement. Environment Department World Bank, Washington D.C.

World Bank. 1994b. The World Bank and participation. Operations Policy Department World Bank, Washington D.C.

World Bank. 1996a. The World Bank's experience with large dams: a preliminary review of impacts. Operations Evaluation Department (SecM96-944) World Bank, Washington D.C.

World Bank. 1996b. Second review of environmental assessment. Volumes 1 and 2. Environment Department World Bank, Washington D.C.

World Bank. 1996c. Participation Sourcebook. World Bank, Washington D.C.

# FOLLOWING A DIVERSIFIED STRATEGY TO ACHIEVE THE SUSTAINABLE USE OF THE MEKONG RIVER BASIN

C.E. Hunt

*World Wildlife Fund – US, Freshwater Ecosystem Conservation, 1250 24th Street, NW Washington, DC 20037, The United States of America;*
*Present address: World Wide Fund for Nature, Living Waters Campaign, Boulevard 12, NL-3700 AA Zeist, The Netherlands*

## Abstract

This paper examines past and potential future development strategies for the Mekong river basin. Past development strategies have focused on the construction of large dams and other water resources infrastructure to achieve the objectives of hydroelectricity generation, expansion of irrigated agriculture, flood control and inland navigation. While such strategies may produce hard currency over the short term, they present considerable risk for the natural resources of the basin upon which most basin residents depend.

The hypothesis presented here is that if the development objectives are re-cast as meeting regional energy needs, increasing food production, reducing flood damages, and facilitating the transport of goods to and from markets, a wider range of alternative strategies and technologies could be used to achieve development objectives. Arguably, the most important strategies for the Mekong basin overall would be energy systems based on small, decentralised energy sources and demand-side management, and food production strategies that are based largely on mixed agriculture systems, particularly in uplands. Such mixed agriculture systems, to the extent that they imitate the natural ecological structure of the forests, would contribute to reductions in flood damages and in the need for dredging to maintain navigability downstream. A development strategy for the Mekong river basin that is more diverse and relies on more modern technologies than earlier, dam-dependent strategies, could result in a more robust and sustainable regional economy while better protecting natural resources.

## 1. Introduction

Mekong river basin nations are striving to better position themselves in a global economy after decades of civil strife. Contemporary basin development plans (Asian Development Bank 1995, Compagnie Nationale du Rhone *et al.* 1994, Quang 2000) have evolved from development strategies based on large-scale, multipurpose dam construction conceptualised in the 1950s and 1960s. The current iterations of these designs are focused largely on the generation of hydroelectric power, much of which is intended for sale to Thailand. Other project purposes include the expansion of irrigated agriculture, flood control, and navigation.

Several factors have substantially changed the political environment since a dam-based development strategy was first proposed for the Mekong. Over the past four decades, developed nations have realised substantial and often unanticipated economic and ecological costs associated with dam construction and other structural alterations of river systems (see for example Hunt 2000). Over the past several years, research on fisheries in the Mekong river basin has revealed that the extent of the fisheries, in terms of both annual production and number of species, is much greater than was previously thought, and that the majority of Mekong basin communities rely heavily on wild-caught fish as a source of animal protein. Non-governmental organisations (NGOs) have organised and developed power bases in several of the Mekong basin countries. Finally, the Asian financial crisis in 1997 substantially slowed the rate of growth in the Mekong region in general and specifically in the Thai energy market. In light of these contextual changes, it seems appropriate to review current development strategies and assess the feasibility and desirability of altering or re-directing them.

Industrialised nations have exported industrial-scale technologies to the developing world for many decades. Industrial-scale technologies seek to mold the structure and function of existing landscapes and cultures to fit the means of mass production, rather than adjusting the means of production to fit the landscape and culture. The input-intensive agricultural technologies employed by the Green Revolution to produce commodity crops and the use of large, thermal plants to produce power are two examples of industrial approaches to development.

While such large-scale and indifferent approaches to development have produced substantial benefits, they are also associated with substantial costs. Industrial scale technologies often require virtually irretrievable commitments of resources and therefore have the effect of limiting future development options. They can impose considerable costs by disrupting existing social and ecological patterns and processes.

Development approaches that are designed to fit with local social and environmental conditions can avoid many of these potential problems. Such approaches rely on the integration of a variety of methods for achieving development objectives. Reliance on any single method of production can be increased or decreased in response to changing social preferences and environmental conditions.

To move from the industrial approach to development to the diversified approach in the Mekong river basin, it is useful to reframe development objectives. So long as the objectives of water resources development in the basin are considered to be hydropower generation, increases in irrigated farmland, flood control, and expansion of inland waterway navigation routes, the preferred technology for development will be dam construction. If development objectives are re-formulated as meeting regional energy demands, increasing food production, reducing flood damages and facilitating the transport of goods to and from markets, the range of options broadens considerably. Energy demands could be met using a combination of demand-side management, solar photovoltaic systems, wind mills, and natural gas in addition to or in place of additional hydropower generation. Food production could be increased through a combination of agro-forestry, fish/rice culture, and improved management of existing irrigation systems in addition to or in place of irrigation expansion. Flood damages could be reduced through a combination of watershed restoration and floodplain management in addition to or in place of flood control structures.

The objective of this paper is to provide a general overview of current water resources development objectives and plans for the Mekong river basin, discuss the potential negative costs associated with these plans, and investigate potential alternative strategies for regional economic development.

## 2. Development objectives

The primary objective of water resources development in most of the Mekong basin is the generation of hydropower. Hydropower generation is driving the plans for mainstream dams in Yunnan Province of China and Laos, as well as tributary development in Vietnam. Because of the prominence of power generation as a factor motivating basin development, the following discussion will focus on this objective. Other purposes of water resources development include the expansion of irrigated agriculture (particularly in Cambodia, Thailand and the Vietnam delta), flood control, and navigation expansion. Substantial structural works are also planned for the delta in Vietnam, primarily to combat saltwater intrusion.

Prior to the Asian economic crisis of 1997, the Asian Development Bank (ADB) estimated that 12,000 MW of new generation would be needed in the greater Mekong subregion between 1995 and 2003. The ADB defines the Greater Mekong Subregion as Cambodia, Laos, Myanmar, Thailand, Vietnam and the Yunnan Province of China. The greatest rate of growth has been in Thailand, which was experiencing a growth rate of about 1,000 MW per year (Figure 1). Thai base energy demand was estimated at over 411,000 GWh in the year 2020 (Asian Development Bank 1995).

A great deal of the dam construction that has been proposed for the Mekong river is intended to produce electricity for sale to Thailand. Roughly half of the hydropower potential in the lower Mekong river basin, 20,000 MW, is located in Laos, a country with few exportable commodities other than timber and hydropower.

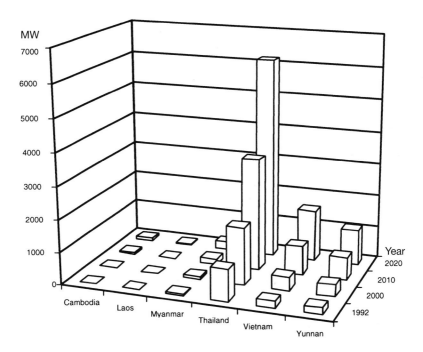

*Fig. 1.* Projected energy demands for Greater Mekong Subregion (MW). Data from Asian Development Bank (1995).

## 3. Current water resources development plans

The Mekong river basin nations (Figure 2) have an abundance of plans for water resources development in various stages of progress (Quang 2000). Some are at the very general level of basin studies, which assess the development potential of specific tributary watersheds. Others are blueprints for specific dams and are accompanied by detailed engineering and environmental assessment work. Some have been developed bilaterally; some are within the province of a single country. Despite the past efforts of the Mekong River Commission and the ADB, the myriad of plans for water resources development have not been assessed from a systematic perspective. Such a perspective would require consideration of the full range of hydrologic, social and economic impacts that implementing all or a subset of these plans would have on the region as a whole. In fact, basic economic, sociological and environmental data regarding the potential impacts of individual dam plans is lacking in many cases.

The "run-of-river" concept constitutes a revision of plans to construct large, multi-purpose dams on the lower Mekong river originally drawn up in the 1960s. Revised plans published by Compagnie Nationale du Rhone *et al.* (1994) aim to reduce environmental impacts by decreasing dam size and making hydropower generation the sole objective.

The objective of this study was to create an inventory of suitable projects that would avoid, to the extent practicable, environmental impacts, relocation of communities, inundation of agricultural land, and other adverse effects. Preliminary design concepts were developed for 10 sites that would create low steps on the river where electricity could be generated. Each dam would have a gated spillway, one or two powerhouses, and a navigation lock. All of the projects considered, with the exception of a project on the Tonle Sap in Cambodia, would be connected to the Thai energy system.

A "run-of-river" project is traditionally defined as one based on straight flow-through of water or minimal water storage. All 10 of the proposed "run-of-river" dams would increase water levels to some extent, ranging from a minimum increase of 5 meters in extremely high water levels at new Stung Treng to a maximum increase of 49 meters in minimum waters levels at Luang Prabang. The dam at Luang Prabang would maintain the operating pool level at 320 meters above mean sea level, or 46 meters above the current low water level and 26 meters above the high water levels. The dam would back up the Mekong mainstream for 200 kilometres.

### 3.1 Cambodia

The ADB estimated the exploitable hydropower potential in Cambodia at about 8,000 MW, including the mainstream "run-of-river" projects, Stung Treng and Sambor.

The exploitable hydropower of the Cambodian tributaries to the Mekong, including tributaries of the Tonle Sap, is estimated at around 1,200 MW installed capacity. The most significant projects proposed in Cambodia would be located in the Se San and Sre Pok rivers. Most of the proposed Cambodian dams would be low

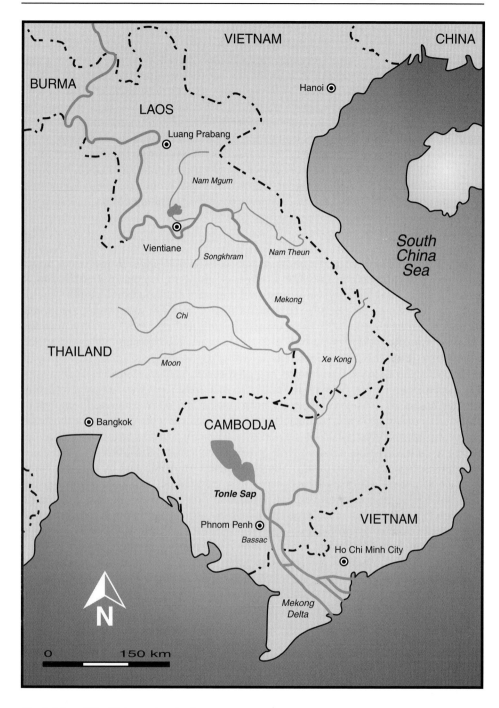

*Fig. 2.* Map of the Mekong river basin.

and impound shallow reservoirs, primarily for irrigation purposes. The ADB (1995) found that the inundation of large land areas, with the attendant environmental impacts and relocation requirements, would generally be out of proportion to the energy generated by these projects. ADB therefore characterised the proposed Cambodian tributary projects as multi-purpose with electricity generation as a side benefit.

Achieving the sustainable development of fisheries is another high priority for the Cambodian government, as fish contributes some 40 to 60 percent of the population's protein intake. Other objectives of water resources management in Cambodia include expanding irrigated acreage, with a focus on small systems; providing water supply and sanitation services to urban and rural areas; rehabilitating ports; and eliminating a backlog of maintenance dredging on inland waterways (General Directorate of Irrigation Meteorology and Hydrology 1996).

### 3.2 Laos

Laos has abundant water resources, but lacks the financial capital needed for water resources development. In the 1990s, however, the government of Laos began to consider harnessing private sector investment in dam construction through "Build-Own-Operate-Transfer" (BOOT) schemes. Under a "BOOT" agreement, the private sector builds the project with their own financing and operates, and manages the facility for a concessionary period of 25 to 30 years, after which ownership of the dam is transferred to the government.

In 1993, the Laotian government signed a memorandum of understanding with Thailand to export 1,500 MW of power by the year 2000. This was followed by a similar agreement in 1996 promising an additional 1,500 MW of Laotian energy to Thailand by 2006. In 1995, Laos also signed an agreement with Vietnam for the transfer of 1,500 to 2,000 MW of power by 2010. By 1995, Laos had signed 23 Memorandums of Understanding with private firms around the world to build dams with a total capacity of 6,676 MW. The government estimated that by the year 2000, receipts from royalties, taxes and proceeds from power sales would be worth approximately US$120 million and would constitute Laos' largest source of foreign exchange earnings. Since the Asian economic crisis of 1997, however, Thailand has decided to delay power purchases from Laos. Recent projections are that Laos will be selling around 467 MW to Thailand by the year 2000 (International Rivers Network 1999).

Laos has a number of hydropower dams in various stages of development (including Nam Theun 2, Nam Ngum 2 and 3, Xe Pian-Se Namnoi, Xe Kaman 1) and several that have been completed (including Nam Ngum 1, Nam Theun-Hinboun, Nam Leuk, and Houay Ho (Figure 3; International Rivers Network 1999).

In addition to producing hydroelectric power for export and for domestic consumption, objectives of water resources management in Laos include expansion of irrigated agriculture, and providing water supply to urban and rural populations (Rasphone *et al.* 1996).

### 3.3 Myanmar (Burma)

Only a small portion of Myanmar, the eastern tip of Shan State, is located within the Mekong river basin. The basin area within Myanmar covers an area of 24,000

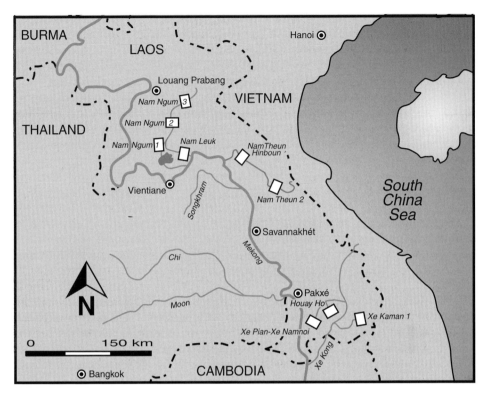

*Fig. 3.* Location of dams constructed or under development in Laos (Modified from International Rivers Network 1999).

square kilometres, or 3 percent of the total Mekong basin, and shares border with Yunnan Province, Laos and Thailand.

Thai and Myanmar authorities have discussed eight potential joint hydropower projects, including the 12.5 MW Nam Mae Sai and 294 MW Mae Kok projects. No definite construction schedules have been developed for these projects (Hirsch & Cheong 1996).

## 3.4 Thailand

Thailand contains an estimated installed capacity of 7,000 MW of which 2,429 MW had been installed as of 1992. An additional 516 MW were under construction or committed at that time and the Electrical Generating Authority of Thailand (EGAT) estimated that a further 186 MW of hydropower would be added to the system by 2001. Most of the proposed hydropower projects in Thailand include irrigation and flood control as objectives (Asian Development Bank 1995).

Investments in new hydropower generation in Thailand have slowed significantly since these projections were made. First, in 1994 EGAT launched a private power programme and invited private generating companies to submit bids to own and operate new plants and sell their output to EGAT. In response, EGAT received over

30 bids to supply 32,000 MW, which exceeds EGAT's projected expansion needs for at least the next 15 years. Many of these bids were for highly efficient combined cycle gas turbine plants, which could produce electricity for a lower cost than hydropower (International Rivers Network 1999). In 1997, Thailand was hit hard by the Asian economic crisis and EGAT was faced with rising costs, debts worth US$5 billion, excess generating capacity, declining electricity demand, and poor returns on its investments (Probe International 1999). Other factors, including growing public opposition to dam construction and increasing investment in energy efficiency, make it unlikely that Thailand will develop significant additional hydropower capacity in the near future.

### 3.5 Vietnam

Vietnam contains the mouth of the Mekong river and is therefore vulnerable to changing conditions in the basin upstream. Water resources development priorities for Vietnam including increasing water supply in the dry season, primarily for irrigation and prevention of salt water intrusion, and reducing flood damages in the wet season.

The ADB (1995) divided Vietnam's exploitable hydropower capacity into 21 potential projects. Plans earlier this decade were to construct hydropower plants in North-western Vietnam, to provide connections with transmission systems in Laos and allow for energy sales to Thailand. The Asian economic crisis has also led to downward revisions in energy demand projections in Vietnam, leaving the fate of many of these projects in question.

### 3.6 Yunnan Province

Yunnan Province Electric Power Bureau has planned 15 cascade hydropower projects on the Lancang, as the upper Mekong river is known in China. One project, Manwan, has been completed and another, Dachoashan, is under construction. Construction of two additional dams , Xiowan and Nuodhadu, is expected to begin soon. The construction of these four dams would flood over 2,300 hectares of farmland and require the resettlement of 52,000 people (Shisong & Zhe undated).

The dams in Yunnan Province will generate electricity for use in China and for sale to Thailand. Because the hydrological year in the Mekong subregion consists of a wet season and a dry season, dams with large reservoirs that can regulate electricity generation according to demand are preferred to "run-of-river" schemes. Most of the reservoirs planned for the Lancang would serve other purposes as well, such as flood control and navigation enhancement.

## 4. Potential adverse impacts of dam construction

The potential adverse impacts of dam construction include population resettlement, hydrologic disruptions, changes in sediment dynamics, reductions in water quality, saltwater intrusion into aquifers, inundation and fragmentation of wildlife habitat, and disruption of fisheries (Goodland 2000). Because of the importance of wild-caught fish in the diets of Mekong river basin residents, the discussion of potential impacts presented below focuses on fisheries disruption.

The Mekong river basin is globally outstanding in terms of its aquatic biodiversity and productivity. About 60 million people live in the lower Mekong river basin. Approximately 85 percent of this population are rural dwellers with a typical land holding of one or two hectares and a per capita income of US$186 to $400. Fish is the single most important source of animal protein in the diet of Mekong river basin communities, forming together with rice the basis of food security. The average per capita consumption of fish is not less than 20 kilograms of fish per year. In areas closer to the Tonle Sap in Cambodia, per capita fish consumption of 60 to 70 kilograms per year have been registered. Most other animal products from low-income, rural households such as chicken and pigs are raised for cash income. Total production from capture fisheries alone amounts to at least one million tonnes, giving a total estimated value of annual fish production of US$750-800 million. Retail market value based on US$ 0.75 per kg. Aquaculture production is considerably less, at around 200,000 tonnes per year (Jensen 1999).

The Mekong river basin supports an estimated 1,300 species, and knowledge of their life histories and migratory patterns is sparse (Mekong river Commission Secretariat 1999). It is certain, however, that fish production in the Mekong river and its tributaries is highly dependent on the occurrence of a wide range of processes (sediment and nutrient transport and flow regimes, for example) and habitats.

Fish species with longitudinal migrations normally begin to spawn in the Mekong river at the beginning of the rainy season (May-June), when the first flood waters are coming in and water levels are starting to rise again. Fish eggs and fry are carried by the currents and swept into the floodplain areas that are being inundated. Synchronisation in the arrival of the first floods and the spawning process may be crucial. The filling of hydropower storage will cause delays in the patterns of flooding and diminish it. It may disrupt this cycle and lead to a decrease or failure in recruitment and a decline of the migratory fish stocks, especially of the longitudinal migrants, which constitute about 63 percent of the total catch taken in the Tonle Sap area (Van Zalinge *et al.* 1998). Investigations supported by non-governmental organisations operating in the Mekong river basin suggest that declines in fisheries have already occurred in response to the construction and operation of hydropower dams on tributaries in Laos (International Rivers Network 1999, Shoemaker 1998).

## 5. Alternatives

The challenge facing Mekong river basin managers, as in other river basins around the world, is to develop an integrated strategy for basin management. Such a strategy would consider the often conflicting demands of various subsectors in the basin as the components of a sort of Rubik's cube and investigate various alternatives for satisfying these demands until a harmonious pattern emerges that optimises uses of the available resources. The following discussion presents alternatives for the energy and agriculture sectors that could fit into such an optimisation strategy for the basin.

## 5.1 Demand side management in the energy sector

Demand side management has the potential to reduce the need for hydropower generation particularly in Thailand, Vietnam and Yunnan Province. Preliminary estimates indicate that the hydroelectric projects listed in the Asian Development Bank's subregional energy study and the Mekong River Commissions proposed "run-of-river" dams, in addition to ADB estimates of natural gas potential and existing regional energy resources, would provide an installed capacity of 91,082 MW before the year 2020. These estimates do not include complete fossil fuel data or estimates of non-hydropower renewable energy resources. Regional energy demand in 2020 is estimated at 64,102 to 128,106 MW (Asian Development Bank 1995). Therefore, planned hydropower development is in the ballpark for supplying forecasted energy demands without taking other renewable energy sources (solar, wind, and geothermal for example) and demand side management into account. These figures indicate that investments in source substitution and demand side management could be used to supplant some of the proposed hydropower developments.

Two of the Mekong river basin countries with the most rapid growth in power demands, China and Thailand, have invested in demand side management and have the potential for significantly expanding these programmes. As of 1992, the Gross National Product (GNP) generated per ton of coal equivalent in China was 15 to 30 percent that of industrialised countries, while the unit energy consumption for major industrial products is 30 to 90 percent higher than in industrialised countries (Long-Hai & Lu-Jun 1992). In Thailand, the energy intensity of GNP has risen by 15 percent since 1982. Low energy efficiency is widespread across all sectors of the economy in the region, depleting scarce financial and economic resources (Ramani1992).

China began a large-scale energy efficiency programme in 1980 by directing about 10 percent of its energy investment to improve energy use in minor industries. Since then, energy conservation has become a priority for all industries and sectors in China. Over five years, China cut its annual growth in energy from 7 percent to 4 percent without slowing growth in industrial production. Ninety percent of the savings were from efficiency improvements. As a result, China's energy consumption expanded at less than half the rate of economic growth from 1980 to 1988 (Lenssen 1992).

Losses of energy during transmission and distribution represent 22 percent of generation in Thailand (World Bank 1993). Thailand may spend up to US$35 billion to meet projected energy demand up until the year 2001 (International Institute for Energy Conservation 1995). Thailand has also invested US$189 million in a demand-side management programme that was expected to result in 1,400 MW of power savings by 1998. Based on the estimated costs of demand-side management investments compared with estimated costs of energy produced by dams, the average cost of power saved through demand-side management is 15 percent less than the estimated cost of hydroelectricity. Mainstream hydropower projects along the Thai border range in estimated cost from US$940,000 per MW at Ban Koum to US$1,544,000 per MW at Ching Khan (Compagnie National du Rhone *et al.* 1994). The Thai demand-side management programme will cost only US$135,000 per MW saved. Estimated costs of Thai tributary dams planned for construction by

EGAT range from US$ 0.0370 per kWh to US$ 0.1005 per kWh, with an average cost of US$ 0.0678 per kWh (Asian Development Bank 1995). The costs of the Thai demand-side management programme for lighting, refrigerators, air conditioners commercial buildings and industrial motors ranges from US$ 0.0256 per kWh to US$ 0.1217 per kWh hour, with an average cost of US$ 0.0579 per kWh. Additional energy-saving initiatives by the Thai government include a fund that provides grants and low-interest loans for conservation and renewable energy activities and the adoption of an Energy Conservation Promotion Act in 1992.

Thailand could achieve a reduction of 25 percent in the projected increase in electricity demand in just 10 years (Lenssen 1992). According to the International Institute for Energy Conservation (1995), great potential exists to reduce the rate of energy growth in Thailand while maintaining economic stability, allowing the country to reduce its dependence on foreign oil and its anticipated expenditures on new power plants. Electrical appliances and energy-using equipment not yet available in Thailand could reduce energy use by 10 to 50 percent or more.

A shift in focus from construction of hydropower plants on the Mekong river and tributaries to supply Thailand's growing demand for electricity to a focus on reducing growth in demand and supplementing existing sources with non-hydropower renewables includes the following. First, the adverse environmental and social impacts associated with dam construction could be reduced by minimising the number of dams constructed primarily for power generation. Second, water resources infrastructure that is developed in the basin could serve other objectives more efficiently, since releases of water would not need to be timed with peak periods of energy demand.

## 5.2 Product diversification in the agriculture sector

Diversification of products from agricultural systems can reduce the demand for water relative to expansion of paddy rice cultivation, particularly in Cambodia Laos, Thailand and Vietnam. Crop diversification also provides farmers and other resource users with opportunities to increase the compatibility of their production systems with native ecosystems, thus reducing negative environmental impacts of agriculture.

Countries in the Mekong river basin, while interested in exporting rice to the world market, are also experiencing a trend towards crop diversification. In Thailand, for example, the rice field component of agricultural production dropped from 62 to 50 percent from 1977 to 1988, while upland crops (including mungbean, soybean, groundnut, watermelon, corn, sorghum, vegetables, and sugarcane) and tree crops (including fruit trees) increased from 20.5 percent and 8.8 percent to 24.1 and 13.2 percent, respectively. As of 1992, only 13 percent of the irrigated land in Thailand was used for diversified crops and fish farming, but these uses were growing at a rate of 1.25 percent per year (Kalwkilaya 1994).

Agricultural sector priorities in Vietnam include increasing the productivity of the sector's resource base and expanding the base into previously neglected commodities, such as livestock, fruits, and vegetables (Fforde & Goldstone 1995). Traditional Vietnamese agriculture systems include small-scale production of livestock, poultry, fish and shellfish, fruits, vegetables and fuel wood. Recent studies of agriculture in the Mekong delta in Vietnam have shown that the introduction of aquaculture into a double rice crop system can increase financial returns by 40 to 60 percent over a triple rice crop system. The Mekong river delta is also experiencing an increase in perennial crop introduction into paddy rice areas in order to reduce irrigation water and labour requirements and to increase income (Sandoz 1995). Successful experiments with mixed crop, fish and livestock farming have also been undertaken in Laos (Sluiter 1992). Cambodia already has a relatively diverse crop base. Main exports include rubber and timber, though Cambodia also exports small amounts of maize, sesame and pepper. The growing demand of industrialising countries in the region for livestock, rice, sugar, rubber and other agricultural products offers potential for strong economic growth in Cambodia (Shawcross 1994).

The sustainable harvest of non-timber forest products constitutes another approach to agricultural diversification that can provide positive returns to the regional economies and ecosystems. Non-timber forest products from Southeast Asia typically include various foods, spices, fodder, animals and animal products, fish and aquatic invertebrates, medicinal plants, rattan, bamboo, ornamental plants, chemical components, wood, and fiber. Thailand, which has lost much of its native forest cover, is experiencing two outstanding trends: the increase in imports of formerly exported non-timber forest products and the increasing percentage of total forest revenue provided by non-timber forest products (De Beer & McDermott 1996). The value of these products to community and national economies is often overlooked even though most forest dwellers in Southeast Asia are critically dependent on these products and Southeast Asian sources account for most of the several billion dollars in annual world trade in non-timber forest products, including nearly three billion dollars in finished rattan products alone.

If Mekong river basin countries substituted some planned investments in irrigated agriculture instead on diversified agriculture strategies, including the maintenance and promotion of non-timber forest products industries, the demand for dams and reservoirs in the basin to supply irrigation water for rice fields could potentially be reduced even as per hectare revenue increases. Other economic sectors could potentially benefit from a relative increase in the availability of water that otherwise would have been consumed in irrigated agriculture. In addition, mixed agriculture systems in upland areas are likely to have advantages over both deforestation and crop monocultures in maintaining soil stability and watershed integrity. Benefits of such systems could therefore extend to reduced run-off rates during the wet season (and reduced flood peaks), increased groundwater recharge (and water availability during the dry season), reduced soil erosion (and therefore, longer-lived reservoirs and reduced dredging costs for navigation maintenance), and improved water quality.

## 5.3 Other sectors

Other strategies for achieving integrated management of the Mekong river basin might include non-structural flood damage reduction; designing barges specifically to conform to the geomorphology of the river; and making use of water conservation technologies in urban, industrial, and agricultural water supply systems. A mix of technologies that facilitate an increase in the standard of living for Mekong river basin residents while protecting and maintaining the fisheries sector might prove to be the most economically advantageous pathway for the basin countries to follow.

## 6. Implementation

The delays in implementing development plans for the Mekong river basin over the past half century, including the Asian financial crisis, may prove to be blessings in disguise for the countries in the basin. Rising concern among local communities and non-governmental organisations is placing pressure on the countries to design development strategies that protect the people and natural resources of the basin. Donors are also searching for more sustainable pathways to economic development of the Mekong region. The following steps might help pave the way for the emergence of such a strategy.

- A basin-level assessment of the potential effects of planned water resources development. This assessment should consider the places (communities and key habitat sites) as well as the processes (sediment and nutrient transport and flow regimes) that would be affected by structural alterations of the river and tributaries.
- Assessment of alternative strategies for achieving the objectives of planned water resources development in the basin. Such an assessment should consider the past track records of alternatives and the factors contributing to their relative success or failure; geographic areas where such alternative strategies are being successfully applied and where such programmes could be expanded; geographic areas where the adoption of alternatives could help to increase the economic viability of development plans while avoiding negative environmental and social consequences.
- Dialogue with basin residents from the community to the national government level to promote understanding of the 'pros' and 'cons' of various development alternatives and ascertain their preferences and priorities.
- Dialogue with the donor community and with multi-lateral lending institutions to encourage funding of the preferred alternatives.

## 7. Conclusion

The global knowledge base regarding the links between ecology, hydrology and economy has expanded significantly since the first plans for development of the Mekong river basin were compiled in the 1950s. Society is more aware of the potential adverse social, economic, and environmental impacts of water resources development, and less damaging and more efficient alternatives to many of the approaches to water resources development have evolved. These include the use of demand-side energy management in preference to hydropower development and the expansion of diversified agricultural production systems, including management of forests for non-timber forest products, as a preferred alternative to expansion of irrigated agriculture and deforestation. Through innovation and modernisation, it is possible that the countries in the Mekong river basin can reap the rewards of development that are enjoyed by most industrialised countries while learning from, and avoiding, the mistakes that the latter have made in the history of water resources development.

# References

Asian Development Bank. 1995. Subregional energy sector study for the Greater Mekong Subregion. Final Report. Asian Development Bank, Manila.

Compagnie Nationae du Rhone, Acres International & Mekong Secretariat Study Team. 1994. Mekogn mainstem run-of-river hydropower: main report. Mekong River Committee Secretariat, Bangkok.

De Beer, J.H. & McDermott, M.J. 1996. The economic value of non-timber forest products in Southeast Asia. Netherlands Committee for IUCN, Amsterdam.

Fforde, A. & Goldstone, A. 1995. Vietnam to 2005: Advancing on all fronts. The Economist Intelligence Unite, London.

General Directorate of Irrigation Meteorology and Hydrology, Ministry of Agriculture, Forests and Fisheries, Royal Government of Cambodia. 1996. Country paper of Cambodia. In: Arriens, W.L., Bird, J., Bcrkhoff, J. & Mosely, P. (Eds.). Towards effective water policy in the Asian and Pacific Region 2. Country Papers Proceedings of the Regional Consultation Workshop. Asian Development Bank, Manila. pp. 7-22.

Goodland, R.J.A. 2000. Is there a future for big dams? In: Smits, A.J.M., Nienhuis, P.H. & Leuven, R.S.E.W. (Eds.). New approaches to river management. Backhuys Publishers, Leiden. pp. 187-207.

Hirsch, P. & Cheong, G. 1996. Natural resource management in the Mekong river basin. Final overview report to AusAID. Australian Development Co-operation, Sydney.

Hunt, C.E. 2000. New approaches to river management in the United States. In: Smits, A.J.M., Nienhuis, P.H. & Leuven, R.S.E.W. (Eds.) New approaches to river management. Backhuys Publishers, Leiden. pp. 119-139.

International Institute for Energy Conservation. 1995. Thailand's energy efficiency industry: potential for investment. Prepared for the Office of the Board of Investment, Office of the Prime Minister, Royal Thai Government.

International Rivers Network. 1999. Power struggle: the impacts of hydro-development in Laos: executive summary (http://irn.org/programs/mekong).

Jensen, J.G. 1999. MRC Fisheries Programme: Living aquatic resources management and conservation. Produced for the WWF-MRC Secretariat meeting, Mekong River Commission (MRC) Secretariat, Phnom Penh.

Kalwkilaya, J. 1994. Thailand. In: Heim, F. & Abernathy C.L. (Eds.). Irrigated agriculture in Southeast Asia beyond 2000. Proceedings of a workshop held at Langkawki, Malaysia. German Foundation for International Development, International Irrigation Management Institute, Colombo. pp. 51-76.

Lenssen, N. 1992. Empowering development: the new energy equation. Worldwatch Paper 111. Worldwatch Institute, Washington D.C.

Long-Hai, S. & Lu-Jun, L. 1992. Energy development and environmental protection: dual challenges for China. In: Ramani, K.V., Hills, P. & George, G. (Eds.). Burning questions: environmental limits to energy growth in Asian-Pacific countries during the 1990s. Asian and Pacific Development Centre, Kuala Lumpur. pp. 255-268.

Mekong River Commission Secretariat. 1999. MRC programme for fisheries management and development co-operation (2000-2004). MKG/R.95063, Rev. 4. Mekong River Commission Secretariat, Phnom Penh.

Pantulu, V.R. 1986. The Mekong River system. In: Davies, B.R. & Walker, K.F. (Eds.). The ecology of river systems. Dr. W. Junk Publishers, Dodrecht. pp. 695-719.

Probe International. 1999. Thailand's flawed electricity privatisation: the case for citizen-oriented reform. Power Sector Reform Series Paper 4, PL-266. Probe International, Toronto.

Quang, N.N., 2000. Management of the Mekong river basin. In: Smits, A.J.M., Nienhuis, P.H. & Leuven, R.S.E.W. (Eds.). New approaches to river management. Backhuys Publishers, Leiden. pp. 85-96.

Ramani, K.V. 1992. Environmental challenges for Asian-Pacific energy systems in the 1990s. In: Ramani, K.V., Hills, P. & George, G. (Eds.). Burning questions: environmental limits to energy growth in Asian-Pacific countries during the 1990s. Asian and Pacific Development Centre, Kuala Lumpur. pp. 255-268.

Rasphone, S., Bodhisane, S. & Phongphaypadith, O. 1996. Country paper of the Lao People's Democratic Republic. In: Arriens, W.L., Bird, J., Berkhoff, J. & Mosely, P. (Eds.). Towards effective water policy in the Asian and Pacific Region 2. Country Papers Proceedings of the Regional Consultation Workshop. Asian Development Bank, Manila. pp. 79-87.

Sandoz, M. 1995. Agricultural water use in Vietnam. In: World Bank, Asian Development Bank, Food and Agricultural Organisation, United Nations Development Programme, & the NGO Water Resources Group. Vietnam water resources sector review: selected working papers. Water Resources Sectoral Group, Hanoi.

Shawcross, W. 1994. Cambodia's new deal. Contemporary Issues Paper 1. Carnegie Endowment for International Peace, Washington D.C.

Shisong, M. Zhe, S. Undated. Extent of development within China's portion of the Mekong basin and the potential impact of future plans. Paper prepared at the International Workshop on Sustainable Development through Co-operation, Washington D.C.

Shoemaker, B. 1998. Trouble on the Theun-Hinboun: A field report on the socio-economic and environmental effects of the Nam Theun-Hinboun hydropower project in Laos (http://irn.org/programs/mekong/threport.html).

Sluiter, L. 1992. The Mekong currency. Project for Ecological Recovery/TERRA, Bangkok.

Van Zallinge, N., Thouk, N., Tana, T.S. & Nuoy, S. 1998. It's big, unique, and important: fisheries in the lower Mekong Basin, as seen from a Cambodian perspective. Mekong Fish Catch and Culture 4/1: 1-5.

World Bank. 1993. The World Bank's role in the electric power sector: policies for effective institutional, regulatory, and financial reform. A World Bank Policy Paper. Washington D.C.

# TECHNICAL SUPPORT OF PUBLIC DECISIONS TO RESTORE FLOODPLAIN ECOSYSTEMS: A STATUS REPORT ON THE ILLINOIS RIVER PROJECT, USA

R.E. Sparks[1], J.B. Braden[2], M. Demissie[3], P. Mitra[4], D.W. Schneider[4], D.C. White[2] & R. Xia[3]

[1] *Illinois Water Resources Center, University of Illinois at Urbana-Champaign, 1101 West Peabody Dr., Urbana, IL 61801, The United States of America;*
[2] *Department of Agricultural and Consumer Economics, University of Illinois at Urbana-Champaign, 332 Mumford Hall, 1301 West Gregory Dr., Urbana, IL 61801, The United States of America;*
[3] *Illinois State Water Survey, 2204 Griffith Drive, Champaign, IL 61820, The United States of America;*
[4] *Department of Urbana and Regional Planning, University of Illinois at Urbana-Champaign, 111 Temple Hoyne Buell Hall, 611 Taft Drive, Champaign, IL 61820, The United States of America*

## Abstract

The history and consequences of river alterations are similar in most of the industrialised nations, where rivers have been increasingly regulated and isolated from their floodplains to increase commercial activity, but where the flows of natural services from these river/floodplain systems have declined as a result. Now there is widespread public support in developed river basins to recover lost or diminished natural functions. In developing basins, loss of natural services may not be an inevitable consequence of commercial development, if citizens, government officials, planners, and engineers learn from previous experience in developed basins. Where long-term data have been collected, as in the upper Mississippi river system, a comparative historical approach is especially useful in identifying impacts of alterations, but such insights need to be incorporated in models to predict effects of alternative development or recovery plans. On the Illinois river, a major tributary of the upper Mississippi river, many recovery projects are being undertaken by a variety of partnerships among private landowners, non-governmental conservation and environmental organisations, and state and federal government agencies. In an effort to support these projects, inter-related hydrological, ecological, and economic models are being developed to predict what will happen to total social benefits (from both commercial and natural sources) if selected portions of the floodplain and of the annual flood cycle are restored. Similar models could be used to evaluate effects of development alternatives in other river basins. This work is in progress, but initial results indicate that the flood regime must be naturalised for full benefits to be achieved on restored floodplains. A significant problem is that low water levels that naturally occurred for several weeks in the summer season have been artificially raised (and de-stabilised) to benefit river shipping. A stable period of low flows during the summer allows floodplain soils to dry out. This seasonal drying is particularly critical to floodplain vegetation which, in turn, is critical for support of animal life, including species highly valued by people. One management solution is to maintain existing dikes or levees, or to construct new ones, so that water levels behind the levees can be artificially maintained in a pattern that is more "natural" than in the regulated river of today. Another approach is to modify the operation of

*New approaches to river management, pp. 225–247*
*edited by A.J.M. Smits, P.H. Nienhuis and R.S.E.W. Leuven*
© *2000 Backhuys Publishers, Leiden, The Netherlands*

the existing navigation dams to create a more natural water regime along the entire river, while also maintaining water depths required for navigation. The most cost-effective approach may be a hybrid of the two: managed flooding of selected parts of the floodplain as well as new operating criteria for existing dams. The cost (in terms of capital and operating costs, and impacts on commercial activity) and quality of the restoration (in terms of "naturalness," biodiversity, recovery of fisheries, and outdoor recreational opportunities) are key factors in public decisions regarding floodplain restoration. In retrospect, it would have been less expensive and more beneficial to have preserved more of the floodplain and to have included a more natural range of water level variation in the design criteria for river development projects-lessons that might be applied to current projects elsewhere.

## 1. Introduction

The Upper Mississippi River System (UMRS; Figure 1) represents an intermediate condition between the highly developed and regulated large rivers of Europe and the western United States (US), and largely unregulated rivers (e.g., the Paraguay in Brazil and Argentina). This intermediate level of river regulation results from the rather late start in river development in the Midwestern region of the US (compared to Europe), from lack of suitable terrain for high storage dams, and from the rise of a conservation movement before the rivers were so greatly altered (Galloway 2000,

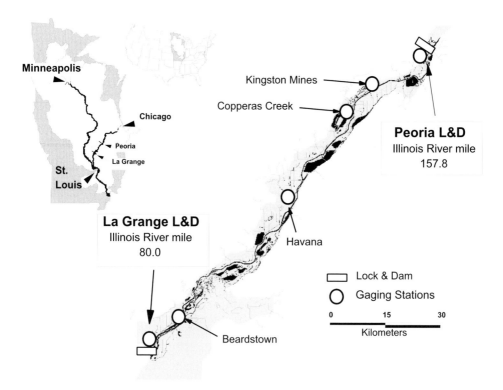

Fig. 1. The upper Mississippi river system is located in the upper Midwest of the USA. The 124 km study reach of the Illinois river is bounded upstream by the Peoria Lock and Dam (L&D) and downstream by the La Grange L&D.

Scarpino 1985). Europe had been modifying its rivers for at least 2000 years before 1818 (*cf* Havinga & Smits 2000), for example, when Illinois finally had enough residents to become a state.

This paper describes the UMRS and its comparatively brief history of commercial development and ecological decline. This history documents long term lag effects and threshold responses that led to persistent, sometimes rapid, degradation and loss of natural benefits. Effects that should now be anticipated and avoided in river development projects elsewhere (Sparks 1992). The paper describes the recent rise of public support and public involvement in river recovery, particularly along the Illinois river, a major tributary within the UMRS. Greater involvement of the public, including local stakeholders who are most directly affected by river development, appears to be a growing, world-wide phenomenon. On-going modelling efforts are described that provide a more scientific basis for choosing among alternative approaches to recovery. The same modelling techniques could be used elsewhere to predict the effects of river development.

Preliminary results indicate the importance of restoring a more natural water level regime, particularly the low flow portion of the annual flood cycle. The discussion uses naturalisation to describe the goal. Naturalisation is: the shifting of some components of an altered ecosystem (*e.g.,* floodplain vegetation) closer to a natural condition, while maintaining or enhancing existing social and economic uses of the ecosystem (Rhoads & Herricks 1996). In river basins that are being developed, a better goal might be the preservation of the ecosystem characteristics and processes that maintain desirable natural services, products, and amenities while instituting compatible commercial development. An ecosystem approach to both preservation and naturalisation involves maintaining or re-creating the water and sediment regimes that support the plants and animals, rather than attempting to maintain the biota by direct human intervention, as in fish hatcheries or botanical parks (Sparks 1995). The motivating hypothesis for our efforts in the UMRS is that the total flow of social benefits (broadly defined to include both natural and commercial services) from regulated floodplain-river ecosystems can be increased by selective re-connection of rivers to their floodplains and re-creation of more natural flooding regimes. The comparable hypothesis for developing basins is that the greatest total flow of benefits will occur from commercial development that retains critical natural processes. Essential to the evaluation of both hypotheses is identification of the critical processes and critical range of natural variation that need to be maintained.

## 2. Site description and history

The UMRS is defined in the Water Resources Development Act of 1986 as the navigable portions of both the Illinois river and the main stem of the upper Mississippi river (2,080 km), from Minneapolis-St. Paul in Minnesota downstream past St. Louis, Missouri to the mouth of the Ohio river. The same legislation recognises both the natural and commercial value of the UMRS by designating it as both a "nationally significant ecosystem" and "nationally significant waterway" (for commercial navigation). Short navigable portions of other tributaries are also included. The Illinois river, the primary focus of this paper, flows 523 km south-east across the state of Illinois before joining the Mississippi near St. Louis (Figure 1).

The early developments affecting the Illinois river occurred in the 19th and early 20th centuries. As part of the process of converting the prairies of the American Midwest into cropland, upland wetlands were drained and streams were channelled to improve drainage in the 1880s and 1890s. On the main rivers of the UMRS most flood protection levees were built between 1909 and 1922 (Mulvihill & Cornish 1929, Thompson 1989). A few of the agricultural levees subsequently failed during floods, the levee districts that owned them went bankrupt, and the lands were purchased for fish and wildlife refuges during the Great Depression of the 1930s (Bellrose et al. 1983). A conservation organisation, the Izaak Walton League, was largely responsible for building public support and persuading the US Congress to preserve natural floodplains and backwaters along the upper Mississippi. As a result, a national fish and wildlife refuge system was started in 1924 with 112,000 ha arranged in a corridor along the river (Scarpino 1985). Today, another 400,000 ha of largely unleveed floodplain in the upper Mississippi is owned by individuals, private duck hunting clubs, state natural resource agencies, conservation organisations, and local units of government, as well as by the federal government.

The Illinois river became the waste receptacle for the rapidly-growing population in Chicago in the latter half of the 19th century (Sparks 1984). In 1848, the headwaters of the Illinois were connected to Lake Michigan at Chicago by a man-made navigation canal (the Illinois and Michigan Canal, I&M Canal) that also carried wastes from the city. The canal cut through the 4 m high natural divide that separated the Mississippi drainage basin from the Great Lakes-St. Lawrence river basin. However, the I&M Canal had insufficient conveyance capacity during rain storms, so the Chicago river still carried wastes into the lake, polluting the city's water supply. Therefore, in 1900 the flow of the Chicago river was reversed and directed into the newly-completed, much larger Chicago Sanitary and Ship Canal (CSS Canal). Today an average of 91 $m^3s^{-1}$ of lake water and effluent is released into the Illinois river via the CSS Canal.

The predominantly organic pollution (human sewage, animal wastes from the Chicago stockyards, offal from the meat packing plants) delivered by the CSS Canal initially damaged just the upstream portion of the Illinois river, creating an anoxic zone devoid of fishes and other aquatic life. However, fish yields actually increased downstream of the anoxic zone. In fact, the peak yield in the commercial fishery occurred in 1908, eight years after the opening of the CSS Canal (Sparks 1984). In 1908 2,000 commercial fishermen were employed along a 300 km reach of the Illinois river and their catch constituted 10 percent of the total US harvest of freshwater fish. The annual yield was about 10 million kg, or approximately 159 kg $ha^{-1}$ (Lubinski et al. 1981).

The boost in downstream productivity was attributable to two causes; although the causes persist, the productivity boost unfortunately proved to be temporary. The first cause was the permanent rise in the downstream water levels (due to diversion of lake water and waste water), which increased the amount of permanent aquatic habitat for fish (but also drowned bottomland forests). Second, the nutrients in the wastes were mineralised in the upstream reaches and carried downstream where they fertilised the expanded aquatic habitat and increased production (Sparks 1984). After 1910, however, the increasing pollution load caused the anoxic and hypoxic zones to extend downriver, destroying the bottom fauna that served as food for many fishes and diving ducks (Sparks 1984). In the 1920s, the earlier gains in aquatic habitat resulting from the rise in water level were offset by leveeing and draining of half (81,000 ha) of the floodplain for agriculture along the Illinois river (Mulvihill & Cornish 1929, Thompson 1989).

By the 1950s the annual yield had dropped to 34 kg ha$^{-1}$; in the 1970s the yield reached a low of 3 kg ha$^{-1}$, totalling only 0.32 percent of the total US freshwater harvest (Sparks 1984). Sparks (1984) attributed declines in yield to declines in productivity, rather than to declines in prices (which remained relatively constant, or even increased, for preferred species) or over-harvest (commercial harvest has been low to non-existent on the Illinois river for decades, giving the fish populations more than enough time to recover). If regional demand for freshwater fish had fallen off, there should be comparable declines in the upper Mississippi. Instead, the commercial yield has been relatively stable on the upper Mississippi (Sparks 1984). Nutrient depletion is not the problem because nutrient concentrations remain high in the Illinois river and its backwaters. In the last 20 years, the annual fish yield from the Illinois river has recovered slightly, to about 9 kg ha$^{-1}$, primarily in response to improvements in water quality starting with the federal Clean Water Acts in 1972. However the most dramatic gains in water quality (improvement of dissolved oxygen levels, reduction of acute toxicity) have already been made, and water quality alone will not revive the fisheries in the Illinois river. The commercial fish yield on the upper Mississippi remained relatively stable during the decline on the Illinois suggesting that the better quality of spawning, nursery, and over-wintering habitat for fishes and better conditions for invertebrates the fishes feed upon played major roles in maintaining fish populations there (Sparks 1984).

The decline in quality of fish and wildlife habitat in the Illinois river has been blamed primarily on intensification of agriculture in upland basins and the associated increase in soil erosion and sediment delivery to the main river, although other factors (*e.g.,* fluctuating water levels) also contribute (Bellrose *et al.* 1979, 1983, Sparks *et al.* 1990). The navigation dams, in contrast to high dams for water storage, generally do not impede fish migrations that occur during the flood season, because the gates are out of the water and the river is essentially free-flowing. The gates are lowered during the low flow season to maintain water depths for navigation. The sediment certainly has filled in formerly deep backwaters and floodplain lakes and suspended sediment has reduced light penetration, thereby restricting the growth of aquatic plants, which provide substrate for invertebrates and shelter for young fishes. Sparks *et al.* (1990) point out that habitat deterioration was not gradual, but sudden, occurring between 1958 and 1961, and was associated with the loss of submersed aquatic plants and certain groups of benthic macroinvertebrates (fingernail clams, burrowing mayflies, and snails). The lakes and backwaters changed from vegetated, clear waters to turbid, plantless deserts. The plants evidently had served as biotic mediators, anchoring the sediments and shorelines with their roots, damping wind-generated waves (which resuspend bottom sediments) with their leaves and stems, and slowing entry of sediment-laden water from the main channels and tributaries into the backwaters. The pattern of decline suggests that a threshold was crossed: once aquatic plants began to weaken or die, the wind fetch increased, resulting in larger waves that uprooted more plants and increased turbidity further by resuspending bottom sediments and eroding shorelines. This positive feedback caused rapid degradation of the remaining plant beds. The loss of the plants may also be associated with an increase in toxic ammonia in the pore water of sediments and the resulting loss of burrowing macroinvertebrates (Sparks et al. 1993). Aquatic macrophytes oxygenate sediments around their roots and are capable of taking up nitrogen as a nutrient either in the reduced form that is very toxic to invertebrates and fish (ammonia) or in the oxidised, non-toxic form (nitrate) that exists in the root zone. Without the aquatic plants, the organic and inorganic nitrogen delivered from agricultural lands and urban sources may be deposited in the anaerobic sediments and converted by microbial processes into toxic ammonia.

The seeds of degradation may well have been sown by a combination of factors, rather than the increased sediment loads alone. The permanent rise in water levels on the Illinois river in 1900, and again in the 1930s when modern navigation dams were installed on both the Illinois and upper Mississippi rivers, killed portions of the floodplain forests and removed an effective windbreak that was especially important in the late winter and early spring floods that were often accompanied by storms and high winds. The permanent impoundments and expanded floodplain lakes created by the dams also served as efficient sediment traps. The floodplain levees also forced the sediment-laden waters into the half of the floodplain that remained unleveed, possibly accelerating the sediment deposition. Finally, unnaturally frequent and rapid fluctuations in water levels during the summer growing season inhibit both submersed and moist soil vegetation (Bellrose et al. 1979). The results of hydraulic modelling reported in this paper indicate that operation of the navigation dams contribute to these excessive fluctuations.

It is ironic that the severe pollution and resulting anoxic conditions in the past were beneficial to some degree because they created a barrier that protected the Mississippi and the Great Lakes ecosystems from each other's introduced aquatic pests. Since the 1972 Clean Water Act, US$4 billion have been spent on improved municipal waste treatment in the Chicago area, water quality has improved, and aquatic organisms can survive in the Chicago canals (Stoeckel et al.1996). Within the last five years, the European Zebra mussel (*Dreissena polymorpha*) has spread from the Great Lakes into the Mississippi drainage through the Chicago connection and at least six other non-native pests are poised to enter. Conversely, the Asian Grass carp (*Ctenopharyngodon idella*) and an African zooplankter (*Daphnia lumholtzi*) are advancing upstream in the Illinois river and could soon enter Lake Michigan (Stoeckel et al. 1996). The zebra mussel can plug water intakes and has been associated with declines in populations of native mussels in the upper Mississippi (Miller, A., personal communication). The Grass carp could compete with several native species of waterfowl, because the carp and the ducks prefer to consume the same species of aquatic plants. The African zooplankter is not palatable to young fish because it has protective spines, and it may compete for food with more palatable native zooplankters.

In summary, the biological productivity and biodiversity of the UMRS diminished as commercial use of the river and its floodplain increased. This is conceptually represented in figure 2. The declines were especially acute and well documented in and along the Illinois river. Sparks et al. (1990) note several reasons why the dramatic changes in the Illinois river were not predicted and averted. First, when the diversions and land alterations were carried out, there was little thought given to downstream effects. The paramount concerns were protection of drinking water and

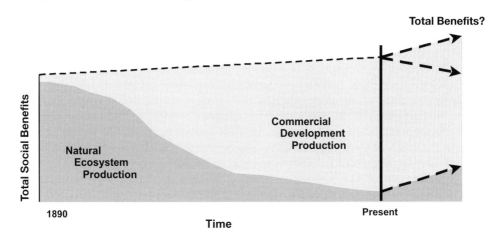

*Fig. 2.* The flow of social benefits from the Illinois river has shifted from predominantly natural to predominantly commercial during more than a century of development. The current policy focus is on whether natural service flows can be restored at little, or no, net cost to society.

putting land into agricultural production. The state of ecological knowledge was not sufficient to identify the variety of causative factors that acted in a complex, decompensatory way, often after time lags of decades. A major stressor, sediment loading, increased gradually until an effect threshold was reached, triggering an abrupt and persistent change in the state of the backwater and lake habitats that were critical spawning, feeding, and wintering areas for fishes. Prior to this change, the floodplain-river ecosystem produced fish in abundance and seemed to absorb the sediment without great harm, just as it had earlier absorbed the organic wastes from Chicago. The existing water quality monitoring network did not detect changes in the critical backwater habitats because all the monitoring sites were in the main channel. Moreover, only the water column was monitored. Biological monitoring used macroinvertebrates colonising artificial substrates suspended in the water column, so development of toxic ammonia concentrations in the sediments initially went undetected. One of the gravest continuing threats to the UMRS is an increasing rate of introduction of invasive species and their parasites and diseases from outside the system (via the Great Lakes and other distant points of introduction). This threat is related to expansion of world trade and, ironically, to the removal of former pollution barriers. Finally, the commercial fishermen and other river users affected by drainage of the floodplain and the increased sediment and pollution loading simply did not have the sustained political influence needed to retain public access to backwaters and to prevent conversion of the floodplain to cropland (Schneider 1996). The latter situation has changed recently.

## 3. Rise of public interest and public participation in recovery

There is strong public and government interest in a greater recovery of the natural productivity and services of the UMRS. Since 1988, Congress has provided

US$176 million for monitoring of biological resources and for habitat rehabilitation and enhancement in the UMRS, and the five states in the UMRS have contributed US$10.5 million (USACE 1997). The Lt. Governor of Illinois chairs the Illinois River Co-ordinating Council, which comprises leaders from government, industry, agriculture, universities, and non-governmental organisations who are charged with implementation of 33 recommendations for recovery of the Illinois river. The recommendations were developed by 150 citizens representing a diversity of interests from throughout the river basin, who worked with a professional facilitator and technical experts in hydrology, ecology, and economic development. The facilitator helped the planning group of citizens to develop operating rules for the discussions and a consensus-based approach to decision-making. In the opening workshops, participants described personal associations with the river and worked together on a shared vision for the future of the river.

The most substantial achievement to date of the Co-ordinating Council has been the commitment of nearly US$500 million in federal and state funds over the next 15 years for riparian restoration and other practices in selected tributary watersheds, practices that will reduce excessive yields of sediment, water, nutrients, and contaminants from agricultural land (the dominant land use in the Illinois river basin). Participation in the programme is entirely voluntary and the response of private landowners has been gratifying, with the number of enrolees exceeding the funds initially available during the first two years of the programme.

Citizens have other opportunities to confront issues and prepare recommendations in both state-wide programmes and programmes within the Illinois river basin. Illinois has a Conservation Congress that is modelled after a representative legislative process, with citizens from all over the state convening every two years to address natural resource issues, build public consensus, and advocate specific policies and procedures to be implemented by state agencies and the state legislature. Ecosystem partnerships are coalitions of local and regional interest groups who seek to merge natural resource stewardship (usually within individual watersheds) with compatible economic and recreational development. Both of these programmes are managed by the Illinois Department of Natural Resources. Watershed management plans are being developed by residents of watersheds throughout Illinois with funding provided by the federal and state environmental protection agencies and natural resource agencies, and technical advice furnished by the agencies, universities, consultants, and non-governmental conservation organisations. In the case of the Mackinaw river, a tributary of the Illinois river, a non-governmental conservation organisation, The Nature Conservancy (TNC), managed the watershed planning grant and facilitated the work of the watershed planning committee. TNC is also developing a conservation plan for the Illinois river itself, focusing on recovery of biodiversity. TNC has purchased a 440 ha agricultural levee district where it plans to restore the aquatic and terrestrial communities that characterised the original Illinois river floodplain. The Illinois river and most of its tributaries now have "friends" groups (*e.g.*, Friends of the Illinois River, Friends of the Chicago River), who organise clean-ups by volunteers and build consensus for political action. Some of these groups are well funded and politically effective; some have full time or part time technical staff and publish newsletters.

The results of recovery efforts are being assessed not only by federal and state environmental agencies in the course of their work, but also by a network of citizen volunteers who monitor habitat conditions and biological indicators in streams and rivers throughout the state as part of the Illinois River Watch Programme. A separate programme (Illinois Rivers Project) involves secondary school teachers and students who use local streams as an educational resource for science, biology, and social studies classes. The River Web Project, funded by the US National Science Foundation, involves the National Centre for Supercomputing Applications at the University of Illinois, and three museums in Illinois, Missouri and Minnesota that are co-operating in the development of computer-based exhibits and educational materials that focus on the science and social history of the river system.

Both in education and in public policy decisions, it is important to understand that many of the attributes and services of rivers and floodplains that humans value and wish to restore depend upon the master variable: the water regime (Figure 3). Floodplain services include the conveyance of floods and the reduction of flood peaks. Both stage and frequency of major floods have increased in both the upper Mississippi and the Illinois river in the last 20 years, in comparison with the previous 60 years, and flood damage has consequently increased (Leopold 1994, Singh & Ramamurthy 1990). The US Army Corps of Engineers (the federal agency in the US responsible for flood control and for navigation in the UMRS), is addressing the causes of the increases in magnitude and frequency of the big floods.

In contrast to the more typical modelling of the physical capacity of a river-floodplain system to accommodate major floods, the work reported here examines

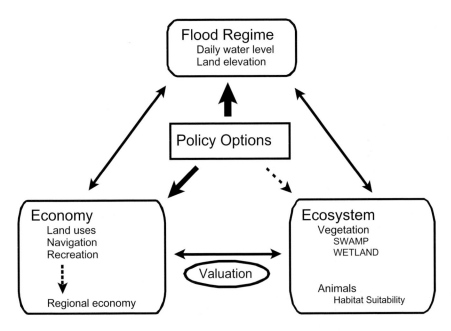

*Fig. 3.* Simulation of the hydrology, ecology and economy related to a section of the Illinois river involves developing a set of inter-related models. The thickness of the arrows from policy options to the other boxes indicate the expected relative cost-effectiveness of recovery options aimed at changing the river's flood regime versus efforts to protect selected plant and animal populations by isolating them from the river.

a neglected part of the seasonal flood cycle, the low water levels that occur during the summer growing season. Figure 4 illustrates the impact that development has had on the annual pattern of water levels in the Illinois river. Small fluctuations of the water level during the critical summer growing period for floodplain plants appear to have a dramatic impact on the ecology of the riparian vegetation, of the floodplain lakes and of the main river channel.

## 4. Hydraulic modelling and effects of operations of navigation dams

We are using UNET (Barkau 1995), an one dimensional hydraulic model, of the study reach to examine effects of dam operations on summer water levels. The 129 km study reach is divided into segments and water is routed from one segment to the next (Figure 5). In each segment, water can be added from tributaries. Water flow and elevation are affected by the size and shape of the cross-section of the segment and by factors such as flow resistance during overbank flows, caused by vegetation growing on the floodplain. Flow resistance results in higher water levels within the segment. In the summer of 1997, an unusual repetitive weekly pattern in water levels was recorded at several river gages (Figure 6). We subsequently learned that maintenance work was being performed during this period on the gates at the upstream dam. Water was being released during the week to facilitate work on the downstream side of the gates. For the weekend, the water above the dam was allowed to rise again to the normal summer elevation, to better accommodate recreationists using the lake above the dam.

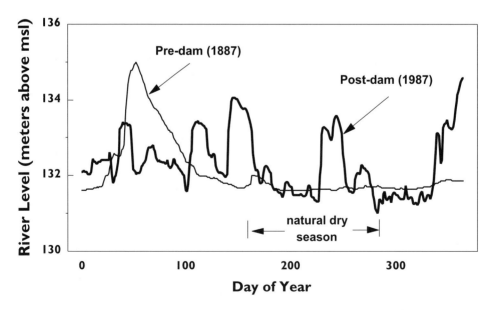

*Fig. 4.* Since the navigation dams have been in place on the Illinois River, the natural pattern of a spring flood pulse followed by a summer season of low flow has been replaced by an unpredictable, chaotic pattern year-round (msl: mean surface level).

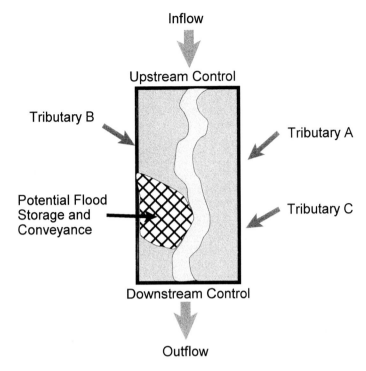

*Fig. 5.* Modelling the hydraulics of the river is key to simulating the behaviour of the river/flood-plain system.

When we included these dam operations in our model, the model predicted the measured water level changes very accurately (Figure 6). Opening the gates caused relatively small changes upstream of the dam, because of the significant storage volume of the upstream channel, which broadens into a mainstem lake. Downstream, however, where the river is more constricted, the water releases caused maximum water fluctuations of 2.5 m immediately below the dam and fluctuations of nearly 2 m at Havana, 54 km below the dam (Figure 6). The Chautauqua National Wildlife Refuge is located at Havana, as are several state conservation areas, public hunting and fishing areas, and private duck clubs. The moist soil plants that supply food for migratory waterfowl are drowned by short term water fluctuations of this magnitude or even much lesser magnitudes, thereby decreasing waterfowl use, hunting opportunities, and income to local communities that service the hunters. The fluctuations gradually dampened out further downstream. Near the La Grange dam, 124 km below the upstream dam, the fluctuations were scarcely measurable (Figure 6).

Some of the harmful water level fluctuations in the Illinois river and its floodplain are probably attributable to unnaturally rapid drainage of stormwater from urban areas and from agricultural areas where artificial drainage systems have been installed beneath the soil surface and where streams have been channelled. The higher and faster flowing water erodes soil from the fields and from the upland channels, and carries it to the main river where it is deposited as sediment in flood-

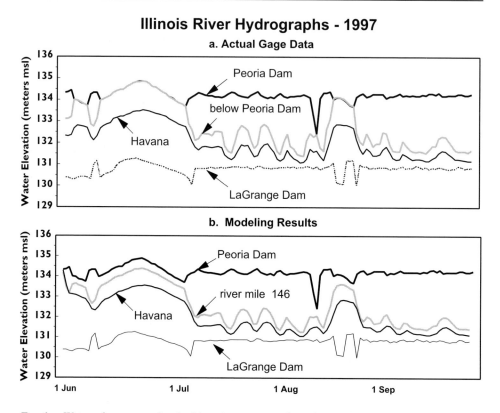

*Fig. 6.* a: Water releases associated with maintenance work on the Peoria Dam produced stage fluctuations ideal for calibrating our hydraulic models; b: Simulation results agreed closely with the
measured water levels (msl: mean surface level).

plain lakes and backwater areas during overbank flows. This sedimentation is
another dimension of river hydrology threatening the health of the river-floodplain
system. The filling and resulting degradation of the floodplain lakes has been well
documented (Bellrose *et al.* 1983).

Incorporating the upland processes impacting the main stem of the Illinois river
is beyond the scope of the modelling project, to date. Future hydraulic model development is intended to assess sediment impacts by modelling the routing and deposition of various sediment loads assumed to be entering the boundary of the river-
floodplain system. This effort will require the development of a two dimensional
hydraulic model, at least for selected sites. The feasibility of modelling at this level
of detail has been preliminarily tested using the TABS modelling system developed
by the USACE (Thomas & McAnally 1991, Brigham Young University 1992).

## 5. Vegetation modelling and effects of unnatural water regimes

Since species of plants vary in their tolerance of flooding and of saturated soil, the
flood regime determines what vegetation will occupy a floodplain site. Therefore,

floodplain vegetation models require either an actual water level record or simulated record generated by a hydraulic model. Another critical piece of information is the elevation of the site: the lower the site and the higher the flood, the longer the site will be inundated. Eventually our models will include both a floodplain forest model and an herbaceous wetland model (Figure 7). We have chosen to run the floodplain forest model first, because the effects of altered water regimes on forests are not so obvious to decision-makers and local residents as the more immediate effect of unnatural floods on herbaceous duck food plants. An unnatural flood in the summer kills some moist soil plants in a matter of days and the losses are immediately noted by duck hunters and refuge managers. In the case of the forest, however, it may take decades before unnatural water levels change the composition of the forest through death and replacement of species. The forests also provide habitat for wildlife (hence, forest attributes are required input variables for the wildlife models we will eventually use) and woody debris that furnishes a solid substrate for many invertebrates that fish feed upon.

The floodplain forest model is an adaptation and extension of the SWAMP model originally developed by Phipps (1979) and Phipps & Applegate (1983). The model simulates the germination, growth and death of individual trees within a forest stand. The model accounts for individual growth factors, such as flood tolerance, and for competitive interactions among trees, such as growth reduction of small trees as they are shaded by other taller trees. The model has been calibrated using 130 years of river stage records, floodplain forest descriptions from early 19th

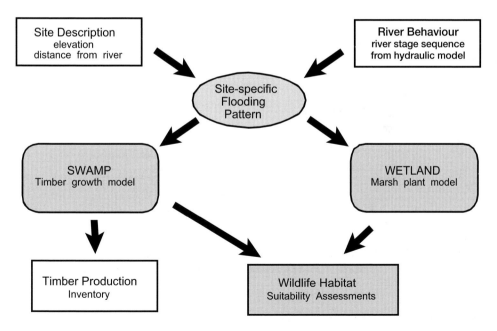

*Fig. 7.* Site elevation and the water level of the river determine the inundation pattern at the floodplain site. The inundation pattern in turn determines the type of vegetation (woody or herbaceous) and its rate of growth.

century surveyor notes, and information from present-day vegetation surveys. The model was initialised with a forest stand having the species composition that existed between 1817 and the 1830s, and then that stand was subjected to the historical pattern of changing water levels that has been recorded over the last 130 years. The model predicted correctly that the contemporary forest is dominated by flood-tolerant Willow (*Salix niger*). In contrast, Pin oak (*Quercus palustris*) was most abundant in the presettlement forest, with many other valuable species also present in substantial numbers, *i.e.*, relative abundance among tree species was much more even in 1817 than it is now (Figure 8).

The most important variable in the forest growth model is the period of inundation during the growing season. One refinement made to the original SWAMP model was to allow the inundation period to vary from year to year. In the original version of SWAMP the inundation period is a constant (an average computed for the period of record: 130 years in our case). We refer to this as the "static" form of the model. When we replaced the average inundation with the actual inundation recorded each year (a more realistic approach that we term the "dynamic" form of the model), the model still predicted a willow-dominated contemporary forest, but with more species present (Figure 9).

The importance of year-to-year variations in maintaining forest diversity is even more evident in recent model runs over spans of 500-1,000 years. We created an artificial 500 or 1,000 year water level record by randomly selecting years from the pre-1900 hydrographic record. If major floods are excluded, the forests become monocultures, dominated first by a single pioneer species that is eventually replaced by a single overstory species. A greater number of species are maintained if infrequent, great floods occur. These preliminary results support the "intermediate disturbance" hypothesis of Connell (1975, 1978): an intermediate level of

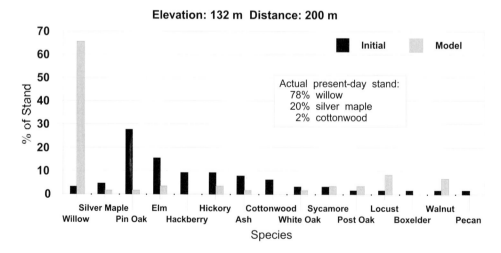

*Fig. 8.* In response to the actual pattern of river level fluctuations over the last century, the floodplain forest simulation model converted a pre-settlement forest composition into a less diverse forest typical of today.

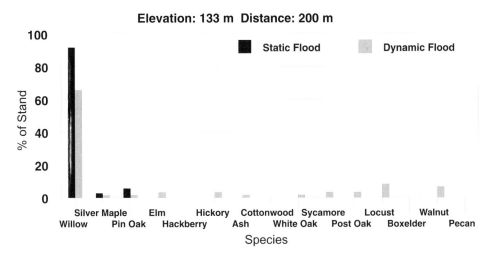

*Fig. 9.* A floodplain forest model that is sensitive to year-to-year differences in inundation produces stands with more species diversity (dynamic flood) than does a model using a single average inundation computed for an entire simulation period (static flood).

disturbance allows more species to co-exist, whereas only a few superior competitors will ultimately dominate a static environment and only pioneer species can survive in frequently-disturbed environments.

To further examine the effects of the modern water level regime on forests, we compared two additional simulations. One simulation used the actual water levels during the past 100 years. The other made 100 random draws from 25 years of late 19th century hydrographs to approximate a 100-year record of conditions that might have occurred in the absence of dams, levees, and releases of water from Lake Michigan. The more natural, simulated flood regime supports a more even distribution of species (Figure 10); *i.e.*, the forest is not dominated by willow, but includes substantial percentages of Silver maple (*Acer saccharinum*), Elm (*Ulmus americana*), Ash (*Fraxinus* ), Boxelder (*Acer negundo*), Walnut (*Juglans nigra*) and Pecan (*Carya illinoensis).*

In the near future, we intend to extend our modelling to non-forest vegetation, particularly the moist soil plants that provide food for migratory waterfowl. In the case of herbaceous plants, the approach will be analogous to the physically-driven models used to simulate marsh succession in the Mississippi delta (Costanza *et al.* 1990, Sklar *et al.* 1985). The flooding tolerances of the moist soil plants are so well documented that manuals have been developed for waterfowl managers who grow moist soil plants in leveed compartments on the floodplain (Fredrickson & Taylor 1982). Water levels within the compartments are controlled with gates and pumps. One goal of our modelling is to determine whether the navigation dams could be operated to recreate the stable low water levels that characterised the summer growing season prior to 1900, thereby encouraging the growth of moist soil plants over much larger areas and perhaps at lower costs than can be achieved in the floodplain compartments (Sparks *et al.* 1998). The output from the hydraulic models and

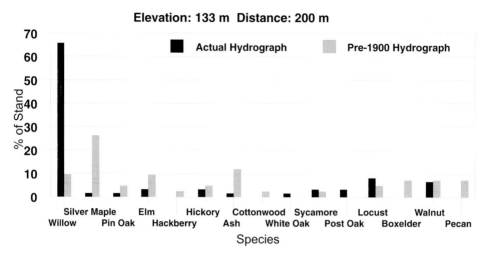

*Fig. 10.* Comparing the simulated response of a floodplain forest to a regulated (actual hydrograph) and to an unregulated (pre-1900 hydrograph) river indicates that regulation results in dominance by one species (Willow). Abundance among species is much more even with an unregulated river.

vegetation models will be used in existing habitat suitability models for selected fishes, birds, and mammals (Fig. 7). Although each of the intermediate steps in the modelling process provides useful information and insights (such as the importance of flood dynamics in maintaining forest diversity), our ultimate goal is to assess the net effects of alternative floodplain naturalisation strategies on both the economy and the ecosystem. The broader interdisciplinary framework shown in Figure 4 will enable comparison of alternatives in terms that are understandable and useful, both to the public and to public officials.

## 6. Economics of flood easements

The physical and biological modelling reported here has not progressed sufficiently to directly support assessment of the economic impacts of reconnecting floodplains to the Illinois river. However, members of the research team have been involved in a related study of the economics of flood easements; specifically, flood easements in sparsely settled agricultural levee districts in order to protect populous urban areas (Hirschi 1999). This research provides some useful insights into how land use is affected by government subsidies and how current land use would be affected by changes in flood risk (*e.g.*, if a levee was to be lowered or breached).

Hirschi (1999) used a constrained, non-linear optimisation model to examine profit maximising farming decisions as the level of flood risk varied from a 1 in 200 chance (or 0.5% probability) to a 1 in 2 chance (or 50% probability). The management alternatives available to the optimising model included a range of crops and production practices common to the agriculture of the region (including a more flood-tolerant crop of hay), the ability to delay planting as needed to accommodate spring floods, and current government agricultural support programmes. The government programmes examined were subsidised crop insurance, and annual government land rent payments paid to farmers who convert crop land to some perennial vegetation for at least 10 years. Such rent payments are available through either the Conservation Reserve Programme (CRP), for highly erodible land, or the Wetland Reserve Programme (WRP), for wetland areas.

Results from the model are summarised in Table 1. These results, for a risk-neutral farmer, suggest that when the annual risk of flooding increases to the level of 1 year in 25 (or a 4% probability), enrolling the land in crop insurance becomes necessary to maximise the expected profit. At lower flood risks, expected loss to flooding does not justify paying the crop insurance premium, even at the government subsidised rate (Hirschi 1999). As one would expect, the availability and the subsidised cost of insurance increases the level of flood risk the farmer is willing to face by choosing to produce a row crop rather than to put the land into CRP/WRP, in which case the returns would be assured.

Another interesting aspect of the optimisation is that the currently preferred crops (corn/maize and soybeans) remained preferred as the flood risk increased until the risk rose to the frequency of one year out of two (a 50% probability of flooding in any given year), at which point all of the land was converted to the CRP/WRP conservation programme. The results suggest that the cropping decision is an "all or nothing" choice. Either the land is used to raise conventional crop of corn or soybeans or, when the risk gets too high, it is put into the conservation programme. At least as modelled, no circumstance justified a risk management strategy of putting some land in CRP/WRP, while continuing to farm the rest; or of growing more flood tolerant crops (Hirschi 1999).

The expected net incomes shown in Table 1 can be interpreted as the level of compensation that the farmer would require to choose some cropping pattern or land use other than the one generating the returns. These results are for a decision-maker with a neutral attitude about risk, neither averse to nor preferring to take risks. Since farmers are by and large risk averse, Hirschi (1999) also examined the influence of risk aversion on these results. As one would expect, increasing the reluctance to assume risk caused the decision-maker to become more cautious and to convert more land to CRP/WRP at lower flood risk, and/or accept less compensation for the conversion.

The modelling work by Hirschi (1999) provides useful insights into the decision-making process of floodplain landowners. More lessons are being learned in the real world. A major new government programme similar to the CRP/WRP has been created to benefit the Illinois river. The Conservation Reserve Enhancement Programme (CREP), begun in 1998, is targeted specifically within the Illinois river watershed, providing US$459 million in federal and state funds over 15 years for conversion of highly erodible and flood-prone land from cropland to permanent vegetation. CREP targets riparian zones, with a goal of enrolling 206,500 ha, or 2.5% of the entire 8,341,000-ha drainage basin. Partly as a result of the currently low corn and soybean prices, voluntary requests for enrolment in the CREP programme in 1998 and 1999 have exceeded the funds available (Bruce, D., personal communication).

*Table 1.* Expected net income and optimal land use percentages (from Hirschi 1999).

| Probability of Flooding (% Chance) | Crop Insurance Coverage (% Yield) | ExpectedZ Net Returns (US$) | Percentage of land area | | | | |
|---|---|---|---|---|---|---|---|
| | | | Late April Corn | Early May Corn | Early May Beans | Late May Beans | CRP/ WRP |
| 0.5 | 0 | 094.24 | 22.75 | 22.25 | 31.50 | 18.50 | 0 |
| 1 | 0 | 191.57 | 22.75 | 22.25 | 31.50 | 18.50 | 0 |
| 2 | 0 | 186.04 | 22.75 | 22.25 | 31.50 | 18.50 | 0 |
| 4 | 50 | 176.42 | 22.75 | 22.25 | 31.50 | 18.50 | 0 |
| 10 | 65 | 152.52 | 22.75 | 22.25 | 31.50 | 18.50 | 0 |
| 20 | 50 | 94.13 | 22.75 | 22.25 | 31.50 | 18.50 | 0 |
| 50 | n.a. | 67.34 | 0 | 0 | 0 | 0 | 100 |

CRP/WRP: Conservation Reserve Programme or Wetland Reserve Programme; n.a.: not applicable.

Anecdotal evidence indicates that a market may be developing for lands that are eligible for CREP, WRP, and CRP. Advertisements seeking property which includes land that is eligible for these vegetative conversion programmes have been placed in local newspapers by individuals and groups who apparently are interested in hunting, fishing, or other outdoor recreation associated with riparian areas. The full effect of the CREP programme on land use, land values and local taxes have yet to be modelled or assessed.

## 7. Discussion

There are several lessons that might be taken from the history of river development and river regulation in the UMRS and applied to less developed basins elsewhere. First, there should be an effort to account for the natural services provided by the existing system, so that loss or replacement of these services can be accounted for as well as the benefits provided by commercial development. Such an analysis includes social issues, because the benefits of the natural system may accrue to middle- and low-income local people (*e.g.*, artisanal fishers who supply local markets) who may not benefit from commercial development (*e.g.*, cheap long-distance water transportation to world markets) that favours an entirely different scale and type of economic activity. Draining and leveeing of the floodplain, particularly along the Illinois river, replaced fish, wildlife and timber production with production of dry land commodity crops. In the US, meat can be easily and cheaply substituted for fish, or fish once caught locally in the river can be replaced with fish shipped from aquaculture centres or from the sea. A well known fish market on the Illinois river in the city of Peoria shifted from locally-caught fish to salt water fish and channel catfish produced in aquaculture centres in the states of Arkansas and Mississippi. In some parts of the world, however, it may not be so easy for local people to find or pay for substitutes for fish protein. Along the Illinois river, it appears that local economies became less diverse and self-sufficient and more dependent on world commodity markets which are subject to sharp price fluctuations. To our knowledge, there is no information on whether fishers who formerly derived their income from the Illinois river found jobs in the new economy. In general, commodity agriculture and commodity storage and shipping (*e.g.*, river terminals) are highly mechanised and not labour-intensive. Although agricultural machinery, fuel, and fertiliser used in commodity agriculture are sold in the river towns, these items are produced elsewhere.

In the case of the UMRS, it would probably have been cheaper to preserve natural services than it is to recover them after development. For example, some drainage and levee districts in the floodplains of the Illinois river are being purchased from private landowners by conservation organisations and state and federal natural resource agencies at prices that reflect the current use for row crop agriculture. The intent is to restore floodplain wetlands and backwaters for native plants and animals. In addition to purchase costs, there will be expenses for reshaping the interior basins of the levee districts (which were levelled for agriculture, in many cases) and in providing a natural water level cycle that benefits native biota (with gates to the river, or water pumps). It would have been cheaper to have preserved more of the undeveloped floodplain in the 1920s, when the state of Illinois initially considered the backwaters that were connected to the river as public lands, or a commons, and before court decisions that favoured private ownership and development (Schneider 1996).

In the developed river basins of the world, a key question for the public and for policy-makers is whether the total flow of social benefits (both natural and commercial) from a regulated floodplain-river ecosystem can be increased by selective re-connection of rivers with their floodplains and re-establishment of more natural flooding regimes. The communities along the rivers are particularly concerned about the quality of the naturalised environment that is achieved and the impact it will have on the local economy and quality of life. Attractive natural environments could attract outdoor recreationists and offer an alternative to the agriculture-dependent economy that may be increasingly subject to boom-or-bust cycles governed by world market prices. As recently as the 1950s, many river towns along the Illinois river had more diverse economies that included greater shares of tourism and outdoor recreation.

Preliminary results of efforts to model the river/floodplain system indicate that mere re-connection of the river with its floodplain will not be sufficient to restore high quality native forests and wetlands that attract migratory waterfowl (and hunters and bird watchers!). The water regime of our regulated river is subject to unnatural fluctuations during the summer growing season that limit native plants on the hydraulically connected floodplains. It is encouraging that some of the fluctuations appear to be attributable to operation of the navigation dams, indicating that modification of dam operations alone might improve conditions for native vegetation over extensive portions of the floodplain not currently protected by levees. The US Corps of Engineers has already modified dam operations at several locations on an experimental basis, and early results indicate that the production of wetland vegetation can be increased without adversely affecting commercial navigation. Such operational modifications probably would be inexpensive, compared to costs of artificially reproducing needed flood regimes behind low levees with the aid of gates and pumps, which is another naturalisation approach being used at a number of sites within the UMRS as part of a state-federal Habitat Rehabilitation and Enhancement Programme.

The potential to naturalise the river/floodplain systemically cannot be fully realised just by restoration actions in the mainstem river and its floodplain. Rivers are products of their watersheds, so actions are also needed in tributaries and uplands. A rising tide of public interest in protecting and restoring rivers and floodplains has stimulated expansion of existing government conservation programmes in the American Midwest to encourage farmers to convert erodible and flood prone land that is near streams from crop production into permanent vegetation. The new generations of these programmes concentrate on riparian zones and on specific problem watersheds that deliver excessive amounts of sediment and water. The scope of these watershed restoration efforts represent a tremendous challenge to efforts to model their cumulative impacts on downstream channels and floodplains.

Predictive models that are used in assessing effects of river development and river naturalisation need to be verified by measurements recorded as projects are instituted, to improve the models and to provide a more scientific basis for both preservation and naturalisation. Some development and naturalisation projects should incorporate hypothesis-testing and experiments and the potential yield of information should be considered as one factor in the cost-benefit analysis: an Adaptive Environmental Assessment and Management (AEAM) approach (Holling 1978). AEAM has begun to be applied in the US and around the world, including the Columbia river, Chesapeake Bay, south Florida, and the upper Mississippi river, where shippers, conservationists, transportation and natural resource agencies from five states, the US Corps of Engineers, the US Fish and Wildlife Service, the US Geological Survey, and several technical experts from outside the region, are currently exploring ways of improving the navigation system while maintaining or restoring the river-floodplain ecosystem (Gunderson *et al.* 1995, Holling 1978, Adaptive Environmental Assessment Steering Committee 1997). AEAM includes use of existing data and simulation models to inform stakeholders and to support decisions regarding restoration and conservation of natural resources. AEAM represents a middle ground between the 1950s US model of comprehensive river basin planning by technical experts in development agencies, and the socio-political realities of the 1990s in the US, where power is devolving from the federal to state and local levels, partnerships are necessitated by budget constraints, and there is a public demand for environmental preservation and restoration. In the US greater attention is now paid to in-stream uses of water, including fish production, protection of endangered species, and recreational uses, and at least 465 dams have been removed since 1912 to recover native fish populations, alleviate dam safety concerns, or revitalise local communities (American Rivers *et al.* 1999). There is increasing awareness that the structure and function of natural and restored rivers vary across space and time; indeed, that variation (disturbance regime) is required to maintain many ecosystems (Poff *et al.*1997). Planning and engineering to incorporate this variability requires change on the part of the development agencies, whose historic missions have generally involved reducing variability (in water supply, shoreline configurations, channel positions of rivers, etc.).

Finally, we end with a plea for scientific monitoring and evaluation of both river recovery and river development programmes, for the sake of improving both science and policy. Management cannot be adaptive without information about the current status and trends in the key physical driving variables (*e.g.*, the sediment and water regimes), biological interactions, and indicators of interest (*e.g.*, population status of key species). A management experiment is worthless without data to show whether the hypotheses were rejected or accepted. Failure is instructive, as long as sufficient information was gathered to understand why the failure occurred. Similarly, little is gained by success if the reasons for success are not known; it may be impossible to extend the results to another site, or even to repeat them at the same site. Worse, there may be little confidence that the success was triggered by the management practice, rather than by some natural change that was unaccounted for.

## Acknowledgements

The research project discussed is supported in part by the US Environmental Protection Agency and the National Science Foundation Water and Watershed Programme (Grant DEB-9613562). We gratefully acknowledge long-term support and information provided by the Illinois Natural History Survey (a unit of the Illinois Department of Natural Resources), by the US Army Corps of Engineers, and by the six field stations and the Environmental Management Technical Center (EMTC) of the Long Term Resource Monitoring Programme (LTRMP) for the upper Mississippi river system. EMTC is a unit of the Upper Mississippi Environmental Science Center of the US Geological Survey. The authors are grateful for the advice provided by the two anonymous referees and R.M. Sparks.

## References

Adaptive Environmental Assessment Steering Committee. 1997. Phase 1 report for adaptive environmental assessment on the upper Mississippi river. Upper Mississippi River Basin Association, St. Paul.
American Rivers, Friends of the Earth & Trout Unlimited. 1999. Dam removal success stories: Restoring rivers through selective removal of dams that don't make sense. American Rivers, Washington DC.
Barkau, R.L. 1995. UNET - One-dimensional unsteady flow through a full network of open channels (Revised by CEWRC-HEC USACE). Hydrologic Engineering Center, Davis.
Bellrose, F.C., Paveglio, F.L. & Steffeck, D.W. 1979. Waterfowl populations and the changing environment of the Illinois river valley. Illinois Natural History Survey Bulletin 32: 1-54.
Bellrose, F.C., Havera, S.P., Paveglio, F.L. & Steffeck, D.W. 1983. The fate of lakes in the Illinois river valley. Illinois Natural History Survey, Biological Notes 119: 1-27.
Brigham Young University. 1992. Fast TABS hydrodynamic modeling reference manual. Engineering Graphics Laboratory, Provo.
Connell, J.H. 1975. Some mechanisms producing structure in natural communities: a model and evidence from field experiments. In: Cody, M.L. & Diamond, J. (Eds.). Ecology and evolution of communities. Harvard University Press, Cambridge. pp. 460-490.
Connell, J.H. 1978. Diversity in tropical rain forests and coral reefs. Science 199: 1302-1309.
Costanza, R., Sklar, F.H. & White, M.L. 1990. Modeling coastal landscape dynamics. BioScience 40/2: 91-107.
Fredrickson, L.H. & Taylor, T.S. 1982. Management of seasonally flooded impounds for wildlife. Resources Publication Number 148. US Department of Interior, Fish and Wildlife Service, Washington DC.

Galloway, G.E. 2000. Three centuries of river management along the Mississippi river: Engineering and hydrological aspects. In: Smits, A.J.M , Nienhuis, P.H. & Leuven, R.S.E.W. (Eds.). New approaches to river management. Backhuys Publishers, Leiden. pp. 51-64.

Gunderson, L.H., Holling, C.S. & Light, S.S. (Eds.). 1995. Barriers and bridges to the renewal of ecosystems and institutions. Columbia University Press, New York.

Havinga, H. & Smits, A.J.M. 2000. River management along the Rhine: a retrospective view. In: Smits, A.J.M , Nienhuis, P.H. & Leuven, R.S.E.W. (Eds.). New approaches to river management. Backhuys Publishers, Leiden. pp. 15-32.

Hirschi, R.L. 1999. An economic analysis of flood easements: the case of the LaGrange reach of the Illinois river. Ph.D. Thesis. Department of Agricultural and Consumer Economics, University of Illinois at Urbana-Champaign, Urbana.

Holling, C.S. 1978. Adaptive environmental assessment and management. John Wiley, London.

Leopold, L.B. 1994. Flood hydrology and the floodplain. In: White G.F. & Myers M.F. (Eds). Water resources update. Coping with the flood: the next phase. The University Council on Water Resources, Carbondale. pp.11-14.

Lubinski, K.S., Wallendorf, M.J. & Reese, M.C. 1981. Analysis of upper Mississippi river system correlations between physical, biological and navigational variables. Technical Report in partial fulfilment of Contract No. 895-305. Upper Mississippi River Basin Commission, St. Paul.

Mulvihill, W.F. & Cornish, L.D. 1929. Flood control report: an engineering study of the flood situation in the state of Illinois. Illinois Division of Waterways, Springfield.

Phipps, R.L. 1979. Simulation of wetlands forest vegetation dynamics. Ecological Modeling 7: 257-288.

Phipps, R.L. & Applegate, L.H. 1983. Simulation of management alternatives in wetland forests. In: Jorgensen, S.E. & Mitsch, M.J. (Eds.). Application of ecological modeling in environmental management (Part b). Elsevier Science Publishers, Amsterdam. pp. 311-339.

Poff, N.L., Allan, J.D., Bain, M.B., Karr, J.R., Prestegaard, K.L., Richter, B.D., Sparks, R.E.& Stromberg, J.C. 1997. The natural flow regime. Bioscience 47/11:769-784.

Rhoads, B.L. & Herricks, E.E.1996. Human-induced change in low energy agricultural streams: an example from east-central Illinois. In: Brookes, A. & Shield, F.D. (Eds.). River channel restoration. Wiley, Chichester. pp. 968-973.

Scarpino, P.V. 1985. Great river: an environmental history of the upper Mississippi, 1890-1950. University of Missouri Press, Columbia.

Schneider, D.W. 1996. Enclosing the floodplain: resource conflict on the Illinois river, 1880-1920. Environmental History 1/2: 70-96.

Singh, K.P. & Ramamurthy, S.R. 1990. Climate change and resulting hydrologic response: Illinois river basin. In: Riggins, R.E. (Ed.). Watershed planning and analysis in action: symposium proceedings of Illinois river conference on watershed management. American Society of Civil Engineers, New York. pp. 28-37.

Sklar, F.H., Costanza, R. & Day, J.W. 1985. Dynamic spatial simulation modeling of coastal wetland habitat succession. Ecological Modeling 29: 261-281.

Sparks, R.E. 1984. The role of contaminants in the decline of the Illinois river: implications for the upper Mississippi. In: Wiener, J.G., Anderson, R.V. & McConville, D.R. (Eds.). Contaminants in the upper Mississippi river. Proceedings of the 15th Annual Meeting of the Mississippi River Research Consortium. Butterworth Publishers, Stoneham.

Sparks, R.E. 1992. Risks of altering the hydrologic regime of large rivers. In: Cairns, J., Niederlehner, B.R. & Orvos, D.R. (Eds.). Predicting ecosystem risk. Princeton Scientific Publishing Co. Inc., Princeton.

Sparks, R.E. 1995. Need for ecosystem management of large rivers and their floodplains. BioScience 45: 168-182.

Sparks, R.E., Nelson, J.C. & Yin, Y. 1998. Naturalization of the flood regime in regulated rivers. The case of the upper Mississippi river. BioScience 48:706-720.

Sparks, R.E., Ross, P.E. & Dillon, F.S. 1993. Identification of toxic substances in the upper Illinois river. Final Report ILENR/RE-WR-92/07. Illinois Department of Energy and Natural Resources, Springfield.

Sparks, R.E., Bayley, P.B., Kohler, S.L. & Osborne, L.L. 1990. Disturbance and recovery of large floodplain rivers. Environmental Management 14/5:699-709.

Stoeckel, J.A., Sparks, R.E., Blodgett, K.D., Whitney, S.D. & Raibley, P.T. 1996. Interbasin dispersal of invading aquatic species. Illinois Natural History Survey Reports 341: 4-8.

Thomas, W.A. & McAnally, W.H. 1991. User's manual for the generalized computer programme system, open-channel flow and sedimentation, TABS-MD. US Army Corps of Engineers, Waterways Experiment Station, Vicksburg.

Thompson, J. 1989. Case studies in drainage and levee district formation and development on the floodplain of the lower Illinois river, 1890s to 1930s. Illinois Water Resources Center, Special Report 16: 1-255.

USACE 1997. Report to Congress: An evaluation of the Upper Mississippi River System Environmental Management Programme. US Army Corps of Engineers (USACE), Rock Island District, Rock Island.

# A POLICY ANALYSIS FOR THE UPPER DANUBE RIVER SECTION IN HUNGARY

J. Leentvaar[1] & P.C.G. Glas[2]
*1 Ministry of Transport, Public Works and Water Management, Institute for Inland Water Management and Waste Water Treatment RIZA, P.O. Box 17, 8200 AA Lelystad, The Netherlands;*
*2 WL/Delft Hydraulics, P.O. Box 177, 2600 MH Delft, The Netherlands*

## Abstract

This paper presents the results of a preliminary application of the method of policy analysis to the case of the Gabcikovo-Nagymaros hydropower project in the Danube. The policy analysis method provides a framework for the generation and comparison of technical alternatives for large infrastructural projects. After more than 10 years of dispute between successive governments in (Czecho)Slovakia and Hungary, the countries still have not reached a final agreement about the modalities for the completion and operation of the Gabcikovo-Nagymaros hydropower project in the Danube. The dispute has been submitted for arbitration at the International Court of Justice (ICJ) in The Hague. As a result of the Court's ruling of 25 September 1997, Slovakia and Hungary have been negotiating again about the modalities of the execution of the project. The case is presently (December 1999) still pending in the ICJ, as no agreement has been reached so far. The results presented in this paper relate to the selection of evaluation criteria and comprehensive technical alternatives for the purpose of a policy analysis comparing technical alternatives for this project.

## 1. Introduction

This paper is the result of a request by the Hungarian government in 1997 to the Dutch Ministry of Transport, Public Works and Water Management for technical assistance in the debate on the Gabcikovo-Nagymaros hydropower dams in the Danube between Slovakia and Hungary. The request for expertise from Dutch governmental organisations involved designing a policy analysis to facilitate decision-making on the future of the Gabcikovo-Nagymaros project, in view of the judgement of the International Court of Justice in The Hague (ICJ 1997). The present paper is based on a report presented to the Hungarian government in May 1998 (Leentvaar *et al.* 1998).

The Hungarian government's request for assistance by the Netherlands was inspired by Dutch experience with the method of policy analysis which in the Netherlands has been applied to several large public infrastructural projects. In the Netherlands the continuous threat of the sea, as evidenced by a storm surge catastrophe in 1953 causing 1,800 fatalities and extensive damage, has led to large water management projects to protect the low-lying lands (Van de Ven 1993). In the

*New approaches to river management, pp. 249–266*
*edited by A.J.M. Smits, P.H. Nienhuis and R.S.E.W. Leuven*
© *2000 Backhuys Publishers, Leiden, The Netherlands*

planning phase of these works it was deemed important to involve public and private parties in the decision-making process. Another goal was to find a clear method of deciding between alternative plans, taking into account all the relevant interests. In the 1970s, policy analysis was used for this purpose in the Eastern-Scheldt project, which involved closing off an estuary from the North Sea (Van de Ven 1993). Since then, the method of policy analysis has matured and has been used for water management planning in the Netherlands (Luiten 1990).

On the basis of the Hungarian government's request for assistance, the Dutch Institute for Inland Water Management and Waste Water Treatment (RIZA) and WL | Delft Hydraulics have advised the Danube Programme Office in Budapest on all methodological aspects of its own execution of such an analysis for the Gabcikovo-Nagymaros project. The purpose of the contribution by the present authors to this analysis has been to provide the methodological basis, rather than to carry out the actual analysis. The specific viewpoints and data on the project expressed in this paper therefore reflect the information provided by the Danube Programme Office and do not necessarily reflect the point of view of the Dutch Government or the Dutch experts, who remain strictly neutral in this respect.

## 2. Methodology of policy analysis

### 2.1 General methodology

Policy analysis aims to clarify and rationalise the various options for management actions (Luiten 1990), and provides information on the 'pros' and 'cons' of the range of choices that can be made. It prepares for decision-making, but does not take the actual decision. Policy analysis pays attention to implementation feasibility (financial, legal and organisational aspects), but it does not deal with the actual implementation. The product of a policy analysis is an overview of possible and feasible alternatives with an assessment of their socio-economic, ecological and institutional impacts. An overview is generally presented as a score-card, showing the scores on the evaluation criteria expressing the impacts versus the scenario alternatives.

Policy analysis is part of the so-called policy cycle. Six phases can be distinguished within the policy cycle each with a different political weight (Figure 1).
- *Conflicts.* Signals from society indicate that there is a problem: awareness is raised. For some time there may be a difference of opinion between various groups within society about the extent, causes and effects of the problem. Consensus about the necessity of government intervention (need for policy making) ends this phase.
- *Policy analysis.* Although there is consensus about the fact that there is a problem, there is still difference of opinion on how the problem should be solved. Various alternative solutions and all the relevant interests are considered.
- *Decision making.* The government formulates an adequate policy and initiates a corresponding set of measures, based on the information derived from the policy analysis.
- *Implementation.* The plan is implemented. Investments are made, project designs are constructed. Attention by society and politics may fade.

- *Monitoring.* Controlling the situation is the central focus. A monitoring programme is executed to assess the effectiveness of the measures implemented,
and to identify any unforeseeable effects.
- *Evaluation.* Vigilance is required as new developments, new societal values,
new knowledge and understanding of the situation may require additional measures or lead to new conflicts of interest.

Policy analysis may be viewed as a systematic process which in our opinion can be
divided into five steps: 1. problem analysis; 2. determination of the objectives; 3.
design/pre-selection of alternatives; 4. selection of the criteria; 5. determination of
impacts.

No matter how objective the description of impacts, the final comparison and
decision are not made on the basis of analytical results alone. The selection of a preferred alternative depends partly on the scores for the various criteria, but also on
the political weights given to the various objectives. Considering all information,
and taking into account the weights, the final decision is made by those who are
politically responsible.

In short, the policy analyst clarifies and rationalises alternatives for management
actions, presents information but does not make the final decision. Likewise the
policy analyst considers implementation aspects but does not implement. The
expected positive effects of a policy analysis are: close interaction between all parties involved; public involvement; involvement of interest groups; objectivity of the
evaluation process; clarity of management alternatives before decision making.

## 2.2 Application to the Gabcikovo-Nagymaros case

One of the crucial steps of a policy analysis is to determine in what terms the alternatives should be evaluated. All relevant interests should be represented by a limited number of criteria that will capture all the important effects of the alternatives.

*Fig. 1.* The place of policy analysis in a policy cycle.

In the present case, the "1977 Treaty", the judgement by the ICJ and the objectives formulated provide the main fields for which criteria should be formulated.

The original project as described in the "1977 Treaty" had multiple objectives, as was pointed out by the ICJ (1997). These objectives comprise the following fields: 1) water management, 2) environment, 3) navigation, 4) energy, and 5) finance. The effect of the project on the environment has become increasingly important. Large amounts of environmental information have been produced by non-governmental groups, and this objective of the "1977 Treaty" has received special attention from the ICJ. Another field may be added in view of the current dispute, *viz.*, 6) international law.

For each of the fields of interest criteria had to be determined to represent the most important effects of the alternatives in that field. The effects in terms of these criteria should preferably be easy to determine (*i.e.*, measurable and predictable). For some of the fields selected, the criteria are straightforward, like the production of energy. For others, like the environment, it is very difficult to find criteria that encompass the complexity of the effects. In view of the purpose of the policy analysis, a limited set of criteria should be used, with a maximum of about five for each field.

Somlyódy (1991) also promoted the adoption of this methodology, which he referred to as system analysis, to the case of Gabcikovo-Nagymaros. His conclusion at that time was that a systematic assessment of this project was lacking. A comprehensive assessment, based on common scientific insight and commonly available data is still lacking until this day. This may partly explain why there still is no broad agreement, neither between Slovakia and Hungary, nor within the two countries, about the direction the Gabcikovo-Nagymaros project should take. The present paper does not fill this gap but does attempt to present a concrete structure for the technical assessments, the public debate and political decision making.

In de present case, the authors have been able to work together with a group of specialists from the Danube Programme Office, which was set up especially to provide technical support to the Hungarian delegation that took part in the negotiations with the Slovakian delegation in the period November 1997-March 1998. The authors had interviews with responsible representatives from various Hungarian ministries. Scientists, representatives of the ministries, Non Governmental Organisations (NGOs), municipal and regional authorities were invited to a workshop in March 1998 in Budapest, where the method and the preliminary results were presented. Because the objective of the project was to provide methodological progress rather than to provide concrete quantitative output, this paper does not contain references to sources of data that have been provided by our Hungarian counterparts.

## 3. Analysing the problem

This section presents some background information on the Gabcikovo-Nagymaros problem. After a brief history of the Gabcikovo-Nagymaros project and the related "1977 Treaty", the content of this "Treaty" and the development of the international dispute are described. Finally, the present situation and the boundary conditions for a solution are presented.

## 3.1 History of the Gabcikovo-Nagymaros project

Historically the Danube and its tributaries have played an important role in the social-economic development of the central part of Europe. The catchment area of the second largest river in Europe is shared by 12 countries (Germany, Austria, Czech Republic, Slovakia, Hungary, Croatia, Serbia, Slovenia, Bulgaria, Romania, Ukraine, Moldava). Planning for a large-scale development of the Danube to improve navigation and ice conditions started in the last century. Since then, the volume of traffic on, and the importance of, the waterway have continued to grow. The Danube-Main-Rhine Canal has opened a new chapter of development, creating a Trans-European waterway linking the Black Sea and the North Sea.

Exploitation of the hydropower potential of the Danube started in the first half of the former century. The first river dams including power stations were built in the upstream, steeper sections, at the same time improving the conditions for navigation in the area. These were followed by the development of the downstream Iron Gates section under a joint Yugoslav-Romanian project, the first stage of which was commissioned in 1972. The middle reaches, however, were still undeveloped for hydropower and constituted a bottle-neck for navigation. The river slope decreases considerably between Bratislava and Komárom. Historically, the meandering river deposited sediments eroded from the Alps in a number of branches, creating an approximately 300 km$^2$ alluvial fan. The area on the Hungarian side of the main stream is called Szigetköz, that on the Slovakian side Zitný Ostrov (Figure 2). Both are interspersed with laterals, islands, etc. Sand and gravel bars traditionally formed obstacles in the channel and often obstructed continuous navigation in low flow periods.

The frequent changes in the course of the river over the alluvial fan have created a valuable natural area, but also presented serious obstacles to navigation and flood hazards to the population in the area. From 1885 onwards, attempts were made to regulate the river by constructing flood levees and by selecting one of the major branches as the main navigation channel and largely closing the others. These measures, however, proved insufficient to ensure navigability throughout the year, as the bed remained mobile. More recently, retention of the bed load behind the river dams built upstream, combined with excessive commercial dredging, have resulted in an approximately 1.5 m degradation of the low-water bed. Commercial gravel dredging has since been discontinued, but the damage has been done. Flood protection has also proved inadequate, as serious floods occurred in 1954 and 1965.

In the early 1950s, Czechoslovakia and Hungary started planning a barrage system on the joint Czechoslovakian-Hungarian section of the Danube, in order to eliminate its shallows and develop the river's water power resources. The design of the large dam system was strongly influenced by the ideology and economic system of that period. In the early 1970s, the two sides worked out a joint plan of investment and a draft contract. Possible modifications of the border were negotiated. Finally, the Hungarian government withdrew its demand for a border change and approved the diversion of a 31 km long section of the Danube into Slovakia. In 1977, the countries signed a Treaty "concerning the construction and operation of the Gabcikovo-Nagymaros system of locks" (hereafter called the "1977 Treaty").

## 3.2 The "1977 Treaty"

The Gabcikovo-Nagymaros barrage system planned in the "1977 Treaty" consists of three dams and two hydroelectric power plants. Downstream of Bratislava, the Danube was to be dammed at Dunakiliti to flood an area of 60 square kilometres up to Bratislava. The reservoir would be 6.5 m deep at Dunakiliti. From Dunakiliti the main body of water was to go into a long canal on Slovak territory, bypassing a 31 km section of the old Danube bed. The first 17 km of this canal were to lead to the second dam at Gabcikovo, including a hydroelectric plant and a system of locks. The walls of this 300-650 m wide canal were to be built to a height of 9-18 m above the surrounding gravel and sandy terrain. The Gabcikovo plant was planned to have a capacity of 720 megawatts. From the Gabcikovo plant, the water course was to be routed back in an 8 km canal, to rejoin its old bed at Palkovicovo (Sap). International water traffic was to make use of this bypass canal instead of the old Danube bed, into which only 50-200 $m^3s^{-1}$ would flow instead of the former average of 2,000 $m^3s^{-1}$.

From the mouth of the canal the river continues eastward for another 100 km and then bends southward, entering a steeper valley at Nagymaros in Hungary. This was planned to be the site for the third dam, with another, 158 megawatt hydroelectric plant. The Nagymaros plant was meant to work almost continuously, while the Gabcikovo plant was intended to generate electricity mainly during peak hours. During the rest of the day most of the water of the river would be retained in the reservoir at Dunakiliti. The large changes in water level caused by the surges of water through Gabcikovo would be compensated by the Nagymaros dam. According to the Czechoslovakian-Hungarian bilateral agreement, the two countries would carry out the construction work equally and share the costs. After completion, they would also share the electricity produced (3,775 million kilowatt-hours per year). The area and location of the works are shown in figure 2.

## 3.3 The international dispute

Construction of the Gabcikovo power plant began in 1978, but was suspended in June 1981 when Hungary, caught up in a deepening economic crisis, was unable to continue construction. An agreement with Slovakia was signed to delay the project deadline. In Hungary, controversy over the project grew during the eighties as public debate on the environmental effects of the project became increasingly heated. The reformist wing of parliament started using the Gabcikovo-Nagymaros project as a political tool against communism. In 1989, the government first signed a protocol with Slovakia to accelerate the project and then decided to unilaterally suspend further construction at Dunakiliti. Consequently, the works at Nagymaros were abandoned and the *status quo* was maintained at Dunakiliti.

During this period, negotiations took place between the parties. Czechoslovakia also started investigating alternative solutions. One of them, a solution subsequently known as "Variant C", would create a smaller reservoir by unilaterally diverting the Danube at Cunovo (Figures 2 and 3), some 10 km upstream of the original site at Dunakiliti (Figure 4). The dam would be on Slovak territory and the river would be routed over Slovak territory to the original bypass canal. Work on Variant C

*Fig. 2.* Schematic overview of the area and works included in the "1977 Treaty" [110 x 75 km].

began in November 1991. Discussions continued between the two parties but to no avail, and the Hungarian Government transmitted to the Czechoslovak Government a Note Verbale terminating the "1977 Treaty" as of May 25, 1992. Five months later, Czechoslovakia proceeded with the damming of the river and started operating Gabcikovo. In December 1994 Hungary started demolition of the Nagymaros coffer-dam.

Immediately after the damming of the river by Czechoslovakia, negotiations started between Czechoslovakia, Hungary and the European Community, which led to the decision to put the case before the International Court of Justice in July 1993. On January 1, 1993, Slovakia had become an independent state. Thereafter, Hungary and Slovakia concluded a Special Agreement to establish and implement a temporary water management regime for the Danube. In April 1995, an agreement was signed to ensure the necessary diversion of water by Slovakia to the Szigetköz region. This special agreement was to remain in force until 14 days after court had delivered its judgement. For its part, Hungary agreed to construct a bottom sill at Dunakiliti to direct more water to the branches of the Danube.

## 3.4 The present situation

The ICJ in the Hague reached a verdict in September 1997. The Court ruled that Hungary had no right to suspend and abandon, in 1989, the works on the Nagymaros project and part of the Gabcikovo project. Furthermore, it ruled that the 1992 notification sent by Hungary had not terminated the Treaty. However, the

*Fig. 3.* The Cunovo dam.

*Fig. 4.* The Dunakiliti dam.

Court also ruled that Czechoslovakia had not been entitled to put into operation the "provisional solution" (Variant C), effectively diverting the Danube in 1992 by closing the dam at Cunovo. Both parties agreed to negotiate for six months to find a solution (until March 25, 1998) after the judgement of the ICJ. Should they be unable to reach an agreement within six months thereafter, either Party might request the Court to render an additional Judgement to determine the modalities for executing its judgement.

The judgement of the ICJ (1997) states that: *"the factual situation as it has developed since 1989 shall be placed within the context of the preserved and developing treaty relationship, in order to achieve its object and purpose in so far as that is feasible".*

In the current situation, the first dam downstream of Bratislava is located at Cunovo (Dunacsuny) in Slovakia, diverting the main body of the Danube onto Slovak territory and into the original bypass canal. Approximately 400 $m^3s^{-1}$ of water is diverted into the old Danube bed. Under the "1977 Treaty" this would only have been 50-200 $m^3s^{-1}$, but the total volume of water flowing through the Danube amounts to an average of 2000 $m^3s^{-1}$. The dam, the system of locks and the hydropower station at Gabcikovo are operational and the electricity is used solely by Slovakia. The Dunakiliti dam has been finished and a bottom sill diverts water to the southern branches of the Danube. The construction works for the Nagymaros dam have been dismantled.

## 4. Results

### 4.1 Selection of criteria for the policy analysis

As was explained in section 2.2, a limited number of criteria had to be selected to cover the six policy fields relevant to this case 1) water management, 2) environment, 3) navigation, 4) energy, 5) finance, 6) international law. On the basis of extensive interviews with specialists and representatives of various ministries in Hungary, a total of sixteen criteria were selected (Tables 1, 2, and 3).

### 4.2 Selection of management alternatives for the policy analysis

#### 4.2.1 Reducing the number of potential alternatives

The stretch of the river between Bratislava and Budapest that is influenced by the project is divided into two separate areas. The upstream area runs from Bratislava to Palkovicovo (Figure 2), where the bypass canal and the old Danube bed rejoin. It comprises the reservoir, the old Danube bed and its branches and the bypass canal. The analysis of the upstream area considered possible futures of the Cunovo, Dunakiliti and Gabcikovo dams. The downstream area runs from Palkovicovo to Budapest and the analysis of this area may include *e.g.* the construction of one or more downstream dams. The possible functions of these large structures define the main alternatives for the upstream and downstream areas.

The choice of main alternatives in terms of structural design was clearly the most important decision in this policy analysis. There were, however, several other issues that had to be included in the analysis, *viz.,* a) the flow regime in the old Danube bed, b) mitigating measures (such as underwater weirs), and c) the application of peak power at the Gabcikovo hydropower station.

It was important to take these three issues into account, without however ending up with an unmanageable number of alternatives. If the upstream alternatives, the three issues mentioned above and all downstream alternatives had been combined in one set of alternatives, the evaluation matrix would have become very complex.

Figure 5 illustrates the number of alternatives resulting from only one upstream alternative, taking into account three different flow regimes in the old Danube bed, mitigating measures, peak power and four downstream alternatives.

In this approach, four upstream alternatives combined with three flow regimes, mitigating measures, peak power and four downstream alternatives would have added up to a total of 192 alternatives. It was obvious that the policy analysis had to be structured in a different way in order to remain practical. Therefore the following approach was adopted.

First of all, a distinction was made between upstream and downstream alternatives, because in principle they do not effect each other and can be considered separately in the analysis. (For example, the effect that a downstream dam would have on shipping does not depend on the choice of upstream alternative.) This means that in fact two analyses were made, one for the upstream area and another for the downstream area. These analyses resulted in two evaluation matrices.

In a second stage, the other important issues were considered such as flow regime in the old Danube bed, mitigating measures (such as underwater weirs) and peak power.

– *The flow regime* in the old Danube bed is crucial to the Szigetköz area and it is therefore important to determine the effects of the various flow regimes for the upstream area. However, the effects of the choice of main alternative and flow regime do not influence each other, but may be added to produce the overall effect. Therefore the additional effects of each flow regime were included in a separate matrix and added to each main alternative to determine the overall effect.

– *Mitigating measures* have the same effect on each alternative. These were therefore considered separately. For any decision on the basic alternatives mitigating measures can be used to soften or undo all or part of the undesirable side effects. In this analysis it was assumed that each flow regime includes the mitigating measures that meet the requirements for habitat development in the area.

– *Peak power* is mentioned in the operational plans relating to the "1977 Treaty" and influences practically all fields selected. Upstream, the use of peak power affects the amount of hydroelectric power that can be generated, as well as the revenues from the power production. On the downstream part of the river, peak power has more structural effects, which are the same for each alternative and may be added to the effects of each main alternative. The downstream matrix was evaluated for each alternative with and without the use of peak-power. It was noted that an extreme peak power regime would give very distinct and sudden elevations of the water level ('tidal waves'). At the confluence, these waves would also induce an upstream flow into the old Danube and the Mosoni Danube up to Györ, partly obstructing the flow of the river and possibly hindering the downstream dilution of the Györ waste water treatment plant effluent. This negative effect on the flow regime in the upstream area has been included in the upstream matrix as a footnote.

Consideration of all of these arguments resulted in the following framework for this policy analysis. For the upstream area there are two matrices, one that compares the effects of the main upstream alternatives and another that lists the additional effects of various flow regimes in the old Danube bed. The analysis assumes that for each

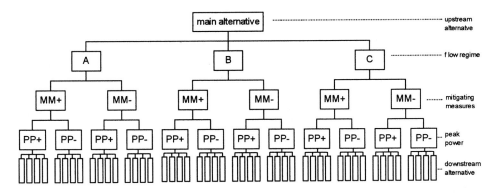

*Fig. 5.* The number of alternatives resulting from one upstream alternative when all important aspects are incorporated as separate issues into the final matrix. A, B and C are the three different flow regimes. Mitigation measures, mainly to be taken in the original Danube, can either be present (MM+) or not present (MM-). Electricity can be generated in peak-power mode (PP+) or by the run-of-the-river method (PP-).

flow regime, all mitigating measures will be taken. For the downstream area, there is one matrix, which compares the main downstream alternatives, with an extra column that lists the additional effects on the downstream area if energy is generated in peak power mode at the Gabcikovo hydropower station.

### 4.2.2 The alternatives and flow regimes

Discussions about the possibilities to reconcile the present situation with the "1977 Treaty" or to reach some other agreement with Slovakia have resulted in a number of ideas for a solution. Four alternatives and a reference situation were identified for both the upstream area between Bratislava and Palkovicovo and the downstream area between Palkovicovo and Budapest. Three different flow regimes were considered for the old Danube bed

*Upstream alternatives*
Adoption of the *status quo alternative* would mean that the present Variant C would be operated by Slovakia, without Hungarian participation. Slovakia would operate a hydropower plant at Cunovo and would develop tourist infrastructure. A schematic impression of the upstream situation in this alternative is shown in figure 6a.

In the *adoption alternative*, Hungary would co-operate in the completion and operation of Variant C. Investments and running costs, as well as the income and energy production would be shared (although the 50-50 division agreed in the "1977 Treaty" could only be achieved if a downstream dam were to be built). A schematic impression of this alternative is the same as that for the Status Quo alternative (Figure 6a).

The *Dunakiliti alternative* goes back to the original plan of 1977. The weir at Dunakiliti would be completed and taken into operation as the main regulator of the lake. The original lay-out of the reservoir would be realised, which is about 30% larger than at present under Variant C (Figure 6b). The Cunovo weir would be operated during the construction/completion of Dunakiliti and its associated infrastructure. The Slovak side would be (partly?) compensated for the investments in Variant C (with the exception of the ship locks and power plant).

In *the split reservoir alternative*, the basis for the operation of the diversion channel and Gabcikovo would still be the present Variant C, but Dunakiliti would also be completed. Thus, a second, smaller reservoir would be created with a level of 126-128 m (present level = 123 m, only in the old Danube river bed). This would provide a source of water for improved regulation of water in the branch system (Figure 6c).

For all of these alternatives, the *reference situation* would be the 'natural' situation as it existed before 1992 (*i.e.*, before Variant C became operational). It should be noted that the situation with respect to river degradation and water tables was already deteriorating at that moment, so in effect, the reference is not the 'pristine river'. The reference situation was used in the analysis as the reference point for comparing the alternatives.

*Flow regimes in the old Danube bed*
Three different flow regimes have been evaluated. The flow regimes all include mitigating measures that meet the requirements for habitat development in the area.

Low flow regime:          Winter average 50 $m^3s^{-1}$ ; summer average 200 $m^3s^{-1}$.
                          Flow regime as described in the "1977 Treaty"
Middle flow regime:       Winter average 250-400 $m^3s^{-1}$; summer average 400-
                          600 $m^3s^{-1}$.
                          Current flow regime.
High flow regime:         Annual average up to 800 $m^3s^{-1}$.
                          Substantially more than current flow regime.

These flow regimes in the old Danube bed are options for the adoption alternative, the Dunakiliti alternative and the split reservoir alternative. Therefore these alternatives also include all mitigating measures necessary for habitat development in the area. The Status Quo alternative includes a temporary agreement signed between Hungary and Slovakia on water management that is the same as the middle flow regime.

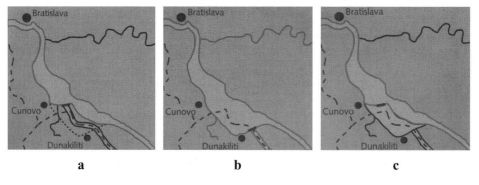

a                              b                              c

*Fig. 6.* The three upstream alternatives (a – status quo and adoption; b – Dunakiliti, c – split reservoir) [29 x 27 km].

*Downstream alternatives*

Five downstream alternatives have been considered: a) the natural dredging alternative, b) the classical river improvement alternative, c) the two barrages alternative, d) the one downstream dam alternative, and e) the reference situation.

*The natural dredging alternative* refers to the situation in which the necessary navigation depth would be maintained by continuous dredging. To prevent further degradation of the river, the dredged material would be recirculated internally in the river.

*The classical river improvement alternative* was developed under the strict assumption that no dams would be constructed. Navigation depth would be maintained by a combination of groins and dredging. Rehabilitation of branches and floodplains could be included to improve the natural characteristics of the river. This method was elaborated earlier by WL | Delft Hydraulics and Vituki (WL | Delft Hydraulics, 1993).

*The two barrages alternative* would follow the example of some rivers abroad, *e.g.,* the Mississippi (Sparks 1992). It would comprise the construction of a series of steps (dams/locks) dividing the length of the river into stretches, each with its own regulated water depth.

*The one downstream dam alternative* would entail the construction of a downstream dam that would include locks and a hydropower plant. An important point would be to prevent river degradation further downstream from the confluence at Palkovicovo.

*The reference situation* is the present situation, including dredging and navigation control at some locations in the Danube between Palkovicovo and Budapest. The reference situation was used in the analysis as a reference point for comparing the other alternatives.

### 4.3 Comparing the alternatives

The alternatives defined in the previous sections were used to complete the evaluation matrices (Tables 1, 2 and 3). All the alternatives were compared with the reference situation, which is the situation as it existed before 1992. Leentvaar *et al.* (1998) presented an elaboration of the scores for all criteria. Here we present the summary in the form of three scorecards for the upstream alternatives, for the flow alternatives and for the downstream alternatives.

### 4.3.1 Upstream alternatives

There are two matrices for the upstream area: one matrix with four alternatives for the upstream area that only analyses the effects due to the structures themselves and an additional matrix for the effects of various flow regimes in the old Danube bed. The comparison between the main structures upstream is made in table 1. Some of the criteria have a more specific focus than the entire upstream area. The environmental criteria are: water quality in the reservoir, opportunities for water level regulation of groundwater and river branches and opportunities for flow regulation. Commercial shipping would take place in the bypass canal and yachting in the old Danube bed. Power would be generated at Gabcikovo.

*Table 1.* Matrix for the analysis of the effect of various upstream alternatives on the upstream area. All alternatives are compared with the reference situation, which is the "natural" situation as it existed before 1992, with a theoretical score of "0". The following scores for the alternatives are used in the matrices: –, 0, +, which means worse, equal or better than the reference situation. The criteria for energy, finance and international law cannot be compared with the reference situation. Therefore energy and finance criteria have been listed quantitatively, while the scores for international law are: *, **, ***, with more stars signifying more compliance with the "1977 Treaty".

| Criteria | Alternatives | Status Quo alternative | Adoption alternative | Dunakiliti alternative | Split reservoir alternative |
|---|---|---|---|---|---|
| W | riverbed erosion | 0 | + | + | + |
| | flood protection | + | + | + | + |
| | ice regulation | 0 | 0 | + | 0 |
| | bank filtration | 0 | 0 | 0 / + | 0 / + |
| E | water quality | 0 | 0 | 0 | 0 |
| | water level regulation | – | – | 0 / + | + |
| | flow regulation possible* | – | + | + | + |
| | nature conservation | – | 0 | 0 / + | + |
| N | commercial shipping | + | + | + | + |
| | yachting | – | – | + | + / 0 |
| $H_p$ | power generated at Gabcikovo: standard / peak ($10^9$ kWh) | 2.6 / 2.5 | 2.6 / 2.5 | 2.6 / 2.5 | 2.6 / 2.5 |
| $ | investment-type costs ($10^9$ HUF) | 15-90 | 15-90 | 16-91 | 16-91 |
| | annual revenues from power: standard / peak ($10^9$ HUF) | 26 / 30 | 26 / 30 | 26 / 30 | 26 / 30 |
| | operational costs | 0.5 | 0.5 | 0.5 | 0.5 |
| | compensation | ? | ? | ? | ? |
| I | compliance with "1977 Treaty" | * | ** | *** | ** |

E: Environment; $H_p$: Hydropower; I: International law; N: Navigation; W: Water management; $: Finance in Hungarian Forints (HUF).

## 4.3.2 Flow regime alternatives

The effects of the flow regime in the old Danube bed have been analysed in table 2. The focus is slightly different for some of the criteria. The criteria for water management (W) were evaluated for the old Danube bed. The environmental criteria (E) were all evaluated for the Szigetköz area and the opportunities for water level regulation and flow regulation have been changed into water level and flow conditions. Hydroelectric power would be generated at Gabcikovo.

## 4.3.3 Downstream alternatives

There is only one matrix for the downstream area (Table 3). This includes one extra column for the additional effects of peak power that can be added to the effects of the main alternatives if the energy at Gabcikovo is generated in peak power mode. The environment (E) section includes the flow criterion of natural flow conditions, and the nature of river banks. The amount of power shown would be generated at the lower dam(s).

*Table 2.* Matrix for the effects of various flow regimes in the old Danube bed on the upstream area. All alternatives are compared with the reference situation, which is the "natural" situation as it existed before 1992, with a theoretical score of "0". The following scores for the alternatives are used in the matrices: −, 0, +, which means worse, equal or better than the reference situation. The criteria for energy, finance and international law cannot be compared with the reference situation. Therefore energy and finance criteria have been listed quantitatively, while the scores for international law are: *, **, ***, with more stars signifying more compliance with the "1977 Treaty".

| | Criteria | Winter average: 50 m$^3$s$^{-1}$ summer average: 200 m$^3$s$^{-1}$ | Winter average: 250-400 m$^3$s$^{-1}$ summer average: 400-600 m$^3$s$^{-1}$ | Yearly average up to 800 m$^3$s$^{-1}$ |
|---|---|---|---|---|
| W | riverbed erosion | 0 | 0 | 0 |
| | flood protection | 0 | 0 | 0 |
| | ice regulation | 0 | 0 | 0 |
| | bank filtration | − | 0 | + |
| E | water quality | − | 0 | + |
| | water level | − | 0 | + |
| | flow conditions | − | 0 | + |
| | nature conservation | − | 0 | + |
| N | commercial shipping | 0 | 0 | 0 |
| | yachting | − | + | + |
| H$_p$ | power generated at Gabcikovo: standard / peak (10$^9$ kWh) | 2.9 / 2.8 | 2.6 / 2.5 | 2.0 / 1.9 |
| $ | investment-type costs (10$^9$ HUF) | 25 | 20 | 15 |
| | annual revenues from power: standard / peak (10$^9$ HUF) | 29 / 35 | 26 / 30 | 20 / 24 |
| | operational costs | 0.3 | 0.2 | 0.2 |
| | compensation | ? | ? | ? |
| I | compliance with the "1977 Treaty" | *** | ** | * |

E: Environment; H$_p$: Hydropower; I: International law; N: Navigation; W: Water management; $: Finance in Hungarian Forints (HUF).

## 5. Conclusion and discussion

The details of the policy analysis are given in Leentvaar *et al.* (1998). The present paper only discusses the methodological conclusions.

The main basis for a policy analysis as described in section 2 is an agreement on the methodological aspects of the analysis. Part of this common basis is the definition of a set of criteria ("yardsticks") against which the alternative policy options can be measured and evaluated. If predictions of future effects (environmental, social, economic etc.) are essential in the evaluation process, a common set of predictive data or models should also be developed.

To date, these prerequisites for the execution of a rational policy analysis have not been met between Hungary and Slovakia. Although the Hungarian side did provide assistance in the design of such a method, this approach would by definition have to be two-sided for the resolution of a transboundary policy problem. The main

*Table 3.* Matrix for the analysis of the effect of downstream alternatives on the downstream area. All alternatives are compared with the reference situation, which is the "natural" situation as it existed before 1992, with a theoretical score of "0". The following scores for the alternatives are used in the matrices: –, 0, +, which means worse, equal or better than the reference situation. The criteria for energy, finance and international law cannot be compared with the reference situation. Therefore energy and finance criteria have been listed quantitatively, while the scores for international law are: *, **, ***, with more stars signifying more compliance with the "1977 Treaty".

| Criteria | Alternatives | natural dredging | classical river improvement | two barrages | one down-stream dam | peak power |
|---|---|---|---|---|---|---|
| W | riverbed erosion | 0 | – | + | + | – |
| | flood protection | 0 | 0 | – | – / 0 | 0 |
| | ice regulation | 0 | 0 | – | – | 0 |
| | bank filtration | 0 | – / 0 | 0 / + | + | – |
| E | water quality | – | 0 | 0 | 0 | 0 |
| | water level | 0 | – / 0 | + | + | – |
| | natural flow conditions | 0 | 0 | – | – | – |
| | nature of river banks | – | 0 | + | + | – |
| S | commercial shipping | 0 | 0 | + | + | – |
| | Yachting | 0 | – | + / 0 | + | – |
| E | power generated at downstream dam: standard / peak ($10^9$ kWh) | 0 | 0 | 0.7 / 0.7 | 1.0 / 1.0 | – |
| $f$ | investment-type costs ($10^9$ HUF) | 0 | 41.5 | 20 + 401 | 20 + 191 | |
| | annual revenues from power: standard / peak ($10^9$ HUF) | 0 / 0 | 0 / 0 | 7.3 / 9.1 | 10.4 / 12.9 | + |
| | operational costs | 0.03 - 0.1 | 0.4 | 10 | 5 | |
| | compensation | ? | ? | ? | ? | |
| I | compliance with the "1977 Treaty" | * | * | * / ** | ** / *** | + |

E: Environment; H$_p$: Hydropower; I: International law; N: Navigation; W: Water management; $: Finance in Hungarian Forints (HUF).

aim of the assistance has so far been limited to opening up the issue to public debate in Hungary by means of a broad forum, based on generally available data. Therefore it is at present impossible to conclude whether application of the method would lead to other, better or more acceptable solutions in the case of Gabcikovo-Nagymaros.

The question is also relevant whether the outcome of the decision-making process would be straightforward if all objectives of a full policy analysis were met, and a complete analysis of the evaluation criteria were made. In approaching this question we want to draw attention to a study by Driessen *et al.* (1997) in which the authors reflect on quality criteria for a decision-making process. The authors consider seven criteria to be 'explanatory variables' for social and administrative acceptance. The more positive the opinion about each of the criteria, the broader the acceptance will be. The authors point out, that other factors besides the seven process-oriented criteria may also play a role. These include project organisation, project management, project budget and the possibility to link various projects and to identify win-win solutions. These are the quality criteria proposed, formulated in seven questions.

1. Have the interest groups been able to express their opinions?
2. Have the interests been mapped (safety, economy, landscape, nature conservation, cultural values, etc.)?
3. Have alternatives been developed and have they been compared for the various conflicting interests (the policy analysis phase)?
4. Have compensation options been developed and have they been used to try and solve potential conflicts?
5. Have interest groups been able to express their opinion about the plans and have the authorities made clear what they have done with these opinions?
6. Has the decision been clearly motivated by the authorities?
7. Is there a clear system for citizens to file objections to a project or appeal to an administrative or civil court?

Looking at this list of seven 'explanatory variables' for the quality of decision making, proposed by Driessen *et al.* (1997), it may be concluded that most of these criteria have not been met in the Gabcikovo-Nagymaros case, or at best only partially. In so far as they have been met, their value has largely not been recognised by interest groups and by the general public.

With respect to the process of decision making about the future of the Gabcikovo-Nagymaros project we therefore conclude that neither the evaluation criteria that we have proposed, nor the quality criteria proposed by Driessen *et al.* (1997) have been duly taken into account.

Finally, it must be realised that even if all available data and knowledge could be mustered in the decision-making process, there would still remain a lack of information and, consequently, uncertainties in the final decision on the rules of operation for the project's installation. Whereas some might argue that under the precautionary principle both countries should therefore abandon the Gabcikovo-Nagymaros in any form, it may also be argued that the remaining uncertainties should be referred to in the Treaty and dealt with jointly in the operational phase. This leads to redefinition of the operational rules and/or compensation between the Slovak and Hungarian governments under a shared responsibility for the future and sustainable management of the Danube river.

## Acknowledgements

The authors would like to express their gratitude to the members of the Danube Programme Office, especially Dr I. Mayer, Dr Á. Szentiványi and Dr J. Poroszlai for their hospitality and their contributions to numerous discussions which have led to the framework presented here. We are also indebted to Dr A. Lindenbach and M.T. Wiechers for their contributions to the project.

## References

Driessen, P.P.J., De Gier, A.A.J., Glasbergen, P., Van Hall, A. & Lammens, M.C. 1997. Uit nood geboren, VUGA Uitgeverij B.V., 's-Gravenhage. (in Dutch).

ICJ. 1997. Judgement of the International Court of Justice (ICJ). ICJ General List 92 (http://www.icj-cij.org), The Hague.

Leentvaar, J., Glas, P.C.G., Wiechers, M.T. & Lindenbach, A. 1998. From powerplay to policy analysis. Institute for Inland Water Management and Waste Water Treatment (RIZA) and WL | Delft Hydraulics, Lelystad and Delft.

Luiten, J.P.A. 1990. Policy analysis of water management for the Netherlands, In: Koudstaal, R., Pennekamp, H.A. & Wesseling, J. (Eds.), Planning water resources management in The Netherlands. WL|Delft Hydraulics / ICW – Institute for Land and Water Management Research, Delft/Wageningen. pp. 47-58.

Somlyódy, L. 1991. Application of system analysis in water pollution control: perspectives for Central and Eastern Europe. Wat. Sci. Tech. 24/6: 73-87.

Sparks, R. 1992. The upper Mississippi river. In: Maurizi, S. & Poillon, F. (Eds.), Restoration of aquatic ecosystems. National Academy Press, Washington D.C. pp. 406-412.

Van de Ven, G.P. (Ed.). 1993. Man-made lowlands – history of water management and land reclamation in the Netherlands. Matrijs, Utrecht.

WL | Delft Hydraulics. 1993. Danube environmental and navigation project. WL | Delft Hydraulics / VITUKI, Delft / Budapest.

# NEW CONCEPTS IN RIVER AND WATER MANAGEMENT IN THE RHINE RIVER BASIN: HOW TO LIVE WITH THE UNEXPECTED?

A.J.M. Smits[1,4], H. Havinga[2,4] & E.C.L. Marteijn[3,4]
*[1] Department of Nature Management of Stream Corridors, University of Nijmegen, P.O. Box 9010, NL-6500 GL Nijmegen, The Netherlands;*
*[2] Delft University of Technology, Faculty of Civil Engineering and Geoscience, Section Hydraulic and Offshore Engineering, River Morphology and Engineering group, P.O. Box 5048, NL-2600 GA Delft, The Netherlands;*
*[3] Ministry of Transport, Public Works and Water Management, Institute for Inland Water Management and Waste Water Treatment, RIZA, River Research Department, P.O. Box 9070, NL-6800 ED Arnhem, The Netherlands;*
*[4] Member of the Netherlands Centre for River Studies (NCR), P.O. Box 177, NL-2600 MH Delft, The Netherlands*

## Abstract

River basins, especially those in the industrialised world, have undergone great changes. In Europe, this is most evident in the Rhine river basin. Over the last two centuries, far-reaching hydrological and river management measures have been introduced, which have had a large impact on the natural water system of the Rhine basin. Generally, these interventions were focused on adapting spatial user functions such as agriculture, urbanisation and navigation. Eventually, underestimation of the effects of these interventions has led to a major reduction in the hydrological (and ecological) resilience of the Rhine river system. Future flooding disasters along the midstream and downstream sections of the Rhine can only be prevented by increasing the number of interventions and at high management costs.

In addition to the common problem-solving approach, a plea is made to pay attention to a fundamentally different approach of using and managing the river basin. The general starting point of this new approach is the philosophy that, firstly, user functions must be adapted to the natural environment and not vice versa. In this context, recent developments relating to water and river management provide intriguing perspectives. Our views are illustrated with examples from the lowland parts of the Rhine basin (in particular the Netherlands). Examples include a new role of agriculture in the rural area, handling precipitation in urbanised areas by allowing more infiltration, and new navigation concepts. Secondly, we suggest that more investments have to be made towards developing new monitoring and management techniques which can be used in a river system providing more room for hydromorphological dynamics. Therefore, the present paper also describes recent studies focusing on the monitoring of relatively fast changing ecological and (hydraulic) roughness characteristics of floodplains. It is our conclusion that, in addition to the technical innovations, this new approach also requires a more pro-active involvement of the water and river manager in the spatial planning process.

*New approaches to river management, pp. 267–286*
*edited by A.J.M. Smits, P.H. Nienhuis and R.S.E.W. Leuven*
© 2000 Backhuys Publishers, Leiden, The Netherlands

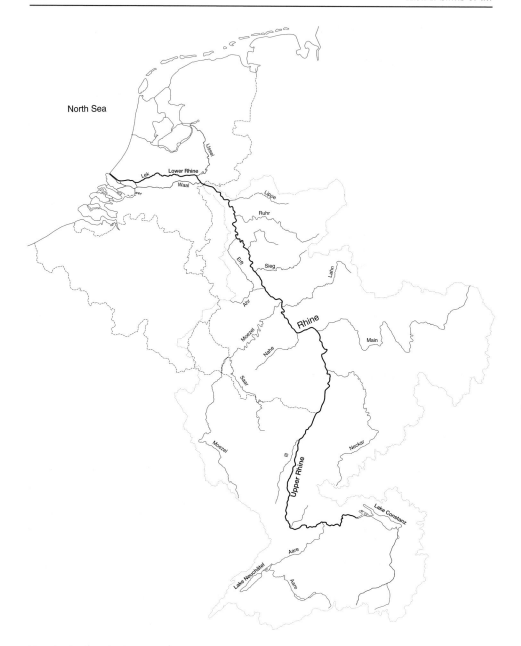

*Fig. 1.* The length of the Rhine river is 1,320 km and its basin area comprises 185,000 km².

## 1. Introduction

Water plays an important role in various spatial user functions (*e.g.*, agriculture, urbanisation and navigation). The growth of the European population inevitably resulted in a growing demand for a fully controlled water system. Therefore, interventions in the water system aimed to change an unpredictable, dynamic system into a more predictable, static system. Eventually, this approach has led to the simplification of an originally complex river basin. As a consequence, moderate fluctuations in precipitation almost immediately result in high or low water levels in the river system, which negatively affect flood protection, navigation and ecology (*i.e.*, a reduced hydrological resilience). At present, the majority of the problems relating to water quantity in the Rhine river basin (Figure 1) proceed from ignorance and an underestimation of the long-term effects of interventions in the water system. The present paper retrospectively reviews the development of spatial user functions, which have had a major impact on the natural water system of the Rhine basin. These user functions have occasioned far-reaching interventions in the natural water system. Many of the interventions have involved large-scale drainage, river regulations and canalisations (Zinke & Gutzweiler 1990, Huisman *et al.* 1999, IKSR 1993). Subsequently, we discuss the development from a regional and sectoral approach to these user functions towards an international integrated approach. This integrated approach in river management however, appears to be insufficient to cope with future effects of climate change in the Rhine river basin. New concepts of land and water management, leading to an increase in the resilience of the water system, are presented here, using examples of the user functions of agriculture, urbanisation and navigation.

## 2. The loss of hydrological resilience in the Rhine river basin

### 2.1 Agriculture

The rapid growth of the European population has resulted in an enormous pressure on agricultural productivity. Drainage of large areas, the introduction of heavy machinery and the use of artificial fertilisers in particular, have spectacularly increased agricultural productivity. In order to speed up water run-off in spring, small meandering streams and rivers in the Rhine basin have been regulated and canalised on a large scale. It is especially in the lowland parts of the Rhine basin (the Netherlands), that the effects of large-scale drainage have drastically changed the original landscape. In the so-called 'embanked polders', drainage has caused a major subsidence of the peat soil (Van der Ven 1976, Huisman *et al.* 1999, Havinga & Smits 2000). As a consequence, the difference in surface level between the land- and the river-sides of the dikes has gradually increased over the last centuries and is nowadays up to 6 m. At present, the water system in the Netherlands is fully controlled. Large-scale drainage has made it necessary to tap the groundwater reserves during periods of reduced rainfall. As a consequence, a growing proportion of the Netherlands, a country internationally known as a "land of water", is suffering from ecohydrological changes as a result of the systematic lowering of water tables (Veel 1999; Figure 2). The disturbed ecohydrological relations in these areas have led to a loss of unique plant and animal species. At the same time, the low-lying polders near the coast are threatened not so much by falling water tables but by the intrusion of saline groundwater.

*Fig 2.* Regions in the Netherlands suffering from systematic lowering of groundwater levels. Dark shaded areas: regions with nature as main function or that will be acquired in behalf of nature. Light shaded areas: regions with nature as additional function (Source: Veel 1999).

## 2.2 Urbanisation

Apart from agriculture, urbanisation has also had a substantial effect on the natural water system in the Rhine basin. Virtually along the entire Rhine river, dikes have been constructed close to the river bed, substantially decreasing the original floodplain area (Havinga & Smits 2000, IKSR 1998, Van de Ven 1976). The embanked areas have been made suitable for intensive agriculture and urbanisation. Population densities, especially, in the low land parts of the Rhine river and its tributaries (the Netherlands), have shown a major increase (Figure 3). The conurbations withdraw huge amounts of groundwater for sanitation and drinking water, thus amplifying the systematic lowering of water tables. In the conurbations, vast areas are covered with impervious materials such as roofs, roads and pavements. Rainwater is collected in extensive sewerage systems and discharged with or without purification, to the surface water. Because of these sewerage systems, the ground water supplies can hardly be replenished. Apart from this low infiltration rate, the swift run-off of rainwater also contributes to high water discharges in the river system.

## 2.3 Navigation

The Rhine is an important economic artery for Europe, and inland shipping has played a crucial role in the economic development of many countries along the river (Middelkoop & Van Haselen 1999, Blom & Silva 1997). The management measures that have been introduced to improve navigation conditions have been extensively described by Havinga & Smits (2000), Huisman *et al.* (1999) and Middelkoop & Van Haselen (1999). These interventions have suppressed most of the natural hydromorphological dynamics. Together with the disappearance of riverine habitats connected to these processes, a large number of plant and animal species have disappeared (IKSR 1998). Moreover, the construction of dams and locks has blocked important migration routes of aquatic fauna (Cazemier 1998, De Groot 1989).

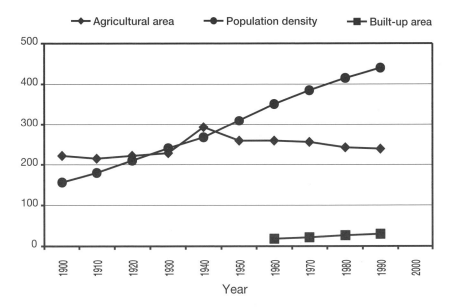

*Fig. 3.* Population growth (numbers per km$^2$), agricultural and built-up area (x 10$^4$ ha) in the Netherlands. Total area of the Netherlands: 4,153 x 10$^3$ ha. Built-up area = cities including industrial area: first registration in 1961 (Source: CBS 1999).

## 3. From a regional, sectoral approach towards an international, integrated approach

Despite the economic prosperity that has proceeded from the classic water and river management in the Rhine basin, the responsible authorities have come to realise that, especially in view of the climate change, this approach can only be maintained at high costs and risks (Anonymous 1999a, Havinga & Smits 2000). Due to the climate change increases of water peak discharges are expected to occur more frequently in the future (Grabs *et al.* 1997). These higher water discharges in the Rhine basin will require huge investments in flood protection.

The above described developments have severely reduced the hydrological resilience of the Rhine river basin. Intensive agriculture and urbanisation have reduced the water storage capacity of the landscape and the confined riverbed of the Rhine river has been reconstructed and rearranged to speed up water run-off. In the historical, much more varied landscape of the Rhine basin, water discharge used to take place in a gradual and phased manner. At present, flood waves from the tributaries of the upper Rhine appear rapidly and unexpectedly in the riverbed and amplify each other (Zinke & Gutzweiler 1990). In the highly regulated and confined Rhine, this can lead to dangerous situations, especially for the middle and lower sections of the river basin. Following the warning signs of December 1993, the high water discharges of January 1995 constituted a serious threat to large cities in Germany and polders in the Netherlands (Anonymous 1999a).

Originally, the tasks and responsibilities of the water and river managers in the Rhine river basin were restricted to water quantity issues (Huisman *et al.* 1999). From that point of view, it was a matter of course that only regional and sectoral solutions were generated. The threat of flooding and a surplus of water on agricultural land were combated mainly by constructing dikes, regulating rivers and draining polders. Since the Middle Ages, several dike improvements have proved necessary. In the Netherlands, the height of the dikes along the Rhine tributaries has increased from several feet in medieval times to 6 metres at present.

After World War II, the problem of water quality was added to the tasks and responsibilities of the water and river managers. In 1950 the Rhine river states, *viz.* the Federal Republic of Germany, France, Luxembourg, the Netherlands and Switzerland, created the International Commission for the Protection of the Rhine (IRC) against Pollution. However, it took several environmental "accidents" before the IRC was charged in 1971 with developing elaborate conventions and an operating working programme to provide concrete arrangements to combat pollution (Dieperink 1998). From that time, the water quality of the Rhine has started to improve (Middelkoop & Van Haselen 1999, Blom & Silva 1997). Figure 4 depicts the developments of two important water quality parameters, *viz.*, cadmium and dissolved oxygen, illustrating the success of the combined efforts.

About 1985, there was a growing awareness that improvement of the water quality was not enough for the desired ecological rehabilitation of the Rhine. Various revolutionary plans were developed along the river. These plans aimed to reduce intensive agriculture in the floodplains and to increase the interaction between the river and its floodplain by removing minor dikes from the floodplains and reintroducing side channels (De Bruin *et al.* 1987, Van Dijk *et al.* 1995, Cals *et al.* 1998,

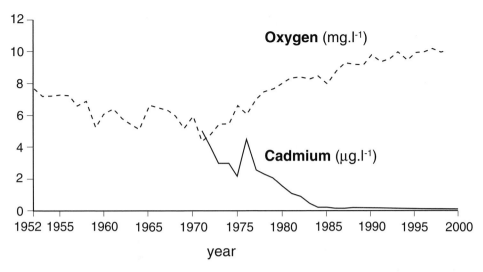

*Fig. 4.* Due to an international collaboration and conventions between the Rhine states, the water quality of the Rhine river has been substantially improved since the seventies. Here, the developments of two important water quality parameters, cadmium and dissolved oxygen in the Rhine water near the Dutch-German border (at Lobith) are shown (Source: Blom & Silva 1997).

Zinke & Gutzweiler 1990). New opportunities for the original biodiversity of the Rhine floodplains were to be provided through low-intensity management of floodplains, with (Vera 1997) or without the introduction of large herbivores (Baumann 1994, De Jong 1999). Based on this philosophy, an increasing number of habitat rehabilitation projects are being initiated along the river (Busskamp 1998, IKSR 1998). Unfortunately, after the high water levels in the Rhine in 1993 and 1995, river managers have hesitated to approve a number of rehabilitation projects that could increase the roughness of the floodplains. Little is known about the rate at which floodplain forests along the Rhine will develop and how extensive they might become, and the river managers tend to prefer certainty over uncertainty. Thus, the general usefulness and necessity of habitat rehabilitation projects in the floodplain are once again subjects of debate.

It is evident that the pressure exerted by various conflicting user functions in the Rhine basin has increased over the last decades (Anonymous 1999b, Marteijn *et al.* 1999). In all Rhine river states, water and river managers are searching for solutions that would satisfy multiple interest groups. The integrated water management approach has become common practice in the Netherlands since 1989 (Anonymous 1993, Nienhuis *et al.* 1998, Van de Kamer *et al.* 1998). Since that time, many interest groups have been more closely involved in river management and the timely input and involvement of these groups is of great importance for a successful policy (Hendriksen 1999). Nowadays, all Rhine river states, explicitly use an open planning process for policy development. This has had a favourable effect on both the support for sustainable water management policy and its implementation. Sustainable water and river management aim at an economic development with preservation of natural and cultural values.

## 4. A new approach to using and managing natural water systems

Despite the international, integrated approach and the involvement of an open planning process for decision-making, the conclusion which is forcing itself upon the
administrators is that this will not be sufficient to achieve a sustainable and safe
Rhine river basin in this millennium. This is well illustrated by a study recently conducted in the Netherlands, entitled "Room for the Rhine Branches" (Hendriksen
1999). This study used an open planning process to identify sustainable interventions that can increase the water discharge capacity of the Rhine tributaries to
16,000 m³ s⁻¹ at Lobith (at the German-Dutch border). However, when the effects
of climate change are included, the "Room for Rhine branches" measures appear to
be insufficient. Water flows of 18,000 m³ s⁻¹ have to be expected (Hendriksen
1999). Figure 5 depicts the monthly variations in the discharge of the Rhine at
Lobith. These data also support the expectation that the hydrological resilience of
the Rhine basin will be further reduced. Although there is much scientific uncertainty about the climate change, authorities in the Rhine basin are seriously considering the possibility that winter and spring discharges will increase, primarily as a
result of higher winter precipitation rates. Rising average temperatures would cause
winter precipitation in the Alpine area, which is presently stored as snow until late
spring, to become available for discharge in the winter or early spring period. This
would also cause a reduced discharge in summer and autumn. The reduction of the
summer discharge from the Alpine region would be amplified by the reduced discharge from the middle and lower sections of the basin. In general, the Rhine

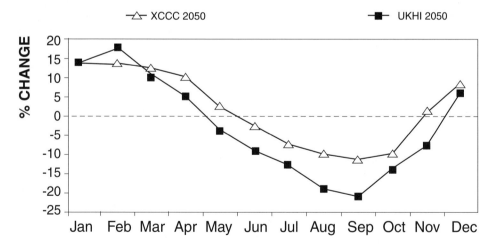

*Fig. 5.* Changes in monthly Rhine discharge at the German-Dutch border according to two different
climate change scenarios. Scenario UKHI 2050: temperature + 2°C; annual precipitation + 2% to
+10%, wet winters and dry summers, Scenario XCCC 2050: temperature + 1.5°C; annual precipitation +5%, drier summers. Scenario runs based on the RHINEFLOW model. Both scenarios show
that the winter discharge of the Rhine increases while summer discharges will decrease. More scenarios are available but all show similar trends. However, the extent of this trend varies per scenario.
Hence, there is a large extent of uncertainty considering the precise impact of climate change
(Source: Grabs *et al.* 1997).

discharge regime would shift from a combined snow-melt/rain-fed regime to a more rain-fed regime, with increased average winter and spring discharges, and reduced summer and autumn discharges (Grabs *et al.* 1997).

Quite apart from the precise effects and rate of the climate change, other processes that increase the flood damage potential are continuing. Sedimentation is causing the surface level of the floodplain to rise (Middelkoop 1997), while the landside of the dikes in the downstream parts of the river basin continues to subside as a result of permanent drainage. Behind these dikes, huge investments are being made in housing, industry and infrastructure, gradually increasing the flood damage potential. Simultaneously, the ecological rehabilitation of the floodplains threatens to stagnate, because it is believed that all the space which has remained in the river bed is needed for water discharge. It appears that the classical approach to water and river management has led us up a dead-end street, where protection against flooding can only be provided by constructing even higher dikes and bigger drainage pumps. In this scenario, natural values are tolerated but are not regarded as an integral part of the river system. In view of the impending climate change, this does not offer us a bright prospect.

We support the hypothesis that this black scenario can only be avoided by the rehabilitation of the hydrological resilience of the Rhine river basin. Restoring this hydrological resilience requires more room for the natural processes in the water cycle. The storage capacity of the river basin and the hydromorphological diversity of the various streams which discharge into the entire Rhine, as well as the Rhine bed itself, have to be restored as much as possible. The space required to achieve this goal can only be found by adapting the various user functions to the natural dynamics of water systems. We present here some new concepts for the three user functions, which have had a major impact on the water system of the Rhine river basin: agriculture, urbanisation and navigation. These concepts are currently under investigation. Additionally, we discuss the latest developments in floodplain management, which anticipate on a synergistic relation between flood protection and ecological rehabilitation.

## 4.1 Concentration, allocation and changing function of agriculture

After the United States, the Netherlands is the largest net exporter of agricultural products in the world (LEI 1999). However, this comes at price. The Netherlands is experiencing considerable environmental problems caused by the systematic lowering of ground water tables and the leaching of herbicides and pesticides into the groundwater. The other Rhine river states have to contend with more or less comparable problems. As a result of stricter environmental laws in the European Union and recent developments on the international agricultural market, there is a trend in the Netherlands towards a smaller but vigorous and sustainable agricultural sector. To improve its competitive position on the international market, it is predicted that the land-requiring agricultural sector will be concentrated in parts of the country, which do not need intensive, systematic drainage. From this point of view, the former sea-clay areas of the Netherlands provide the best perspectives the more so as, unlike the parts of the country with sandy soils, the nutrient-rich clay does not require huge amounts of fertiliser. This trend will increase as the traditional agricultural crops are substituted by more salt-tolerant crop species because sea-clay areas are prone to saline groundwater intrusion. Some farmers have already started experimenting with salt-tolerant crop species (NIOO-CEMO 1999). This development is not confined to the Netherlands. Among many examples, an interesting case is the Mekong delta, where farmers experiment with saline tolerant agriculture that requires less irrigation water and makes a rigid separation between the estuary and the sea unnecessary (combined rice-shrimp culture; Sluiter & Ryder 1993).

In addition to the spatial and technological changes, there is also a new trend concerning the role and function of agriculture along the Rhine. It is even likely that there will be a greater need for farmers as managers of the rural area rather than producers of foodstuffs. In this new role, the farmer will be paid for managing the rural area in such a way as to increase the hydrological resilience. Because sustainable management of land and water is for the benefit of the community, it seems obvious that the governments of the Rhine river states must provide the financial requirements. As far as the financing methodology of this new aspect of agriculture is concerned, the idea of "fisquality" suggested by Corporaal (2000) is most intriguing. The concept of "fisquality" is based on reducing taxes for farmers who manage their land in such a way as to improve water retention. In view of these trends, it is likely that in the near future, the agricultural function of the floodplains will be greatly reduced and there will be more room for water, riverine conservation areas and recreation.

*4.2 Urban water management*

Over the last decades, the total surface area of the Rhine river basin, which is covered with impervious materials, has increased enormously. Sewage systems in the urbanised areas and infrastructure have generally been designed for a rapid run-off of rainwater. However, a number of modifications could be applied in the design and construction of urban areas. These modifications can be interpreted as adaptations of the user function "urbanisation" to the natural water system. For example, it is quite simple to improve the infiltration of rainwater into the subsoil by using an infiltration facility. Such facilities could be constructed in a bed of coarse sand, rather than in clay or peat soil. This would substantially increase the infiltration capacity. Another option, which could be used additionally, used in residential areas is that of constructing so-called "wadis" (Geldof & Van de Ven 1998; Figure 6). Instead of a rapid run-off of rainwater via sewerage systems, water is collected in wet depressions in the residential area and allowed to replenish groundwater reserves. Recently, various innovations such as the application of permeable materials in roads and pavements have been introduced in order to improve urban water management (Pötz & Bleuzé 1998, Geldof *et al.* 1997). When applied on a large scale, this could improve the water storage capacity of urban areas substantially.

*4.3 Innovation of navigation*

The growth of navigation on the Rhine has been a strong incentive for the economic development of Europe and the Rhine river states in particular. To improve the inland water navigation system, a large number of river regulation and canalisation

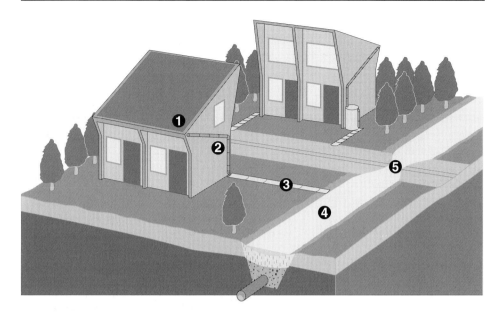

*Fig. 6.* Schematic representation of a so-called "wadi". The name "wadi" is used in arid regions, and refers to riverbeds, which only contain water in the rainy period. Instead of a fast run-off of rainwater via sewerage systems, it is collected in wet depressions in the residential area and allowed to replenish groundwater reserves. The average rainfall in the Netherlands ranges from 650-900 mm per year (Van Boxel & Cammaraat 1999). Rainwater on the roof (1) flows via a down pipe (2) in a special gully located in the garden (3). The gully ends in the so-called "wadi" (4), which has a depth of 25 cm. Also, the rainwater in the streets ends in the wadi (5) (Source: Anonymous 1999c).

projects have been implemented. In view of the large impact that these interventions have had on the natural water system, and the high costs involved in compensating the negative effects (Havinga & Smits 2000), it is meaningful to consider navigation concepts which do not require such major interventions in the river system. An example is the so-called "River Snake" (Figure 7). The principle is simple. The River Snake involves a new type of flat-bottomed vessel in the form of a snake (Gerritse & Prins 1997). The Snake consists of container carriers joined with large ball joints and interspersed with "power units". These units are the propelling and navigating "vertebrae" of the floating river train. They also ensure that the Snake easily adapts to bends in the river. A central computer located at the front end of the vessel controls the power units. We realise that this concept will be of limited use for the Rhine system, because this water system is already almost completely regulated and canalised. However, such vessels could be highly useful for the protection of natural river systems elsewhere. They could be tailor-made for any riverbed and provide economic potential while regulation and canalisation measures could be kept to a minimum. There is a good chance that various countries will be interested in this concept. For instance, along the Elbe river, attempts are being made to construct a navigation vessel with less draught, making further canalisation of this river unnecessary (so-called "Elbe-schiff"; Lamprecht 1996).

Fig. 7. Schematic presentation of the so-called "river-snake". The river-snake consists of container carriers joined-up to a flat-bottomed vessel in the form of a snake. This concept allows transport on a natural river system without far-reaching regulation and canalisation measures (Source: Gerritse & Prins 1997).

## 5. Management of floodplains by cyclic rejuvenation

Following the warning signs of 1993, the January 1995 flood wave in the Rhine, focused the attention of the river managers on the need to increase water storage and discharge capacity (Anonymous 1998a). In the short term, rehabilitation of the natural resilience of rivers, by allowing them more space, is the best strategy to prepare for uncertain future developments (Hendriksen 1999, Anonymous 1999a). Man-made obstacles should be removed wherever possible and dikes repositioned, while floodplains, which have silted up, should be excavated, and non-river based activities such as housing strictly prevented. Apart from plans to construct retention polders (IKSR 1997) and measures aimed at reducing the hydraulic roughness of the floodplain this has also led to the general conception that rehabilitation of riparian vegetation is not in line with flood prevention interests. However, there are other possibilities to synergise both interests. In the suggested approach, two assumptions are essential.
1. Riparian vegetation (*e.g.*, softwood floodplain forests) and side channels strongly influence the hydraulic roughness of a stream corridor and can function as powerful tools to regulate the water run-off. Provided that conservation areas are carefully planned along a stream corridor in place and time, they can be used to dose and phase flood waves in such a way that it decreases flooding risks.
2. The biodiversity of riverine conservation areas is determined by erosion and siltation. These driving forces of living rivers regularly reset the vegetation succession and hydromorphological developments. Therefore, it is suggested to stimulate these processes into the bridled and static river systems within a certain period of time.

These assumptions form the core of a methodology named "Cyclic rejuvenation of floodplains", which is currently under investigation (Smits & Duel 1999).

At present, a flood wave runs more or less straight downstream through the simplified and narrow Rhine bed. Compared with the former situation, nowadays smaller volumes of water cause dangerous situations. By contrast, wide diversiform floodplains of stream corridors have a damping effect and slow down flood waves (Figure 8). Under these conditions, peak levels are relatively low. This effect is caused by the fact that each floodplain has a different structure and vegetation, resulting in different hydraulic roughness. And since side channels tend to silt up, and shrubs and willows can form dense softwood forests, the hydraulic roughness for each floodplain is not constant over time. Under natural conditions, the erosion and sedimentation processes (*e.g.*, meandering) periodically interrupt these successions along a living river. The net effect at the river basin level is a great diversity of ecotopes, providing a broad spectrum of ecological niches in space and time. Ecotopes, such as side channels and river dunes, are hydromorphologically defined units with specific ecological characteristics (Rademakers & Wolfert 1994). At present, unbridled erosion and sedimentation processes along the densely populated Rhine cannot be allowed. As a consequence, habitat rehabilitation projects tend to end up as dense softwood floodplain forests, which unacceptably increase the hydraulic roughness. Therefore, the river manager will not allow a major increase of these projects in the floodplains of the Rhine and its tributaries.

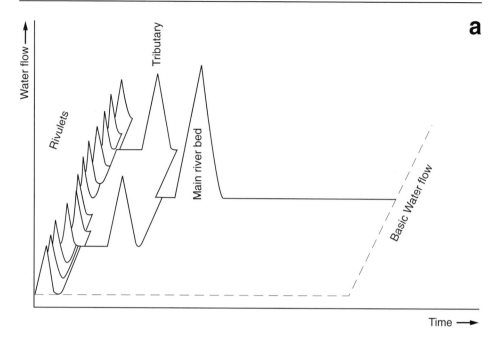

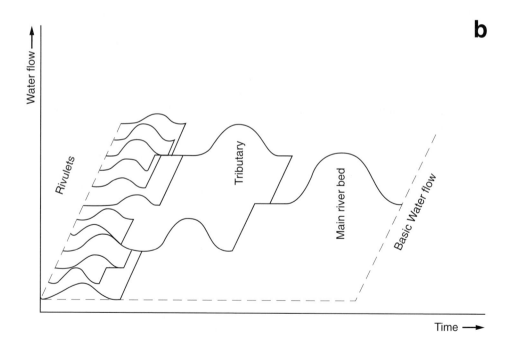

*Fig. 8.* Schematic presentation of the effect of a simplified and a diversiform system of stream corridors on the peak heights of water flow. By providing more room for the stream corridors and allowing the riparian vegetation to develop, water discharge in the main river bed will be damped resulting in lower peak discharge values (Source: Helmer 1999).

The concept of "Cyclic rejuvenation of floodplains" aims at initiating and terminating certain successive stages of riverine habitats along the Rhine. This is done in such a way that the total area of habitat rehabilitation can be increased as well as the damping of flood waves can be accomplished. When the hydraulic roughness of a floodplain attains a critical level, the succession process can be reset by harvesting the floodplain forest and if necessary, by clay and sand excavations. These interventions mimic the natural dynamics of erosion and sedimentation processes, which periodically occur along natural river systems and generate riverine biodiversity. Thus, cyclic rejuvenation aims at reintroducing hydromorphodynamics vital for riverine habitats and simultaneously serving flood protection. Hence, it relates well with the second part of the new approach to river management presented here *i.e.*, developing new monitoring and management techniques. The methodology of cyclic rejuvenation is founded on the Dynamic River Management System (Havinga & Smits 2000) and includes a set of computational instruments, comprising a hydraulic/morphological model and an ecological model using a Geographic Information System (GIS). Geomorphological data-sets of almost all sections of the Rhine are available in GIS. To assess the ecological potential of the river sections, existing ecotope classification systems are used as a starting point (Reijnen *et al.* 1995). The next section elaborates on the linking of ecological and hydraulic roughness data.

## 6. Monitoring ecological developments and hydraulic resistance of floodplains

Over 100 ecotopes can be distinguished in the floodplains of the Rhine and its tributaries (Rademakers & Wolfert 1994, Maas 1998). Because the morphological and vegetative structure of each ecotope is known, these ecotopes can be labelled with a specific hydraulic roughness factor. At present, studies are being conducted to combine the ecological and hydraulic roughness data. The preliminary results provide good perspectives for determining, with improved accuracy, the hydraulic roughness of entire river sections. This will prevent generalisations and reduce the attitude of always preferring certainty over uncertainty, which severely limits the room for dynamic riverine habitat development.

The hydraulic characteristics of river sections vary with time. It is laborious and expensive to monitor adequately any changes, which occur in the floodplains by conventional techniques (aerial photographs and field studies). In the future, faster and cheaper techniques will be needed to monitor the abundance and structure of vegetation in large parts of a river basin. In this context, a method involving laser-altimetry seems promising. Recently, some experiments were carried out with the objective to convert data on the vegetation structure directly into hydraulic roughness data for a floodplain. An aircraft equipped with a special laser camera produces images of a nature conservation project along a Dutch tributary of the Rhine, the IJssel (Figure 9). Using these data as the input for water flow models may provide quick and cheap monitoring of the continuously changing conditions in floodplains, and may enable the river manager to ensure sufficient water flow capacity in a dynamic river bed.

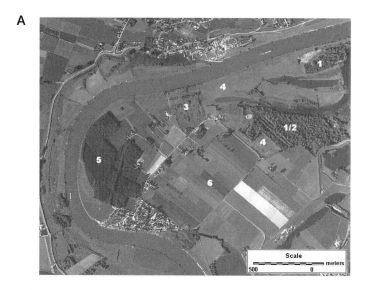

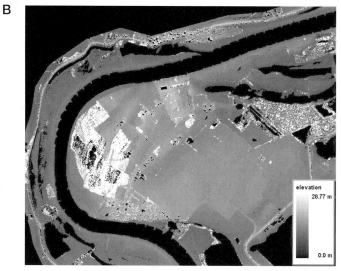

*Fig. 9.* A. An aerial photograph of a floodplain along the IJssel river (Duurse Waarden) in the Netherlands. Various ecotopes can be distinguished in this floodplain. (1) Floodplain forest; (2) low woodland vegetation; (3) herbs and bushes; (4) grass; (5) old floodplain forest; (6) agricultural field and meadows.
B. Average height of the floodplain vegetation in the Duurse Waarden. With the laser-altimetry method the height of each object can be accurately determined. An aeroplane provided with a laser camera flies over the floodplain while the device emits and collects reflected laser light. By collecting and selecting reflected laser pulses from the floodplain the average height of the vegetation can be assessed. Each ecotope has its own characteristics, which can be used for the calculation of the hydraulic roughness (Source: Asselman 1999).

## 7. Future role of water and river manager

Reviewing the new concepts of agriculture, urban water management, navigation and floodplain management it is clear that the tasks and responsibilities of future water and river managers can no longer be confined to water quantity and water quality in the river bed. A more pro-active role in the spatial planning process is required. In the current Dutch situation there are indications that the authorities will adopt this approach. Every 4 to 8 years, proposals for river management and spatial planning are formulated in a National Management Plan. A National Policy Document on Water Management and a National Policy Document on Spatial Planning and Environmental Quality provide the objectives and financial preconditions for these plans respectively. An important area of attention is the relationship between spatial planning and the environment in the Fourth National Policy Document on Water Management (Anonymous 1999d). The Fifth National Policy Document on Spatial Planning and Environmental Quality (Anonymous 2000), which is currently in preparation, will devote a similar degree of attention to "room-for-rivers" issues.

## 8. Conclusions

In the short term, rehabilitation of the hydrological resilience of rivers, by allowing them more space, is the best strategy to prepare for uncertain future developments (Hendriksen 1999, Anonymous 1999a). However, there are clear indications that this is not sufficient in the long term. Therefore, this paper has advocated a new approach to the use and management of river basins. More efforts have to be made to adapt present day user functions to natural water systems. In this manner, hydrological and ecological resilience will increase gradually over time. At present, the technological and socio-economic developments in the Rhine river basin provide good perspectives for further implementation of this new approach. Because sustainable water and river management is an issue of common interest, the governments of the Rhine river states have an important task in initiating and facilitating the required technological and conceptual innovations. From this point of view, the tasks and responsibilities of future water and river managers are no longer confined to water quantity and water quality. A more pro-active role in the spatial planning process is required. It is of great importance that spatial units both on the landside and the riverside of the dikes are used and managed in such a manner as to increase the hydrological resilience. The hypothesis is that nature conservation and rehabilitation will benefit from this development, as is illustrated by some of the examples in the present paper.

Another important question regarding the benefits of adapting user functions to the natural water system presented here is the aspect of upscaling to other river basins. We realise that there are great differences between the Rhine river basin and other large river basins such as those of the Yangtze, Mekong, Nile and Mississippi. Apart from the large differences in dimensions, climatic and geophysical conditions, there are also differences relating to socio-economic, cultural and institutional aspects. However, we suggest that the philosophy of the new approach presented here is basically applicable to all natural water systems and is particularly important for those river basins, which have not been yet regulated and canalised. Good examples of adapting user functions to natural water systems can be found in Central Europe as well as Asia. Each example that can be added to this list increases the evidence that when user functions are adapted to natural water systems, much of the "unexpected behaviour" will no longer be experienced as a threat but will be accepted as natural dynamics of water systems.

# References

Anonymous. 1993. Evaluatienota Water. Ministry of Transport, Public Works & Water Management, Den Haag. (in Dutch).

Anonymous. 1999a. Notitie Aanpak Wateroverlast. Ministry of Transport, Public Works & Water Management, Den Haag. (in Dutch with English summary).

Anonymous. 1999b. Third National Policy Document on Water Management. Ministry of Transport, Public Works & Water Management. Den Haag (in Dutch).

Anonymous. 1999c. Wadi. Een natuurlijke regulering van hemelwater. Municipality of Enschede, The Netherlands and TAUW, Deventer. (in Dutch).

Anonymous. 1999d. Fourth National Policy Document on Water Management. Ministry of Transport, Public Works and Water Management. Den Haag. (in Dutch with English summary).

Anonymous. 2000. Fifth National Policy Document on Spatial Planning and Environmental Quality. Ministry of Housing, Environmental and Spatial Planning; Den Haag. (in prep.).

Asselman, N. 1999. Laseraltimetrie en vegetatieruwheid. Report Q2577. WL Delft Hydraulics. Delft. (in Dutch).

Baumann, L. 1994. Deutsch-Niederländisch Landschaftsentwicklungsproject "De Gelderse Poort"; Machbarkeitsstudie für das deutsche Teilgebiet. Ludger Baumann Freier Landschaftsarchitekt, Kleve und Lana-plan Landschafts- und Stadtökologie, Nettetal. (in German).

Blom, G. & Silva, W. 1997. Towards integrated and flexible river management by an open planning process and basin approach in the Netherlands. In: An appeal from Nagara river to the world harmonizing human activities with rivers. Proceedings Nagaragawa Convention Center Gifu, Gifu.

Busskamp, R. 1998. Rhein-Atlas. Ökologie und Hochwasserschutz. Internationale Kommission zum Schutze des Rheins. Koblenz. (Summary in German, French & Dutch).

Cals, M.J.R., Postma, R., Buijse, A.D. & Marteijn, E.C.L. 1998. Habitat rehabilitation along the Rhine river in The Netherlands: putting ideas into practice. Aquatic. Conserv. Mar. Freshw. Ecosyst. 8: 61-70.

Cazemier, W.G. 1988. Fish and their environment in large European river ecosystems; the Dutch part of the river Rhine. Science de l'Eau 7: 95-114.

CBS. 1999. Vijfennegentig jaren statistiek in tijdreeksen. Centraal Bureau voor de Statistiek. Voorburg/Heerlen. (in Dutch).

Corporaal, A. 2000. Fisquality, a proposal for a tax bonus to improve retention of river cachments. In: Smits, A.J.M., Nienhuis, P.H. & Leuven, R.S.E.W. (Eds.) New Approaches to River Management. Backhuys Publishers, Leiden. pp. 179-186.

De Bruin, D., Hamhuis, D., Van Nieuwenhuijze, L., Overmars, W. Sijmons, D. & Vera, F. 1987. Ooievaar. De toekomst van het rivierengebied. Stichting Gelderse Milieufedereatie, Arnhem. (in Dutch).

De Groot, S.J. 1989. Literature survey into the possibility of restocking the river Rhine and its tributaries with Atlantic salmon (*Salmo salar*). Ecological Rehabilitation of the rivers Rhine and Meuse. (EHR) publication 11-89. Institute for Inland Water Management and Waste Water Treatment, RIZA, Lelystad. (in Dutch).

De Jong, D.M., 1999. Tussen natuurontwikkeling en Landschaftsschutz; Sociaal-cognitieve configuraties in het grensoverschrijdende natuurbeleid. PhD Thesis University of Nijmegen, Nijmegen. (in Dutch).

Dieperink, C. 1998. From open sewer to salmon run: lessons from the Rhine water quality regime. Water Policy 1: 471-485.

Geldof, G.D. & Van de Ven, F.H.M. 1998. Urban water management. In: Huisman, P., Cramer, Van Ee, W., Hooghart, G., Salz, J.C. & Zuidema, F.C. (Eds.) Water in The Netherlands. Netherlands Hydrological Society (NVH), Delft.

Geldof, G.D., De Jong, S.P., De Braal, A.J., Marsman, E.H., Van der Laan, J. & Kruseman, I. 1997. Water in de stad, behandelingstechnieken. RIZA report 97.092. Institute for Inland Water Management and Waste Water Treatment (RIZA), Lelystad. (in Dutch).

Gerritse, G. & Prins, D.G. 1997. River-Snake; large scale container transportation over water. RiverSnake Development Ltd., Dordrecht. (in Dutch with English summary).

Grabs, W., Daamen, K., Gellens, D., Kwadijk, J.C.J., Lang, H., Middelkoop, H., Parmet, B.W.A.H., Schädler, B., Schulla, J. & Wilke, K. 1997. Impact of climate change on hydrological regimes and water resources management in the Rhine basin. CHR-report I-16. CHR, Lelystad.

Havinga, H. & Smits, A.J.M. 2000. River management along the Rhine: a retrospective view. In: Smits, A.J.M., Nienhuis, P.H. & Leuven, R.S.E.W. (Eds.). New Approaches to River Management. Backhuys Publishers, Leiden. pp. 15-32.

Helmer, W. 1999. Natuurlijke Veiligheid. Visie op de Rijntakken in het perspectief van stromende berging. Staatsbosbeheer & Wereld Natuur Fonds, Arnhem. (in Dutch).

Hendriksen, E. 1999. Room for Rhine branches. State of affairs. Summary. Ministry of Transport, Public Works and Water Management, Divion East, Arnhem.

Huisman, P., Cramer, Van Ee, W., Hooghart, G., Salz, J.C., & Zuidema, F.C. 1999. Water in The Netherlands. Netherlands Hydrological Society (NVH), Delft.

IKSR. 1993. KHR-Arbeitsgruppe, Der Rhein unter der Einwirkung des Menschen – Ausbau, Schiffahrt, Wasserwirtschaft. Internationale Kommission für die Hydrologie des Rheingebietes. Änthropogene Enflüsse auf das Abflußregime. Internationale Kommission zum Schutze des Rheins (IKSR), Koblenz. (in German).

IKSR. 1997. Hochwasserschutz am Rhein. Bestandsaufnahme. Internationale Kommission zum Schutze des Rheins (IKSR), Koblenz. (in German).

IKSR. 1998. KÖ-Arbeitsgruppe, Bestandsaufname der ökologische wertvolle Gebiete am Rhein und erste Schritte auf dem Weg zum Biotopverbund. Internationale Kommission zum Schutze des Rheins (IKSR), Koblenz. (in German).

Lamprecht, H. 1996. Container- und Trailertransport auf der Elbe. Schiffahrt und Technik 10: 31. (in German).

LEI 1999. Landbouw-economisch bericht. Landbouw Economisch Instituut, Den Haag. (in Dutch).

Maas, G.J., 1998. Benedenrivier-Ecotopen-Stelsel. Herziening van de ecotopenindeling Biesbosch-Voordelta en afstemming met het Rivier-Ecotopen-Stelsel en de voorlopige indeling voor de zoute delta. RWES report 3. DLO-Staringcentrum, Wageningen. (in Dutch).

Marteijn, E.C.L., Cals, M.J.R. Geilen, N. & Silva, W. 1999. Nature, shipping, & safety from flooding: a challenge for integrated water management of the river Rhine in the Netherlands. In: Nijland, H.J. (Ed). Dealing with nature in deltas. Proceedings Wetland Management Symposium, Lelystad.

Middelkoop, H. & Van Haselen, C.O.G. 1999. Twice a river. Rhine and Meuse in the Netherlands. Institute for Inland Water Management and Waste Water Treatment, RIZA 99.003, Arnhem.

Middelkoop, H. 1997. Embanked floodplains in the Netherlands. Geomorphological evolution over various time scales. PhD Thesis, Utrecht University, Utrecht.

Nienhuis, P.H., Leuven R.S.E.W. & Ragas, A.M.J. (Eds.) 1998. New concepts for sustainable management of river basins. Backhuys Publishers, Leiden.

NIOO-CEMO. 1999. Saline Crops. A contribution to the diversification of the production of vegetable crops by research on the cultivation methods and selection of halophytes Netherlands Institute for Ecology, Centre for Estuarine and Coastal Ecology (NIOO-CEMO), Yerseke.

Pötz, H. & Bleuzé, P. 1998. Zichtbaar, tastbaar, zinvol, de integratie van natuur en techniek in de vormgeving van stedelijk water. Nai Publishers, Rotterdam.

Rademakers, J.G.M. & Wolfert, H.P. 1994. Het Rivier-Ecotopenstelsel, een indeling van ecologisch relevante ruimtelijke eenheden ten behoeve van ontwerp –en beleidsstudies in het buitendijkse rivierengebied. EHR-publication 61-1994. Institute for Inland Water Management and Waste Water Treatment (RIZA), Lelystad. (in Dutch).

Reijnen, R., Harms, W.B., Foppen, R.B.P., De Visser, R. & Wolfert, H.P. 1995. Rhine–Econet, Ecological networks in river rehabilitation scenarios: a case study for the lower Rhine. EHR-publication 58-1995. Institute for Inland Water Management and Waste Water Treatment, Institute for Inland Water Management and Waste Water Treatment (RIZA), Lelystad.

Sluiter, L. & Ryder, G. 1993. The course of the Mekong. Novib, The Hague.

Smits, A.J.M. & Duel, H. 1999. Cyclic rejuvenations of floodplains. Research proposal within the context of IRMA SPONGE Programme. University of Nijmegen, Nijmegen.

Van Boxel, J. & Cammeraat, E. 1999. Wordt Nederland steeds natter? Een analyse van de neerslag in deze eeuw. Meteorologica 1: 11-15.

Van de Kamer, S.P.G., Postma, R., Marteijn, E.C.L. & Bakker, C. 1998. On the way of total water management for large rivers in the Netherlands. In: P.H. Nienhuis, R.S.E.W. Leuven & Ragas, A.M.J. (Eds.) New concepts for Sustainable Management of River Basins. Backhuys Publishers, Leiden. pp. 291-308.

Van der Ven, G.P. 1976. Aan de wieg van de Rijkswaterstaat: wordingsgeschiedenis van het Pannerdens Kanaal. PhD Thesis. University of Nijmegen, Nijmegen. (in Dutch).

Van Dijk, G.M. Marteijn, E.C.L. & Schulte-Wulwer-Leidig, A. 1995. Ecological rehabilitation of the river Rhine: plans, progress and perspectives. Regulated Rivers: Research & Management 11: 377-388.

Veel, P.W. 1999. Verdrogingskaart van Nederland. Landelijke inventarisatie van verdroogde gebieden en projecten verdrogingsbestrijding. Interprovinciaal Overleg en Rijksinstituut voor Integraal Zoetwaterbeheer en Afvalwaterbehandeling (Institute for Inland Water Management and Waste Water Treatment, RIZA). Den Haag. (in Dutch).

Vera, F.W.M. 1997. Metaforen voor de wildernis. Eik, hazelaar, rund en paard. PhD Thesis. Wageningen University, Wageningen. (in Dutch with English summary).

Zinke, A. & Gutzweiler, K.A. 1990. Possibilities for regeneration of floodplain forests within the framework of the flood-protection measures on the upper Rhine, West Germay. Forest Ecology & Management 33/34: 13-20.

# MULTI-LEVEL APPROACH TO FLOOD CONTROL IN THE DUTCH PART OF THE RIVER MEUSE

W. van Leussen[1], G. Kater[2] & P.P.M. van Meel[3]

[1] *Department of Public Works and Water Management (Rijkswaterstaat), Limburg Directorate, P.O. Box 25, NL-6200 MA Maastricht, The Netherlands;*
[2] *Province Limburg, Limburglaan 10, NL-6229 GA Maastricht, The Netherlands;*
[3] *De Maaswerken, P.O. Box 25, NL-6200 MA Maastricht, The Netherlands*

## Abstract

To guarantee an acceptable level of safety with regard to flooding along the river Meuse, measures are being taken at local, regional, national and international levels. All of these work together to ensure the agreed safety level. All of them also have their own technical, political, social and economic constraints, and thus their own timetables. Therefore, flood problems are being tackled at different levels, in a multi-level approach, including administrative, legal and technical measures. In view of the large number of functions of rivers, such measures must be introduced in the context of a variety of perspectives on the river. This makes the flooding problem immensely complex, particularly if a river and its watershed transcend a number of administrative boundaries. The results of such an innovative process in the context of the various physical, political, social, ecological and economic constraints and opportunities are illustrated for the Dutch part of the river Meuse. It is shown that these include enlarging the river's cross section, habitat creation and restoration, contributions to the national ecological network and retaining the water in the watershed for longer periods.

Although there has been a fundamental shift in the philosophy on tackling flooding problems, moving away from harnessing the river towards stimulating its natural behaviour, the above-mentioned constraints and opportunities still allow a wide spectrum of solutions, ranging from more or less traditional solutions to so-called modern sustainable approaches. Coping with risks is at the basis of the choices that have to be made to control flooding. A difficult problem is that of weighing these risks against ecological and economic potentials. The challenge is to look for win-win solutions, optimising the results within available budgets, so that an acceptable level of protection against flooding is achieved, while at the same time the investments contribute to a better economy and to ecological improvements. The present paper illustrates how creativity and perseverance can achieve such solutions.

## 1. Introduction

Flood control is a challenge in many river systems around the world. During the last decade of the 20th century, many floods ravaged the areas along a number of rivers. Examples can be given from the United States of America, China, Korea, the Netherlands, Poland, etc. Notwithstanding the sophisticated technology available today, it seems to be a never ending story, which has moreover been with us for many centuries. In the wake of such a disaster, defence against high water is high on the

*New approaches to river management, pp. 287–305*
*edited by A.J.M. Smits, P.H. Nienhuis and R.S.E.W. Leuven*
*© 2000 Backhuys Publishers, Leiden, The Netherlands*

political agenda. Based on experiences concerning the effectiveness of previous approaches and improved scientific understanding of river systems, a great deal of progress has been made in our thinking on ways to master such problems. At the same time, the complexity of the problem is being recognised; it involves not only technical, but also social, political and economic aspects, so that a workable solution can only be found through a well-balanced mixture of engineering, social, political, and economic aspects (Van Leussen 1999). This means that there is no one simple approach which is always effective, but that a well-balanced approach should be sought, one which tries to find an optimised route amidst a large number of possibilities and limitations. This paper outlines the current Dutch approach with respect to the river Meuse.

The fight against floods has a long tradition in the Netherlands, which is not surprising, since more than 50% of the country is situated below sea level. In fact, ever since the country came into existence, the Netherlands has engaged in a continuous struggle with the water. It is for this reason that the Netherlands is sometimes called "Waterland". Verwey (1980) demonstrated how Dutch culture is interwoven with the story of the water, which is one of many severe inundations (*cf.* Van der Ven 1993, Van Petersen 1978). It is clear that such events have had a great impact on society. In 1926, for example, the river Meuse had an extreme water discharge of 3,000 $m^3$ $s^{-1}$, resulting in large-scale inundations, while many of the Meuse dikes were breached. After such disasters, commissions were usually installed and reports were written with recommendations to prevent such consequences in the future (Lely 1926). This was followed by decisions to implement the recommendations. As a result, dikes were raised and a number of improvements were made to the river, in order to ensure sufficient capacity for the discharge of water and ice.

The most recent extreme floods in the Netherlands were those of 1993 and 1995. In 1993, the discharge of the river Meuse was 3,120 $m^3$ $s^{-1}$, which statistically should happen only once in about 125 years. The 1995 flood involved a maximum discharge of 2,870 $m^3$ $s^{-1}$, but lasted much longer, due to persistent rainfall. In both cases, serious damage was done: more than NLG 250 million (USD 125 million) in 1993 and about NLG 200 million (USD 100 million) in 1995. The less severe damage in 1995 can be attributed to the increased flood risk awareness since 1993 among the people living in this area, who were now better prepared for such calamities. The emotional damage is difficult to quantify, but should not be ignored!

Shortly after the 1995 disaster, the Dutch government accepted the so-called "Delta Plan Large Rivers", which stated that dike levels should be such as to ensure that the incidence of flooding would on average occur only once every 1,250 years (Ministerie van Verkeer en Waterstaat 1995). As a short-term measure, it was decided that unsafe stretches of dikes (with a flooding risk exceeding once every 100 years) should be repaired before the end of 1996. In specific parts of the floodplains of the river Meuse, where the potential damage is relatively large, levees were constructed which should reduce the risk of flooding to once every 50 years for the shorter term and ultimately to once every 250 years. The short-term measures were implemented within two years with the help of a special emergency act, called the "Delta Act on Large Rivers".

The floods of 1993 and 1995, plus some severe high water problems in various parts of the Netherlands in 1998, provided a strong stimulus for the development of a philosophy on short-term and long-term flood control. In addition to the 4th National Policy Document on Water Management (Ministerie van Verkeer en Waterstaat 1998) a special national policy document called "Approach to the high water problems" (Ministerie van Verkeer en Waterstaat 1999) was written. The strategic approach outlined in this document includes the following main points:

- Safety first (national safety standards should be met as soon as possible);
- No shifting of problems (solutions for a specific location must not result in problems in other areas);
- Room for water (water as the regulating principle in spatial planning);
- Tailored approach on a regional scale;
- No guarantees (it will never be possible to guarantee 100% safety against flooding).

The present paper outlines the current attempts to control floods in the river Meuse. Their aim is to ensure a certain level of safety against flooding along this river. Contributions to the achievement of this goal can be found at the local, regional, national and international levels. Each of these has its own technical, political, social and economic constraints, and thus also its own timetable. It seems worthwhile, therefore, to tackle the flood problem at various levels. This so-called multi-level approach is discussed in Section 3, but before that, Section 2 summarises some characteristics of the river Meuse. Future developments, such as climate changes, are included in the discussion section.

## 2. River Meuse

The Meuse is a typical rain-fed river, originating at an altitude of 409 m above sea level at the Plateau of Langres in the north of France and discharging some 850 km further into the Haringvliet in the west of the Netherlands, from where its water flows out into the North Sea. The catchment area of the river (Figure 1) is around 33,000 km$^2$ and is situated in France (9,000 km$^2$), Belgium (13,500 km$^2$), Germany (4,000 km$^2$), Luxembourg (600 km$^2$) and the Netherlands (6,000 km$^2$). The Meuse crosses the border between Belgium and the Netherlands at Eijsden, at an altitude of 45 m, and then runs through the city of Maastricht, after which it forms the border between Belgium and the Netherlands for some 47 km. This stretch of the river is called Grensmaas (Border Meuse). From Stevensweert onwards, the Meuse runs entirely on Dutch territory. Further downstream, the river has been provided with weirs to make it navigable. Downstream of the weir at Lith, tidal influences are present.

As far as its hydrologic properties are concerned, the Meuse has been divided by Berger (1992) into three sections. The upper reaches (Lotharingian Meuse) stretch from the source at Pouilly-en-Bassigny to the mouth of the Chiers. In this section the catchment is long and narrow, the gradient is small and the major bed is wide. The middle reaches (Ardennes Meuse) cover the part from the Chiers to the Dutch border at Eijsden. Here the Meuse cuts through rocky terrain, resulting in a narrow river and a steep slope. These circumstances result in rapid discharge after precipitation, so that this part contributes considerably to the flood waves. The lower reaches consist of the Dutch section of the Meuse. The gradient in the Grensmaas section

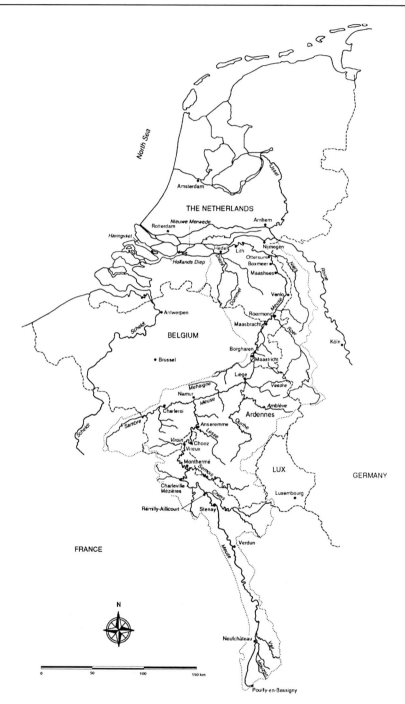

*Fig. 1.* The catchment area of the river Meuse.

is still relatively steep, but downstream, in the area provided with weirs, the gradient becomes less and less steep, resulting in ever finer sediment. The Grensmaas is a typical gravel river, but further downstream, only sand is found in the bed. This part is therefore known as the Zandmaas (Sandy Meuse).

The discharge of the river Meuse shows great fluctuations. Discharge levels at Borgharen, the representative measuring point for the Dutch part of the Meuse, range from 10 m³s⁻¹ during very dry periods to 3,000 m³ s⁻¹ in periods of heavy rainfall in the catchment area. The average annual discharge at Borgharen is 230 m³s⁻¹. The distribution of the river discharge over the year, averaged over the period 1911-1991, is presented in figure 2. The figure also indicates two extreme years: 1966 as a typical wet year and 1976 as a typical dry year.

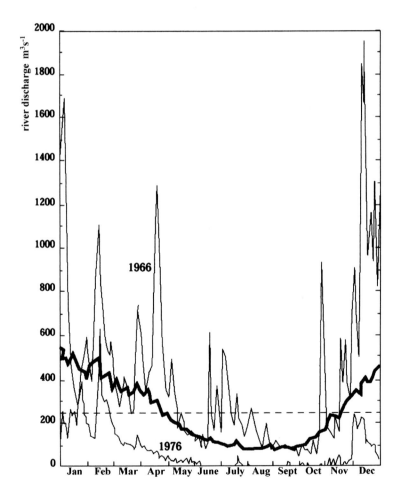

*Fig. 2.* Distribution of river discharge over the year: mean values over the period 1911-1991, and examples of a typical wet year (1966) and a typical dry year (1976); average annual value (230 m³s⁻¹) is also indicated.

*Table 1.* Exceeding frequencies for various river discharge levels at Borgharen.

| Exceeding frequency (once per x years) | Discharge ($m^3 \ s^{-1}$) | Comments |
|---|---|---|
| 1/1,250 | 3,800 | |
| 1/250 | 3,275 | |
| | 3,120 | December 22, 1993 |
| | 3,000 | January 1, 1926 |
| | 2,870 | January 31, 1995 |
| 1/50 | 2,710 | |
| 1/2 | 1,500 | critical discharge |
| | 355 | mean winter discharge |
| | 230 | mean discharge |
| | 105 | mean summer discharge |
| | < 10 | dry period; low discharge |

Table 1 lists the exceeding frequencies for discharge levels at Borgharen. A flood risk of once every 1,250 years (1/1,250) is the required safety risk behind the dikes, while 1/250 is required behind the levees after completion of the Meuse improvement project (Maaswerken; see section 3.2) and 1/50 is the present-day safety risk behind the levees. The extreme discharge levels of 1926, 1993 and 1995 are indicated.

At discharges between 800 and 1,200 $m^3 \ s^{-1}$, the weirs are opened and the river is allowed to flow freely downstream. In the Netherlands, the term 'flood' is used for the river Meuse when the discharge is greater than a critical value of about 1,500 $m^3 \ s^{-1}$, because this is when large areas of the floodplains along the river start to be inundated.

## 3. Approaches to flood control

For many centuries, the answer to flood problems was to build and/or further raise the dikes and to straighten and deepen the river so that the water could be discharged as rapidly as possible. In addition, areas with controlled inundation were used to prevent the inundation of areas with greater potential damage. Gradually, however, the idea began to take form that such an ongoing process of harnessing the river was not a sustainable solution. Therefore raising the dikes is no longer the starting point, but is used only as a last resort when other measures fail. The preferred solution is now the restoration of natural processes, and especially opportunities to create more space for the river. This means that the floodplains should only be used for necessary river-related activities, while measures should be taken to give the river more room to expand. Such measures may include deepening and widening of the main channel, lowering the winter bed, and digging side and flood channels in the floodplains. A more fundamental, long-term solution to the problem should involve the water being retained in the catchment areas for a longer period of time, so that discharges become spread over a longer time and discharge peaks are reduced. In addition, efforts should be made to communicate the risks to the inhabitants of the flood plains.

## 3.1 The "Room for the river" policy document

The experience of the extreme floods of 1993 and 1995, the vulnerability of our country and the awareness of increasing river discharges in the future as a result of the expected climate change, mean that the development of a sustainable protection against floods must have high priority, both now and in the future. It has been realised that the construction of dikes, sedimentation processes and human activities in the floodplains have seriously reduced the space available to the river over the past centuries. This has usually been a very gradual process, with small parts of the river's expansion space being given new functions. This process has resulted in ever increasing high water peaks.

To stop this process, the Dutch government decided to introduce a more stringent policy for the use of the winter bed. The national policy document called "Room for the River", which was published in 1996 and adapted on May 12, 1997, has a strong legal basis and permits only new activities which are necessarily related to the river. Furthermore, each activity that was tolerated had to be accompanied by measures to compensate for any effects on the water level and must not lead to new damage. The objective is defined as: "more room for the river, sustainable protection of human beings and animals against high water and limitation of material damage". Implementation occurs on the basis of the "Spatial Planning Act" and the "Rivers Act". In principle, these acts tolerate no new interventions in the floodplains which could lead to increased water levels, prevent or hamper future measures to increase the discharge capacity or cause potential damage during high water. Generally this means any construction works or obstacles in the floodplains or the extension of existing buildings.

New interventions which inevitably lead to the above-mentioned effects will only be tolerated for activities which are inseparably linked to the river. Such activities include civil engineering works for the actual waterway (bridges, sluices, water defence structures, etc.), provisions for shipping (improvement of the waterway), provisions for shipping safety, transshipment facilities, shipyards for vessels larger than 25 m and habitat creation or restoration in the floodplains. These interventions in the floodplains are only permitted under strict conditions: the resulting increases in the water level, as well as the hindrance to future measures to lower water levels, should be limited to a minimum, while potential water level increases should be compensated for and there should be a flood damage risk of less than once every 1,250 years (below this level no compensation can be claimed from the Dutch Government). Other new activities will not be not permitted unless there is a serious societal necessity to implement them within the floodplains and they produce no problems for water level interventions in the future. The above-mentioned conditions also apply to these exceptions.

It will be clear that these strict rules have major consequences for all activities in the floodplain areas. In fact, developments such as housing, recreation, agriculture and habitat creation will all be subordinate to the effort to guarantee a set level of safety against floods. Not surprisingly, this has led to a great deal of debate in these areas. Nevertheless, it may be concluded from a recent Meuse Valley report (Maaswerken 1999a) that the above policy document still allows many new developments, provided these are designed and executed in a creative way. Designing "win-win solutions" will require a great deal of creativity and co-operation from all the actors.

## 3.2 The Meuse Improvement Project (Maaswerken)

The Delta Plan Large Rivers (Ministerie van Verkeer en Waterstaat 1995) stated that by 1996 the risk of flooding behind the levees in the floodplains of the river Meuse in the Province of Limburg had to be reduced to once every 50 years (1/50), while ultimately it had to be reduced to once every 250 years. The required reduction to 1/50 has already been achieved. The Meuse improvement project (Maaswerken) should further reduce it to 1/250 before 2015, although 80% of this safety target is due to be achieved before 2006. Although flood protection is the starting point, this project is to be carried out as an integrated rehabilitation project, including elements such as flood protection, improvement of shipping lanes and habitat creation. Additionally, attention is given to the extraction of sand and gravel, recreation, agricultural activities in the floodplains, housing, groundwater levels, economic aspects, etc. The philosophy on which the project is based is in fact that of accelerated discharge. This can be achieved by providing more space for the river through a number of activities: widening and deepening the summer bed, lowering the winter bed level, digging side and flood channels and temporary storage of the water in retention basins. Details are presented in sections 3.2.1 and 3.2.2.

Deepening of the summer bed is the most efficient measure, contributing most to the lowering of water levels per $m^3$ of dredged soil. Moreover, the dredged-out sand or gravel is a valuable building material. Widening the summer bed requires more dredging work, as well as construction work along the river banks, while the excavated soil has a lower value. Measures in the floodplain have an even lower efficiency, since the soil in these upper layers is often polluted (Schouten *et al.* 2000), resulting in much higher costs. However, the activities in the winter bed do have great potential for nature conservation. It is especially these activities which can contribute to the sustainable restoration of the river.

Acceleration of the river discharge may have significant downstream consequences (Brookes 1988). This is also true for the river Meuse, where measures to lower the water level by about 0.80 m during extreme discharge situations result in downstream water level increases of a few cm. Because this is not acceptable, compensation works will be carried out to diminish these effects.

The project is carried out in a public partnership of national and regional governmental agencies (the Ministry of Transport, Public Works and Water Management, the Ministry of Agriculture, Nature Conservancy and Fisheries and the Limburg provincial authorities). A covenant was signed on April 10, 1997 and the project should be completed in 2015. Additionally, intensive contacts exist with 48 municipalities along the river Meuse, 5 regional water boards, nature conservancy groups, tourist organisations, agricultural organisations, the regional Chambers of Commerce, and special local interest groups. The project involves two main sections of the river: the Grensmaas (Border Meuse) and the Zandmaas (Sandy Meuse). Environmental impact studies for both parts were published in 1998 and 1999 respectively.

### 3.2.1 Grensmaas (Border Meuse)
Initially, the Grensmaas was characterised by islands, sand and gravel banks and channels with sloping banks. However, as a result of gravel extraction, river normalisation and the construction of upstream water intakes, the Grensmaas devel-

oped into a river whose main channel has cut deeply into the bed and whose flood-plains are inundated only in extreme situations. Thus, the river lost its natural character. The Grensmaas does not allow shipping traffic. The ships travel by way of the Juliana canal, which runs parallel to this stretch of the river.

Due to the relatively steep gradient (an average of 0.50 m km$^{-1}$), this part of the Meuse is a gravel bed river. In the 1980s, a plan was designed in which the restoration of the natural character of the river could be financed by the revenues of gravel extraction (Helmer *et al.* 1991). The slogan for this project was: "Gravel for wildlife; a worthwhile exchange". After the extreme flood of 1995 this natural restoration project was combined with the goal of decreasing the risk of floods. Since 1997, it is a part of the Meuse improvement project (*Maaswerken*).

The project involves three main measures (Figure 3):

1. Widening of the main channel. This will contribute to the goal of reducing flood risks. Within this widened channel, the river can follow its natural course, giving it every opportunity to form islands, meandering channels and sand and gravel banks. This will also provide ideal conditions for the development of typical river ecotopes, so that the original characteristic plants and animals may return.

2. Lowering of the floodplain levels. This will lead to a transitional area from the river to the higher areas at the original level, creating a gradient from frequently to rarely inundated areas, and allowing a variety of ecological habitats to develop.

3. Storage of fine-grained sediment. The fine-grained sediments resulting from the excavation process will be stored in deep pits created by gravel extraction. The pits will be situated in such a way that, after having been filled up with the fine sediment and clay, they will function as zones of low permeability and thus prevent undesirable drops in the local water tables (*cf.* Figure 3).

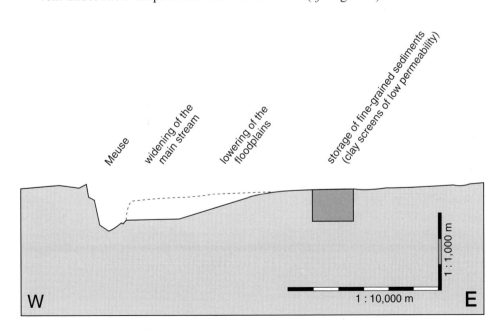

*Fig. 3.* Principles of the Grensmaas project (Source: Maaswerken 1998).

Another aspect which will be given careful consideration is the linkage to areas where no excavation is to take place, allowing the project to contribute to what is known as the national ecological network. Much attention will be given to co-ordinating the project on both sides of the river, which means co-operating with Belgium. In a 1992 declaration of intent, the two countries agreed to develop a joint programme for the spatial planning of this part of the Meuse valley, both to prevent flooding and to stimulate the natural development of the river. The joint programme is called "Living Border Meuse"

### 3.2.2 Zandmaas (Sandy Meuse)

In the 1920s and 1930s, this part of the Meuse was turned into a main shipping lane by deepening and straightening the river and building a number of weirs and sluices. This part of the river thereby lost its typical dynamic character. Figure 4 shows a number of alternative solutions which have been presented, and from which a preferred alternative is to be chosen. Flood protection and improvement of the shipping lane are the main objectives of this project, while habitat creation is also receiving some attention, though not as much as along the Grensmaas. These measures are supposed to reduce maximum water levels for the sort of peak discharge which is likely to occur once every 250 years by an average of about 0.60 m.

The "Combined Alternative" is a solution in which deepening of the main channel is combined with habitat creation at specific locations along the river, depending on local potentials. The intention of this so-called limited habitat creation is to link the nature conservation areas together in a chain, thus contributing significantly to the development of the national ecological network. Wherever possible, erosion of the river banks will be allowed to occur. This should result in more natural, 75 m wide river banks, which link other conservation areas and also make a limited contribution to providing more space for the river. In addition, some flood and side channels are proposed, as well as a retention area near Roermond (the so-called Lateraalkanaal West).

Much attention is also given to the creation of retention areas, which could temporarily store large amounts of water during extreme floods, reducing peak levels

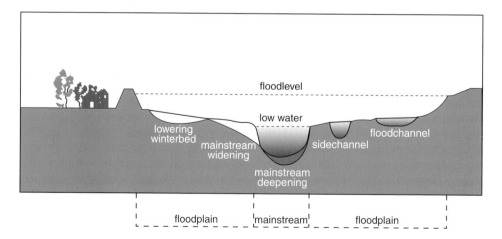

*Fig. 4.* Main measures of the Zandmaas project (Source: Maaswerken 1999b).

further downstream. Of course, if such retention areas are to have a significant effect, they must have a large capacity. Lateraalkanaal West has a total volume of about 19 million m³ (with a net volume of about 13 million m³). At a discharge level of 3,382 m³ s⁻¹, which is expected to occur once every 250 years, this would lower the maximum water level by about 0.06 m. As these data illustrate, the desired flood control in the densely-populated Meuse Valley cannot be achieved by the creation of retention areas alone. However, these could be regarded as a compensation measure for downstream effects. Research on these options is currently underway.

### 3.3 Measures in the tributaries of the river Meuse

There is an increasing awareness of the interconnections between the main river and its tributaries. In fact, they form one water system, in which problems can be solved adequately only by a comprehensive approach; it requires a watershed approach. From a practical point of view, it may be recommended to start at the sub-watershed level. The interconnections between the river and its tributaries concern not only discharge levels, but also the ecological functioning and water quality aspects. Retaining the water in the sub-watersheds of the Meuse for a longer period ensures retardation of discharge in the tributaries in periods of heavy precipitation. As a result, discharge peaks are reduced, because the discharge volume is spread over a longer period of time. The combination of such lower peaks with peaks in the Meuse itself may result in a lower total maximum discharge. Of course, besides lowering the tributary peaks, one should also be aware of the shift of these peaks in time, and look for possible coincidences of peaks in the river Meuse and its tributaries.

The tributaries entering the river Meuse in the province of Limburg can be divided into two types: the slow-flowing lowland streams in the Holocene sands and the fast-flowing upland streams from the Ardennes and the Limburg plateau. Examples of the two categories are the Tungelroyse Beek and the Geul, respectively. The lowland streams have generally been canalised to enforce faster discharge in spring in order to optimise the groundwater level for agriculture. The banks of the upland streams have been protected by stones to prevent erosion. Both types are characterised by high discharge peaks during heavy rainfall. An outline of the discharges of the main tributaries during extreme high water in the Meuse is given in Table 2.

*Table 2.* Outline of the discharges of the main tributaries of the Meuse during extreme high water in the Meuse.

| Tributary | Discharge (m³ s⁻¹) |
|---|---|
| Jeker | 15 |
| Geul | 25 |
| Geleenbeek | 25 |
| Roer | 100 |
| Tungelroyse beek | 20 |
| Groote Molenbeek | 15 |
| Niers | 30 |
| **Total** | **230** |

As the discharge of the river Meuse in such extreme situations amounts to 3,000 $m^3s^{-1}$, the relative contribution of each of the tributaries alone is very low. But the total amounts discharged by all the tributaries together are no longer negligible. It is clear that a real solution in the watershed of the Meuse can only be achieved by international co-operation. By way of a demonstration project, however, the approach used in some of the tributaries can be seen as a valuable contribution to solving the high water problems in the river Meuse. It may be an example how the high water problems in this area can be approached.

The policy in the province of Limburg with respect to the tributaries of the Meuse is to aim for a 20% reduction of the maximum discharges (Provincie Limburg 1999). This aim tries to anticipate on the expected increased river discharges in the coming century as a result of climate change. Additionally, these tributaries are being reconstructed as important linking zones in the ecological network. In fact, attempts are being made to restore the natural behaviour of these tributaries.

The greatest progress has so far been made in the Tungelroyse beek and the Geul, representing the lowland and upland type of stream, respectively. The lowland streams are to be provided with shallower and wider beds, while meandering is stimulated and areas are specified where inundation will be allowed. Existing trenches and ditches are filled in, particularly in the infiltration areas. Spontaneous development of river vegetation is allowed, resulting in a more natural situation in the flat stream valley. Comparable measures are taken in the upland streams, but these are combined with interventions on those slopes which are being used for modern agriculture. During the winter period, ground coverage is prescribed along the slopes, as well as grass strips running parallel with the contours on the map. The steepest slopes will be permanently covered by forest or grass-land. These additional measures are being taken to prevent topsoil erosion during heavy rainfall. The importance of such measures was demonstrated in 1998, when heavy mudslides came down along the slopes during such rainfall situations. These were the result of changed land use on the slopes by the farmers, who had replaced grasslands by crop cultivation.

*3.4 International co-operation in the watershed of the river Meuse*

Of course, co-ordinated measures in the entire watershed of the river are much more effective than the above-mentioned measures in the tributaries which discharge into the Dutch part of the Meuse. However, the watershed as a whole transcends several international borders, and international co-ordination is an important prerequisite for successful flood control.

Such an international approach is exemplified by the "Meuse High Water Action Plan", which originated at a meeting in Arles of the Environment Ministers of France, Germany, Belgium, Luxembourg and the Netherlands on February 4, 1995, during a high water calamity (Anonymous 1995). It was agreed to take joint action to reduce the future risks during extreme river discharges. These actions will take the form of a joint effort by water managers and spatial planners. This has been worked out by the international Working Group on High Water in the Meuse, and the Action Plan was agreed on April 8, 1998. The basic philosophy is to retain water in the catchment area of the river for longer periods and to give more space to the river and its tributaries. This will be done by an integrated approach, because such measures have links with a number of other stakeholders' interests in the watershed. The measures aim to retard water discharge and reduce flood peaks by spreading them out over a longer period. The Meuse High Water Action Plan seeks to achieve a sustainable flood protection on the basis of five principles (Working Group High Water Meuse 1998):

1. Integrated, multidisciplinary and responsible actions in the perspective of sustainable development. This principle is seen as a prerequisite for the success of the Action Plan. Integration is needed because the actions have links with many other functions in the watershed. The multidisciplinary character results from the various policy areas and scientific disciplines involved, while responsible means that measures may not lead to unacceptable downstream or upstream effects.
2. Keeping people aware of the danger. The local populations should realise that, whatever measures are taken, the danger of flooding will always exist.
3. Land use activities from a water perspective. All policy areas for the entire watershed should take full account of possible effects of land use on the water system.
4. Longer storage and slower release of water from the watersheds. The water should be retained in the watershed for as long as possible, resulting in retarded discharge and therefore in reduced peak water levels during large floods.
5. Space for the river and its tributaries. The river should be given sufficient space to ensure retarded discharge without negative consequences.

This approach at watershed level corresponds with the "Framework Directive on Water" of the European Union (EU), which is expected to be accepted by a number of EU countries within a few years. The aim of this document is the protection and sustainable use of water, which will be achieved by management at watershed level. Watershed authorities are to be installed, water management plans are to be presented and implemented, and evaluations are to be made on the basis of agreed monitoring plans. Several projects are already in progress, such as those in the river Geul (together with Belgian authorities) (Overmars 1999) and the river Niers (Van den Brink & Lanphen 1999).

## 4. Discussion

Controlling river floods is a world-wide challenge. Notwithstanding the high level of technology being used and the increased scientific understanding of river behaviour, again and again we seem to be surprised by unexpected extreme floods. From a statistical point of view, such events should not come as a surprise, and it must be said that such calamities have often been expected by a group of specialists, but the general public is usually caught by surprise. The problem is that nobody knows when extreme floods will take place and that their frequency is often lower than the duration of one person's life. Notwithstanding their threatening character, rivers have played an important role in the development of specific areas, through their functions as shipping lanes, sources of fresh water, fisheries, opportunities for recreation and tourism, locations for harbours and industrial estates. Furthermore, rivers are important elements of the landscape, if only because many people enjoy living along the waterside. This means that interventions in the river have a great impact on a large number of activities in the surrounding area, and a large number of related stakeholders' interests must be taken into account. This places the river problem in the context of a number of constraints and opportunities, both from a technical, social, economic, ecological and political point of view. Charting a course through this forest of constraints and opportunities is the great challenge.

First of all, there should be sufficient support within society for spending money to reduce the damage risks. Shortly after an extreme flood with much damage, this is not a problem. However, after some years, and sometimes even after some months, public interest usually starts to decline relative to other topics. Thus societal interest is the first dynamic constraint. Immediately after or even during the disaster, emotions play a dominant role. There is a strong feeling that something ought to be done. Politicians usually sense this momentum and feel they have to contribute to one or more short-term solutions as a part of crisis management. Emergency laws allowing plans to be implemented within a much shorter period of time, as well as technological solutions such as levees, have been exemplified above. In this respect, the combination of limited available time together with emotional feelings in the community are important constraints. Nevertheless, such circumstances also provide opportunities, which would perhaps not have arisen without a crisis (*cf.* Rosenthal *et al.* 1989), especially as regards agreements between politicians. The Declaration of Arles (Anonymous 1995) is such an example.

The extreme river floods in recent years have stimulated extensive thought on the basic principles of flood control. One could say that there has been a fundamental shift in the philosophy on tackling river flood problems. The traditional approach of raising dikes and straightening and deepening rivers is no longer seen as a sustainable solution. Instead, 'natural solutions' are increasingly being sought, which first of all means retaining water in the watershed for a longer period of time, and thus lowering the peak discharges. Similar activities in the tributaries of the river also offer attractive opportunities for ecological restoration.

In specific circumstances 'accelerated discharge', for example by deepening the summer bed, could still be a solution, but downstream effects should be compensated. Furthermore, the classical emergency solution of 'controlled inundation' is also still a real option. Raising the dikes remains only as a final option, when all other solutions have failed. Nevertheless, as such it remains a real option. It may be concluded that, depending on the particular situation, a broad range of solutions is still available, ranging from more or less traditional solutions to so-called modern sustainable approaches.

For specific rivers, the flood problem emerges at a variety of levels, both in time and space. Floods have local effects, but their origin is often found in the watershed at a considerable distance. The frequency of severe floods is much lower than that of several other politically interesting events. River basins often transcend international borders, involving different sets of laws and different stakeholders' interests. Each stretch of the river has its own engineering constraints and opportunities, for example because of the soil conditions or the space around the river. So a real solution requires working at different levels. This so-called multi-level approach has been illustrated above.

Coping with risks is at the basis of making choices in flood control. Guaranteeing particular levels of safety against floods is based on long-term data sets on high water levels. It is not easy to define the level of acceptable risk; this is to a certain extent a political choice. A difficult problem is the weighing of such risks against ecological and economic potentials. In fact, the risk of floods, and measures to reduce them, should be weighed against all aspects of the quality of life. Protection against high water levels is one of these aspects, and one with a high priority. Nevertheless, the problem requires a holistic approach, in which environmental, economic, social and psychological aspects of all actions are considered together. In this approach, risk ranking is not an easy task.

In the meantime, it is now widely accepted that measures for protection against floods should be sustainable. This means that measures must not have a negative effect on the possibilities for future generations to go on living with the river. Developments in the river area should have no adverse effects on future measures to control floods, which look set to become ever more frequent and severe. On the other hand, flood control measures should not block important environmental, social or economic potentials. The challenge is to look for win-win solutions, which optimise results within available budgets, so that an acceptable level of protection against flooding is obtained, while at the same time the investments contribute to a better economy and to ecological improvements. It has been illustrated above that creativity and perseverance can achieve such solutions. Because the larger part of the catchment area of the river Meuse is outside the Netherlands, the greatest potential improvements are to be expected from abroad. Therefore, international co-operation has a high priority. Differences in legislation and stakeholders' interests, however, mean that concluding agreements and especially implementing such agreements is usually a time-consuming process. Therefore, although international co-operation will continue to be very important, local and regional measures will also be needed to control the floods.

It should be realised that the river Meuse is an important part of the national and European ecological network. This means that interventions in the river for protection against high water should also be considered in the light of this role of the river. This has been exemplified above by the Zandmaas project. Of course, the relative weight of this aspect in relation to the primary role of the river (discharge of water, ice and sediment) is a matter of debate.

In addition to technical and engineering measures, attention should be given to administrative and legal measures. This has been exemplified above by the "Room for the River" policy document. It is our experience that large projects such as the Meuse improvement project (Maaswerken) require new legal instruments, because they encounter unprecedented situations, or situations in which real solutions cannot be obtained without new legislature. An example is the handling of polluted soil (Schouten *et al.* 2000). Some parts of the floodplains contain highly polluted fine-grained sediments. Complete removal of this sediment, followed by dumping in storage basins, is too expensive, so that the project would become unfeasible. Granting permits for local transport over short distances, under strict conditions, has allowed restoration programmes to proceed (Ministerie van Verkeer en Waterstaat *et al.* 1998). In fact, the sediment remained in the same area, with no additional effect on the ecological functioning of the particular stretch of the river.

River restoration projects such as the Maaswerken are large infrastructure projects, for which the passage of time is an important focal point. The larger the scale, the more difficult it becomes to obtain all the legal permits in time to start the engineering works. Furthermore it has been found that the old habit of seeing the project as a purely technical problem, which should be solved by technical experts, and then presenting this technical solution for public debate, often results in much community opposition and serious delays. This shows that political and social aspects are at least as important as the scientific and technological ones. Therefore, much time is now being spent on political and social discussions in the early stages of such projects. The Maaswerken project even has a special "communication team" for this purpose.

In the present situation of complex decision-making, overlapping policy areas and limited budgets, innovative partnerships are crucial if the river restoration projects are ever to be implemented. Both the Maaswerken and the co-operative efforts in the tributaries are examples of national and regional interagency partnerships, while public/private partnerships are being prepared for parts of the Maaswerken. Such partnerships often involve the mining industry, as is particularly the case for the Grensmaas project entitled "Gravel for wildlife; a worthwhile exchange".

Although the projects for the Meuse tributaries make a relatively small contribution, in quantitative terms, to flood control in the river Meuse itself, they are nevertheless important as demonstration projects, since the principles are the same on a larger scale. The importance of such projects must therefore be underlined. Moreover, a number of such projects together can make a significant contribution to reducing peak floods.

Comparing the damage caused by the extreme floods of 1993 and 1995 shows the importance of a public awareness of the risks of flooding among people living in the floodplains. The authorities should make continuous efforts to communicate this information to the public, especially after some years without such extreme floods. This communication effort should have the same priority as the engineering works themselves.

Because the Meuse is a rain-fed river, climate change will have a significant effect on its discharge levels. Large amounts of precipitation in a relatively short period, as was the case in February 1995, result in extremely high water levels. The hydrological developments are expected to follow the climatic developments, resulting in higher extremes of river discharges and corresponding water levels (De Wildt & Können 1996). It is expected that at the end of the 21st century, peaks will have increased by about 20%. In the province of Limburg, dealing with these heavy discharges in the future is now a subject of intense debate. It is felt that solutions should take into account the interconnections between land and water. This means that there is an increasing link between water management and spatial planning. One of the options being studied is to reserve sufficiently large areas of land along the river which could be inundated in periods of dangerous high water situations. These problems should really be solved at the watershed level, which means that this problem should have an important place on the international agenda. This is all the more urgent since the required town and country planning will have to be made well in advance.

## 5. Conclusions

Controlling extreme river floods, notwithstanding the present-day high technology and scientific developments in river engineering, remains a difficult task. To begin with, it is difficult from a flood risk management perspective: river discharge generally shows a very dynamic behaviour, whose extremes are very difficult to predict. The extremes with which one has to reckon often occur with frequencies of less than once in a human lifespan. This means that decisions are taken on the basis of extrapolations of scarce data sets. This alone is a source of much disagreement, and the current debate on the possible effects of climate change add even more uncertainty. Secondly, rivers have many functions (shipping, recreation, housing, habitat creation, drinking water supply, etc.), which means that many stakeholders are interested in possible interventions in the river. Thirdly, each river is unique, with its own geometry, soil properties, hydrology and hydraulics, and its own watershed with tributaries. This already causes a number of constraints and/or opportunities from an engineering point of view. Fourthly, the river and its watershed generally transcend a number of administrative boundaries, at local, regional, national or international level. This means that complex negotiations may be needed to agree on specific measures. A joint vision is therefore a first prerequisite. Finally, crisis situations during or shortly after a calamity can, often in a very short time, put a completely different face upon the river and its flooding problems. This tends to make (short-term) solutions possible, which were unthinkable before.

Such a variety of perspectives with differences in time and space make the river flooding problem immensely complex. Each of these perceptions and circumstances creates physical, political, social or economic constraints, but also opportunities. To discover these constraints and opportunities, in the light of the problems to be solved, is a first step on the road that will lead to a solution. It is this innovative process in the context of the various constraints and possibilities which is the great challenge. Because 100% safety from flooding can never be obtained, the objective to control extreme river floods can be described as ensuring a particular level of safety. Contributions to reach this goal can be found at local, regional, national and international levels. Each of these levels presents its own technical, political, social and economic constraints, and hence its own timetable. It is thus worthwhile to tackle the flood problem at different levels. That it why this paper has proposed a multi-level approach, which has been illustrated by a number of examples above. For the Dutch part of the river Meuse, these included the following proposed measures:

– administrative and legal measures (the "room for the river" policy document);
– accelerated river discharge (enlargement of the river's cross-section) with compensation for possible downstream effects;
– widening the channel and lowering the floodplain level (restoration of natural development of the river);
– creation of side and/or flood channels (improved discharge and contribution to the national ecological network;
– measures in the tributaries of the river (retaining the water in the watersheds for longer periods; retarding the discharges);
– co-ordinated measures in the entire watershed of the river (international co-operation).

Measures for protection against floods should be sustainable. This means that measures must not have any negative effects on the opportunities for future generations to live with the river. Developments in the river area should not hamper future measures to control the floods (which are expected to increase), while at the same time such measures against flooding should not block important environmental, social or economic potentials. The watershed approach seems to be most appropriate option, but one has to realise that due to the densely populated area of the Netherlands and the relatively small part of the Meuse watershed that lies within this country, long-term solutions must come from activities at the (international) watershed level. Therefore international co-operation has a high priority, which will become even more urgent in view of the expected higher peak discharges due to climate change.

## Acknowledgement

An earlier draft of this paper was prepared for the Seminar on Flood Prevention and Protection, organised by the Economic Commission for Europe of the United Nations (Berlin, October 7-8, 1999). We gratefully acknowledge their permission to publish the revised version of this paper.

## References

Anonymous. 1995. Declaration of Arles. Tackling the problems caused by the high water level of the Rhine and Meuse. Environment Ministers of France, Germany, Belgium, Luxembourg and the Netherlands, Arles.

Berger, H.E.J. 1992. Flow forecasting for the river Meuse. Thesis. Delft University of Technology, Delft.

Brookes, A. 1988. Channelized rivers. Perspectives for environmental management. John Wiley & Sons, Chichester.

De Wildt, P.J.W. & Können, G.P. 1996. Hydrologie en klimaatverandering. Het Waterschap 6: 190-194. (in Dutch).

Helmer, W., Overmars, W. & Litjens, G. 1991. Toekomst voor een grindrivier. Stroming, Laag Keppel. (in Dutch).

Lely, C.W. 1926. Rapport betreffende De verbetering van de Maas voor groote afvoeren. Algemeene Landsdrukkerij, 's-Gravenhage. (in Dutch).

Maaswerken. 1998. MER Grensmaas. Province Limburg, De Maaswerken, Maastricht. (in Dutch).

Maaswerken. 1999a.Visie Maasdal. Ministerie van Verkeer en Waterstaat, Rijkswaterstaat, De Maaswerken, Maastricht. (in Dutch).

Maaswerken. 1999b. Trajectnota/MER Zandmaas/Maasroute. Ministerie voor Verkeer en Waterstaat, De Maaswerken, Maastricht. (in Dutch).

Ministerie van Verkeer en Waterstaat. 1995. Deltaplan Grote Rivieren. Directoraaat-Generaal Rijkswaterstaat, Den Haag. (in Dutch).

Ministerie van Verkeer en Waterstaat. 1998. Water Kader. Vierde Nota Waterhuishouding Regeringsbeslissing. Ando bv, Den Haag. (in Dutch).

Ministerie van Verkeer en Waterstaat. 1999. Aanpak wateroverlast. Ando bv, Den Haag. (in Dutch).

Ministerie van Verkeer en Waterstaat, Ministerie van VROM, Ministerie van LNV, IPO. 1998. Actief bodembeheer rivierbed. Omgaan met verontreinigd sediment in de grote rivieren. Beleidsnotitie. Ministerie van Verkeer en Waterstaat, Den Haag. (in Dutch).

Overmars, W., Van Winden, A. & Helmer, W. 1999. Stromende berging in het stroomgebied van de Maas. Natuurhistorisch Maandblad 88: 123-125. (in Dutch).

Provincie Limburg. 1999. Investeren in kwaliteit. Schets van het omgevingsbeleid voor Limburg. Uitgave Provincie Limburg. Maastricht. (in Dutch).

Rosenthal, U., Charles, M.T. & 't Hart, P. ( Eds.). 1989. Coping with Crises. The management of disasters, riots and terrorism. Charles C Thomas, Springfield.

Schouten C.J.J., Rang, M.C., De Hamer, B.A. & Van Hout, H.R.A., 2000. Strongly polluted deposits in the Meuse river catchment and their effects on river management. In: Smits, A.J.M., Nienhuis, P.H. & Leuven, R.S.E.W. (Eds.). New approaches to river management. Backhuys Publishers, Leiden. pp. 33-50.

Van den Brink, F. & Lanphen, B. 1999. De Niers. Grensoverschrijdende beekdalontwikkeling van een laaglandrivier. Natuurhistorisch Maandblad 88: 142-148. (in Dutch).

Van der Ven, G.P. 1993. Man-made lowlands: history of water management and land reclamation in the Netherlands. International Commission on Irrigation and Drainage (ICID), Royal Institute of Water Management. Matrij, Utrecht.

Van Leussen, W. 1999. Integrated water management: a sociotechnical challenge. In: Wessel, J., Wind, H.G. & Mostert, E. (Eds.). Paradigms in water management. RBA Centre, Delft University of Technology, Delft. pp. 53-61.

Van Petersen, J.W. 1978. De waterplaag. Dijkdoorbraken en overstromingen achter Rijn en IJssel. De Walburg Pers, Zutphen. (in Dutch).

Verwey, G. 1980. Op zoek naar het wezenlijke in de Nederlandse geschiedenis. Elsevier, Amsterdam. (in Dutch).

Working Group High Water Meuse. 1998. Actieplan hoogwater Maas. Francis Hambye, Namur. (in Dutch).

# USING NATURAL CLEANING PROCESSES IN THE RIVER ECOSYSTEM: A NEW APPROACH TO ENVIRONMENTAL RIVER MANAGEMENT

## Does natural attenuation outbalance the risks of organic and inorganic contaminants in a river ecosystem?

H.J.P. Eijsackers[1] & P. Doelman[2]

*[1] Alterra, Institute for Green World Research, P.O. Box 47, NL-6700 AA Wageningen and Institute of Ecological Science, Vrije Universiteit, De Boelelaan 1087, 1081 HV Amsterdam, The Netherlands; [2] IWACO, International Water Consultants, Advisory Bureau on Water and Environment, P.O. Box 8520, NL-3009 AM Rotterdam, The Netherlands*

## Abstract

In modern river management, natural erosion processes will be facilitated, resulting in the exposure, mobilisation and release of contaminants sedimented in riverbanks and estuarine areas. Based on our analysis of rate characteristics of the various processes (adsorption and desorption, leaching and biodegradation) for heavy metals, polycyclic aromatic hydrocarbons and organochlorines in the various (sub)ecosystems and for various scenarios of mobilisation, we can draw the following conclusions:
- In most riverbanks persistent contaminants are bound to the deeper soil layers where they are subject to little biodegradation and mobilisation. For persistent compounds which easily bioaccumulate, risks may increase in the course of time.
- Stepwise massive release caused by accidents, excavations or massive erosion during high tides results in sudden mobilisation and a flush of released contaminants. At low discharges with limited dilution this causes acute, harmful effects. Due to the short duration of the flush, these effects do not continue long; side channels and river banks provide refugia from which recovery occurs.
- In side channels, rivulets and temporarily inundated areas slow release, in combination with high temperatures, results in increased risks.
- For most other situations, biodegradation usually will be effective (biodegradation rate exceeds release rate) and no contaminants will be set free, given the microflora had enough time to adapt to these compounds.
- Potential release at low discharge levels should be monitored; contaminants pose a risk in such situations, because release-kinetics exceeds degradation-kinetics.

We recommend preventive routine monitoring, combined with specific ecological interpretation and additional monitoring after a positive signal.

## 1. Introduction

Originally river management was a strictly safety-driven approach, optimising water drainage and resulting in gutterlike streambeds, flat riverbanks and high dikes. In recent years it has developed into an ecodynamic and hydrodynamic sys-

*New approaches to river management, pp. 307–328*
*edited by A.J.M. Smits, P.H. Nienhuis and R.S.E.W. Leuven*
*© 2000 Backhuys Publishers, Leiden, The Netherlands*

tem approach, facilitating a diverse river ecosystem. However, the river system still carries and stores the remnants of the past, when rivers were used as gutters and contaminants were discharged freely. It is especially in lowland river areas that these contaminants have become sedimented in riverbanks and estuarine areas. Over the years, these contaminated sediment and soil layers have become covered by cleaner or less contaminated sediment layers.

In modern river management, natural eroding processes will be facilitated, by providing a more natural streambed with more twisting and turbulent river channels. This results in the exposure, mobilisation and consequently the release of contaminants stored in deeper layers of the sediment and riverbanks (Figure 1).

The question is how the mobilisation and release of old contaminants actually occur? One can think of a number of possibilities:

1. Contaminants are gradually released allowing sufficient time for biodegradation. This might result in release at low concentrations which are more or less in the range of natural releases.
2. Alternatively contaminants become available as a flush. The remnants and processes might then pose a risk, because release-kinetics could exceed degradation-kinetics.
3. Hence, one may wonder whether it is reasonable to rely on the natural attenuation processes of the natural river ecosystem?
4. Or whether it would be better to opt for a prudent, more preventive approach, because of the toxicological risks of a flush release and the resulting increased exposure to natural biota?

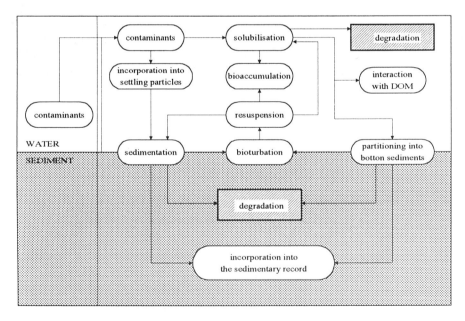

*Fig. 1.* Redistribution pathways of contaminants released from river sediments; the vertical line on the left represents the partition between the river system itself (to the right) and the surrounding environment (to the left).

This paper intends primarily to set an agenda for further discussion on these questions, in order to assess properly the 'pros' and 'cons' of a more natural form of river management, including the management of the contaminants present. Therefore, in the next section, the river system will be described from different perspectives: *i.e.*, in relation to environmental management, to nature development, to natural biodegradation and sanitation mechanisms, and to risk assessment. In the third section, the fate of three major groups of contaminants of the river system, *viz.* Heavy Metals (HM), Polycyclic Aromatic Hydrocarbons (PAH) and Chlorinated Organic compounds (also called Persistent Chlorinated Organics: PCOs, and exemplified by Hexachloro Cyclo Hexane: HCH) will be described. The discussion focuses on their behaviour (biodegradation and leaching) and the related amount of toxicity under various conditions. This is discussed in the context of the various natural river sub-systems and the associated risks.

## 2. Different perspectives of river-system management

### 2.1 Environmental management and conditions

River systems might be characterised as discharge mechanisms for water, loaded with dissolved and mobilised compounds. Most major historical cities were built along rivers because of the water supply and waste discharge possibilities. A number of characteristics of the river system are of importance in relation to these discharge processes (Table 1).

The water discharge volume is important primarily in relation to dilution. The consequences of an accidental spill or tentative release differ greatly for high or low discharge levels. This is not only a matter of water mass and the resulting dilution rate, but also of stream velocity and the resulting turbulence and aeration, which reinforce natural breakdown processes. At high discharge peaks, the water volumes

*Table 1*. River characteristics important for release and further leaching of biodegradation of contaminants.

| | |
|---|---|
| **Water volume**: | dilution, seasonal and incidental peak flows. |
| **River branching**: | deep, cool, turbulent main channels; stationary oxbows; deep cool and dark whirlpools with partly anaerobic conditions; shallow, warm and light side-channels, streamlets and ponds. |
| **Erosion and sedimentation**: | remixing of materials, sequential aerobic and anaerobic conditions at specific places. |
| **Sorption processes**: | depending on acidity (pH), redox conditions (Eh) and the composition of mineral and organic materials in the water and the sediment. |
| **Microbial processes**: | controlled by temperature, Eh, pH, and available electron-donors and electron-acceptors. |
| **River organisms**: | which bioturbate sediments and riverbank soil, but also take up contaminants and might become intoxicated. |

may carry high contaminant loads, while the mean concentrations still remain at an 'acceptable' low level. These high discharges, moreover, pose a threat as the water erodes streambed and riverbanks, which may result in the opening of deeper layers where formerly contaminants have become stored.

Of the two main rivers in the Netherlands, the river Rhine has a spring and early summer peak related to snow smelt in the Alps, combined with a rain peak in late summer and autumn. The Meuse is a typical rain-fed river and has a more erratic discharge pattern. Recently, due to modern river management and stream regulation these peaks have become more frequent and higher resulting in more frequent inundations in the upper as well as the lower streambed.

Until recently, river branching was a more or less 'historical' phenomenon in rivers like the Rhine and Meuse. It is regaining importance as a consequence of more natural river management which restores former side-channels to their original function. These are now permanently fed with river water, only at high water discharges, or by groundwater welling up from surrounding slopes. Historic events may have resulted in partially or completely closed-off oxbows and deep stationary whirlpools, as well as sand and gravel pits. These typical river features provide ecosystems with particular environmental conditions and biotopes.

Hydrodynamic and morphodynamic processes erode, replace and redistribute sediment, meanwhile sorting out coarse and fine minerals as well as organic particles. As a consequence, riverbanks are highly heterogeneous, both in soil mineral and textural composition and in contamination load. Depending on the sorption mechanisms (to clay or organic matter), contaminants may become mainly deposited in shallow areas rich in clay and organic matter or remain in the deeper main streambed areas with coarser bottom material.

Turbulence and stationarity influence the mixing or lack of mixing of the water with the various contaminants. This also includes aeration and the formation of stratification in deeper whirlpools and sandpits with anaerobic conditions in the lower water body.

Environmental conditions like pH and Eh play a major role in the chemical speciation and, hence, in the behaviour of inorganic compounds. The biodegradation of particular classes of organic compounds, like PAHs, depends on the successive occurrence of aerobic and anaerobic conditions, in relation to breakdown processes by microorganisms adapted to this environment.

In addition, pH and Eh influence the behaviour and state of health of soil and sediment organisms and consequently their behaviour. In sediments, but also in riverbank soils, bioturbation by soil and sediment inhabitants (*e.g.*, various worm species) causes a redistribution of contaminants and enhances aeration, biodegradation and desorption.

*2.2 Nature development*

In 1985, the 'Black stork' plan (De Bruin *et al.* 1985) caused a major change in the ideas about river management in the Netherlands. The river was to be returned to its natural streambed and behaviour; riverbanks were to be allowed to go through their natural succession and were to be taken out of agricultural production, building activities in the riverbanks should be stopped. This plan also initiated and catalysed a new approach to nature policy and management, which was to leave more room for natural succession and development processes, instead of the previous more conservation-oriented approach. In this conservation-oriented approach, certain biotopes were maintained by specific management practices and areas were fenced off for the public in order to prevent disturbance.

The implementation of this new approach, required new aims and targets to be formulated. These have been called nature target types (Bal *et al.* 1995) and are effectively the various biotopes or ecosystems, with a list of their key species and the environmental conditions necessary to bring back or maintain these biotopes. The main biotopes, with their stream or soil characteristics and the typical environmental conditions in these biotopes are summarised in table 2.

From a nature development point of view, the seed supply from upstream, in combination with the seed-bank in the soil is of prime importance in a transient system like a river. The establishment and maintenance of vegetation types are affected by soil conditions like pH and clay content, inundation frequency and inundation

*Table 2.* River ecosystem biotopes and conditions (extended from Bal *et al.* 1995).

| Biotope type | Stream or soil characteristics | Environmental conditions |
|---|---|---|
| Main river | High velocity and turbulence, deep | Aerobic, eroding |
| Side channels | Low velocity and turbulence, shallow, temporarily low water levels, seldomly without water | Aerobic, bottom occasionally anaerobic, eroding at peak discharges, partly shaded by bordering vegetation |
| Isolated whirlpools, oxbows, sand- and gravel pits, dammed side channels | Stationary nutrient rich-water, whirlpools and pits deep | Incidentally and deeper water and bottom layer anaerobic (sometimes entire water layer anaerobic), cool and dark |
| River dunes | Gravelly and sandy, wind-erodable, rarely inundated | Low organic matter content, low Cation Exchange Capacity (CEC), aerobic |
| Mud flats | Clayey, very frequently inundated, water-erodable | High organic matter content, high CEC, mostly anaerobic |
| Reed marshes and wasteland willow marshland | Frequently inundated, mostly loamy to clayey, water-erodable | High organic matter content, high to medium CEC, frequently anaerobic, shaded, active rhizobiota, low pH |
| Grassland | Variable inundation and soil type (sandy loam to heavy clay), both nutrient poor and rich, aerobic | Variable aerobic and anaerobic, light, sometimes warm |
| Shrub border vegetation soft and hardwood forest | Occasionally inundated | Shaded, temporarily and partly inundated and anaerobic, sometimes warm |

period, and the sensitivity to erosion of the various vegetation types (Siebel 1998, Van Splunder 1998). In addition to this, adverse impacts of contaminants already present may hamper the establishment and maintenance of natural plant species and vegetation types. Consequently, succession may veer into different directions.

## 2.3 Risk assessment

In order to properly assess the risks that the contaminants already present pose to a more natural river management system, such risks can be described in a very broad ecological sense, evaluating all potential adverse conditions. Risk is defined as: "The probability of the occurrence of adverse phenomena weighed against the profits of the activity causing these adverse phenomena" (Health Council 1995, 1996).

The present paper restricts itself to the risk of contaminating compounds, more specifically HM, PAH and HCH, in relation to their behaviour and fate, and to their toxicity and related impact on river biota.

A generic system for environmental risk assessment has been adopted in the Netherlands based on a statistically derived sensitivity distribution of species (Van Straalen & Denneman 1989), including functional microbial parameters. This sensitivity distribution is used to calculate the Maximum Permissible Concentration (MPC), expressed as the No Observed Effect Concentration (NOEC), as well as the Negligible Concentration (NC) which is 1/100 x the MPC. Two cut-off values have been chosen as a policy aim:
- the Limit Value (LV) indicates safe conditions with less than 5% of the species showing any adverse response (the MPC);
- the Intervention Value (IV) at the other, most contaminated end of the scale indicates that 50% of the species show some adverse impact of the contaminant. At this level, immediate policy action for clean-up needs to be taken.

Moreover, there is the Target value (TV) which corresponds to the NC (= 1/100 x the MPC) and should be the aim of nature management. Compounds are assessed by comparing the NOEC (also called No Effect Concentration: NEC) with the Predicted Environmental Concentration (PEC) expressed as the PEC/NEC-ratio.

In the framework of nature development it seems reasonable to use the TV, assuming that no adverse impacts of contaminants should occur in natural conditions. It is questionable, however, whether a generic system is relevant for the diversified and variable biotopes and conditions of the natural river system. Under different conditions contaminants do not pose the same risk. In clayey spots with a high organic matter content, contaminants will be bound much more strongly than in more sandy and gravelly spots (although standardisation of the sediments before assessment to some extent compensates for this). And as a further step in this line of reasoning: what are the risks in conditions that are optimal for bio-degradation? Therefore a risk assessment procedure should be further specified.
- Firstly, it should be defined what events could pose any risks for contamination, and which compound concentrations will become released or mobilised at certain events, given the prevailing conditions.
- Secondly, the derived risks for the micro-organisms, and plant and animal species present in the various ecosystems under these conditions should be assessed.

The most relevant risk events involve incidental massive spills or continued long-term discharge of contaminants; and the gradual release of bound contaminants from the sediment by natural desorption processes or by enhanced desorption after soil erosion (high tides) or excavations. These events are described in more detail below.

When soils are excavated to create new streambeds in the context of nature development projects, deposited soil layers with high levels of contamination may become exposed and environmental conditions may change from extremely anaerobic to aerobic. This will influence the chemical speciation of contaminants, and their sorption to the soil and may result in increased mobilisation of heavy metals. It may also result in enhanced biodegradation of PAHs under aerobic conditions.

High tides may erode riverbanks, which may also expose, similarly as with excavation, deeper soil layers. Most of the soil material will be taken downstream and become deposited again in the river estuary. Such high tides coincide with high discharge volumes, resulting in strong dilution. Moreover, the high turbulence of the water creates aerobic conditions and hence, as described above, increased mobilisation of heavy metals or improved biodegradation of organic contaminants.

Occasional spills can be either incidental like the Sandoz fire in 1986 or tentative. They result in a more or less massive flush, which passes along the river trajectory with relatively short residence times at the various locations along the river. Depending on the concentration of compounds in this flush, intoxication can nevertheless be considerable. Tentative releases, as observed in the 'Fliessende Welle' campaign and suggested for the salt emissions into the Rhine, mostly coincide with high discharge volumes of the rivers Rhine and Meuse and relatively strong dilution. The sodium and potassium ions released have a direct impact and may interfere with the sorption mechanisms of heavy metals.

Despite the improved water quality of the Rhine and Meuse there is still a certain level of contaminants discharged. Due to the lower stream velocity and different environmental conditions in the estuarine area, contaminants become trapped here, and sediment and estuarine areas become further contaminated. Persistent contaminants like heavy metals and resistant organochlorine compounds bioaccumulate in water, sediment and soil organisms and further bioconcentrate in aquatic and terrestrial food chains (Hendriks 1995). In the case of easily degradable compounds, only a massive and sudden release or mobilisation may lead to transient adverse direct and indirect effects.

After completion of the excavations for nature development, new water channels may cut off and erode formerly deposited and buried contaminated layers, which become gradually exposed and start to release their contaminants. This process can go on as long as these new side channels continue to cut their way through the former riverbank.

*2.4 The cleansing system: principles and versatility of natural breakdown mechanisms*

The question whether nature is a good cleansing system may seem to be somewhat of a rhetorical question, as naturally occurring organic matter shows perfect recycling. This is called "the principle of the infallibility of nature" and means that all

products formed by natural processes can also be broken down completely by natural processes, provided the right environmental conditions prevail. These breakdown processes leave no residues like metabolites (intermediate breakdown products), but $CO_2$ and $H_2O$ (Baas Becking 1942). However, does this also hold for anthropogenic organic compounds, and are microorganisms always so effective under a variety of environmental conditions?
Some observations may serve to illustrate this.

The infallibility of nature developed within an evolutionary timeframe, *i.e.,* in the course of approximately 3.5 x $10^9$ years (Baas Becking 1942, Zehnder & Stumm 1987). In addition to natural organic compounds, this principle also applies to many organic environmental contaminants, given sufficient time to allow the micro-organisms to adapt. Microbial studies in general date back to Louis Pasteur (1821 – 1895), while investigations of sediments and the corresponding water-columns go back at least 50 years. In addition, basic science on biodegradation processes of organic compounds has been carried out for a considerable period of time. As early as 1950, Zobell reported on the assimilation of hydrocarbons by micro-organisms. The complete microbial degradation of DDT (1,1,1-trichloro-2, 2'-bis(p-chlorophenyl)ethane) was unravelled by Focht *et al.* (1972), who also demonstrated the microbial degradation of PCB. Grbic-Galic & Vogel (1987) and Hutchins *et al.* (1991) consolidated the anaerobic degradation of mono-aromatics under respectively methanogenic and denitrifying conditions. In 1989, the role of $Fe^{3+}$ as an electron-acceptor in the degradation of aromatics was clarified (Lovley *et al.* 1989).

Further, we have to realise that the ecological niche of microbes is extremely wide. While one group of micro-organisms can function at pH 2, others can function at pH 11. Some micro-organisms function around freezing point, whereas others function at a temperature of 1100° Celsius. Microbes also function at extreme values of salt concentrations, redox-conditions, organic matter content and many other physical and chemical characteristics. Given the extreme versatility of the microbial world and the extensive small-scale heterogeneity in all ecosystems we should be aware of Beyerinck's adage (app. 1900, cited in Baas-Becking 1942): "Everything is everywhere but it is the environmental conditions which determine what effectively happens"; emphasising the imperative importance of environmental conditions.

The stepwise degradation of organic matter during mineralisation is driven by oxic as well as anoxic processes. In the former oxygen acts as the terminal electron acceptor, through aerobic respiration, while the latter involves fermentation and anaerobic respiration in which nitrate, sulphate, ferric iron, carbon dioxide and other compounds (even contaminants, as has been shown for tetrachloroethene) act as the terminal electron acceptor (Gerritse *et al.* 1996).

Micro-organisms use the organic molecules as nutrient sources and/or energy sources. When we define the organic molecules as electron donors, the micro-organisms use one of the above electron-acceptors to regulate the energy transfer. Moreover, micro-organisms need enzymes to initiate specific reactions. These enzymes are mainly located within the cell, so biotransformation mainly occurs within the micro-organisms. To pass the cell wall or cell membrane, a compound has to be soluble. Hence, only the soluble fraction of the compounds involved is biodegraded. This aspect of solubility should be emphasised as contaminants have to desorb from the sediment, or soil/sediment aggregates, and have to break-free to the water-phase in order to become biodegraded.

Every gramme of natural soil or sediment and every millilitre of a regular river or lake contain at least 1 million micro-organisms. Most of these are in a quiescent, non-active stage. Of these micro-organisms we know of only about 1% how they live and what they can achieve, since those micro-organisms can be cultured on artificial growth media. For the greater majority we are still unable to do that, as their activity depends on as yet insufficiently known specific environmental conditions. Table 3 summarises major anaerobic processes like denitrification, sulphate reduction and methanogenesis for various sediments and wetlands (Westermann 1994). Whatever the characteristics of the sediments, nitrate-reducing, sulphate-reducing and methanogenic processes do occur, but the process rates may vary greatly with the prevailing environmental conditions.

The ideas about the 'cleansing' capacity of the river system fit in well with the current discussion on natural attenuation. Natural attenuation is described as 'the biodegradation, diffusion, solution, sorption, volatilisation and/or chemical stabilisation of contaminants to effectively reduce toxicity, mobility or volume to levels that are protective for human health and the environment' (US-EPA 1996). According to US-EPA (1996) it involves the following processes:

1. characterisation of fate and transport to evaluate nature and extent;
2. ensuring that processes reduce risk to acceptable levels;
3. evaluating the factors that will affect the long term performance of natural attenuation;
4. monitoring to ensure their continued effectiveness.

*Table 3.* Anaerobic processes (denitrification, sulphate reduction and methanogenesis) in various wetlands with different temperature conditions, acidity and carbon content (Westermann 1994).

| Wetland type | Activity (n mol $d^{-1}g^{-1}$ dry weight) | | |
|---|---|---|---|
| | **Denitrification** | **Sulphate reduction** | **Methanogenesis** |
| Low carbon wetland, neutral | 0.16 15°C | 23 15°C | 6 15°C |
| Peat wetland, neutral | 2 10°C | 130 10°C | 160 10°C |
| Acid peatlands | 96 24°C | 670-1,670 8°C | 210-720 8°C |
| Rice paddies | 850-4,800 >20°C | no data | 250-950 17-30°C |
| Oligotrophic lake sediment | 12-180 20°C | 707 10°C | 658 10°C |
| Eutrophic lake sediment | 0-28 no data | 1224 12-16°C | 7,920 12-16°C |
| Marine and salt-marsh sediment | 0-240 23°C | 744-24,000 25-32°C | <1 23°C |

## 3. Fates of different types of compounds

The general fate of contaminants in the river system, with the various processes involved (primarily biodegradation and remobilisation/leaching) is outlined in figure 1. This is elaborated in more detail for the heavy metals (HMs), Cd and Zn, and the organic compounds HCH and PAHs, for the greater part based on research with terrestrial soils and some experiments with slurries. In our opinion there is no fundamental difference between soil and firm sediments, except for aerobicity, which is limited to the uppermost few millimetres in true sediments. Along rivers in particular, soils will become submerged regularly, which gives them an intermediate position between real soils and sediments. However, the very loose top layer of sediment in deeper water bodies should be treated differently. With respect to the physico-chemical behaviour of contaminants these soils and sediments behave in similar ways.

### 3.1 Remobilisation/leaching of heavy metals and natural biodegradation processes

Heavy metals, by definition, are not biodegradable. Nevertheless micro-organisms do influence the behaviour of HM, since micro-organisms use them as electron acceptors, as has been shown for ferric ions ($Fe^{3+}$) by Lovley et al. (1993) and for manganese (Mn) by Langenhoff (1997). Moreover, micro-organisms mediate the oxidation-reduction processes of many heavy metals, as is summarised in table 4. In addition to these series of reactions, Lovley et al. (1993) have summarised reduction reactions for a number of lesser known heavy metals, comprising the following reactions: $U^{6+} > U^{4+}$; $Se^{6+} > Se^{0}$; $Cr^{4+} > Cr^{3+}$; $Hg^{2+} > Hg^{0}$; $V^{5+} > V^{3+}$; $Mo^{6+} > Mo^{5+}$; $Cu^{2+} > Cu^{+}$; $Au^{3+} > Au^{0}$; $Ag^{+} > Ag^{0}$.

The chemical speciation of heavy metals and hence their mobility is strongly influenced by pH and Eh, for which some general trends can be defined (Bourg, cited in Salomons & Stigliani 1995). These have been combined by Salomons & Stigliani (1995) with the changes in Eh and pH resulting from major environmental processes like acidification, inundation, and desiccation by drainage and lowering of the water table (Figure 2). A comparison between these two sets of trends allows the conclusion that, e.g., chromium (Cr) will become more available under desiccating conditions, while cadmium (Cd) and zinc (Zn) do so under acidifying conditions.

Of course, the real situation is not as simple and straightforward as was depicted above. Firstly, there could be more factors involved than just pH and Eh. Janssen et al. (1998) sampled about 20 natural sites on various soils and analysed the

*Table 4.* Micro-organism-mediated heavy metal oxidation-reduction reactions.

| Transformation | Metal |
|---|---|
| Reduction | $As^{5+}$, $Cr^{6+}$, $Fe^{3+}$, $Hg^{+}$, $Hg^{2+}$, $Mn^{4+}$, $Se^{4+}$, $Te^{4+}$ |
| Oxidation | $As^{3+}$, $Cr^{3+}$, $Fe^{0}$, $Fe^{2+}$, $Mn^{2+}$, $Sb^{3+}$ |
| Methylation | $As^{5+}$, $Cd^{2+}$, $Hg^{2+}$, $Se^{4+}$, $Sn^{2+}$, $Te^{4+}$ |
| Demethylation | $Hg^{2+}$ |

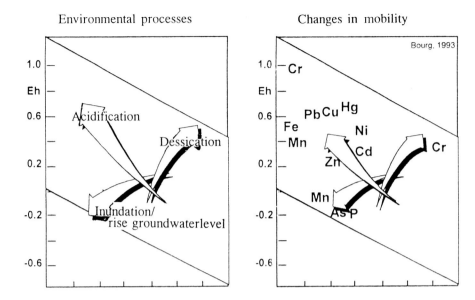

Environmental processes        Changes in mobility

*Fig. 2.* Environmental processes and changes in mobility of metals in relation to the pH and redox condition (Eh) of soils (from Salomons & Stigliani 1995).

amounts of a number of heavy metals as well as all soil factors which might be of relevance. By multiple regression they calculated which soil factors had a significant influence on sorption (kp) to the soil, arranged in descending order of impact in the regression equation (Table 5).

The regressions show that for cadmium and zinc, pH was the only significant factor in these terrestrial soils (aerobic, with low Eh levels). For other heavy metals, like copper and lead DOC (Dissolved Organic Carbon) and iron oxides also play a role. Secondly, the relation between pH and mobilisation is not linear. Salomons (1993) plotted the concentrations of cadmium and zinc in the soil solution of different soils in the Netherlands against the pH values of those soils. Starting from pH 7, a decrease in pH sharply increases the mobility of zinc, with maximum dissolved amounts at pH 5-6. Cadmium shows a similar increased mobility, starting at pH 8, with a more gradual increase. Salomons (1993) calculated, moreover, that for cadmium organic carbon has a major impact. At a pH of 3, the cadmium contents in the

*Table 5.* Multiple regression equations of environmental availability (kp) of cadmium, copper, lead and zinc in relation to various soil factors (arranged in decreasing order of importance), according to the following general formula: Log kp = a*pH(CaCl$_2$) + b*log OM + c*log clay +d*log Fe$_{ox}$ + e*log Al$_{ox}$ +f* log DOC + g*log I + h (Janssen *et al.* 1998a).

**Log kp**

| |
|---|
| Cd $= 0.48*pH + 0.28$ |
| Cu $= 0.15*pH + 0.45*\log Fe_{ox} - 0.71*\log DOC + 1.33$ |
| Pb $= 0.24*pH + 0.40*\log Fe_{ox} + 1.98$ |
| Zn $= 0.61*pH - 0.65$ |

soil solution were 5, 3.5, 2 and 1.25 µg.ml$^{-1}$ Cd at organic carbon contents of 3, 2, 1 and 0.5%. Consequently, the above- mentioned relation between zinc/cadmium and soil-pH is most pronounced for sand and silt soils and also for peat soils but less for clay soils.

Thirdly, the impact of Eh, is not the same for all heavy metals. For zinc it is relevant when the sulphide content is < 3 g S kg ds$^{-1}$, which is especially the case in sediment conditions, but according to recent reports also for river banks (Wijdeveld et al. 1999). For cadmium there is no such relation. Besides, there is a clear interference between Eh and pH: a change in Eh from -50 to 500 coincides with a decrease in pH from 7 to 3. Inundation events may result in alternate aerobic and anaerobic conditions, combined with correspondingly alternating pH levels. This results in repeated mobilisation cycles of the heavy metals stored in sediments or harbour sludge deposits as well as a stepwise drop in the moderately reduced and organic/sulphide bound Zn-forms and an increase of the amount in solution (Calmano et al. 1993).

Fourthly, salinity is important down-stream, in the transition zone between freshwater and saline conditions. It can result in a considerable stepwise increase in the mobility of cadmium.

Finally, adsorption and desorption do not follow the same isotherm-trajectory, and a drop in pH may influence desorption of heavy metals more slowly than a pH rise influences adsorption.

## 3.2 Fate of degradable compounds

Organic components still present in sediments and riverbanks after several years can be defined as persistent. Low availability for microbial attack, unfavourable environmental conditions for degradation (wrong Eh or pH) or just inaccessibility to microbes, or even a toxic environment (due to other contaminants present) are the main reasons for this persistence.

In a series of experiments by Doelman et al. (1990) on the biodegradation of α-HCH in soils or slurries with different dilution rates (Liquid/Solid relations) and either undisturbed or stirred, there were clear effects of dilution rate and treatment. In untreated soil and sediment no degradation occurred, while in treated aerobic and anaerobic soils or sediments degradation occurred at a faster rate and to a final lower content (Figure 3).

As can be seen from this figure, biodegradation for α-HCH starts readily, without a period in which the micro-organisms present have to adapt to this new food substrate; i.e., there is no apparent lag-phase. Moreover, when we plot the desorption rate and the biodegradation rate together (Figure 4), it turns out that the biodegradation rate is far higher than the desorption rate, at all levels of HCH. Between approximately 10 and 180 mg kg$^{-1}$ HCH, the desorption rate increases from 10 to nearly 30 mg kg$^{-1}$d$^{-1}$, whereas the biodegradation rate increased from over 70 to over 90 mg kg$^{-1}$d$^{-1}$ . That means that in this case the desorption factor is the limiting factor rather than the biodegradation. The desorption rate - and hence the desorption conditions - controls the overall mobilisation and degradation process. The moment an -αHCH-molecule comes available, the micro-organisms present readily attack it. This is probably also true for other readily degradable compounds, as has been shown for PAHs (Mulder et al. 1998).

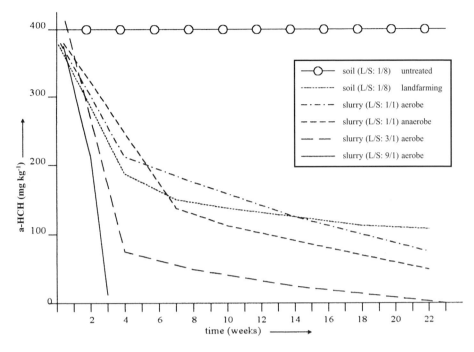

*Fig. 3.* Biodegradation of α-HCH under different soil and sediment conditions (L/S is Liquid/Solid relation).

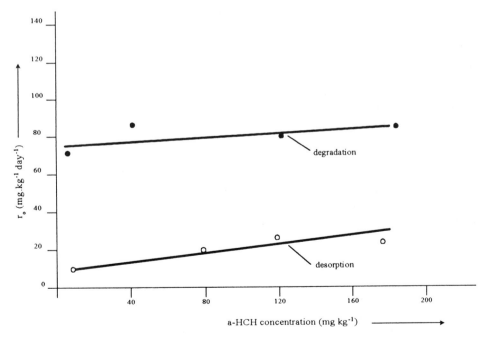

*Fig. 4.* Desorption and biodegradation rate constants $r_o$ in soils with various concentrations of α-HCH (slightly adapted from Rijnaarts *et al.* 1990).

*Table 6.* Half lives (t$^{1/2}$) in days of Naphtalene (Nap) and Benzo-a-Pyrene (BaP) under various redox (Eh) conditions (expressed in milliVolts) at which different electron acceptors are active, and at two pH-levels (Hambrik *et al.* 1980).

|  | **Redox-conditions** | **Eh** | **pH** | **t$^{1/2}$ (d)** | **pH** | **t$^{1/2}$ (d)** |
|---|---|---|---|---|---|---|
| **Nap** | mV-oxidative | 500 | 6.5 | 24 | 8.0 | 33 |
|  | mV-oxidative | 250 | 6.5 | 25 | 8.0 | 22 |
|  | mV-denitrifying | 0 | 6.5 | 32 | 8.0 | 61 |
|  | mV-reductive | −250 | 6.5 | 7,400 | 8.0 | 5,700 |
| **BaP** | mV-oxidative | 500 | 6.5 | 640 | 8.0 | 390 |
|  | mV-oxidative | 250 | 6.5 | 2,970 | 8.0 | 1,340 |
|  | mV-denitrifying | 0 | 6.5 | 8,300 | 8.0 | 7,100 |
|  | mV-reductive | −250 | 6.5 | 23,300 | 8.0 | 28,500 |

This is all the more important for those compounds which also bioaccumulate easily, because one of the main elements of risk assessment in this context is whether a compound which comes available might be taken up by other organisms (see the following section).

However, it should be realised that the results presented here for α-HCH cannot be generalised unconditionally to other organochlorines. For instance, of the other HCH-isomers β-HCH in particular is extremely persistent.

PAHs, especially the larger, more complex ones, are persistent under anaerobic conditions, but are readily degraded under aerobic conditions. Anaerobic conditions mainly prevail in river sediments (only the upper few millimetres are aerobic) and in riverbanks below the groundwater level. Therefore the various hydro-turbating events in the river cause an increase in aerobic conditions, and consequently in availability, so these events may greatly increase PAH biodegradation. Table 6 summarises the half-lives (the period in which the amount of the compounds is reduced to 50%) of naphtalene, which is a simple, degradable PAH, and Benzo-a-Pyrene, a complex and persistent PAH. This degradability relates to the complexity of the compounds as such, and to the corresponding differences in $K_{ow}$ and related water solubility. Neutral and positive Eh values result in about the same half-life, whereas negative (anoxic) Eh values cause major increases in half-life, both for the simple and the complex PAH. The impact of pH is negligible. Moreover, experiments with a very watery slurry have shown PAHs to be fully broken down in less than one hour.

## 4. Derived risks

### 4.1 Ecotoxicity

The relation between PEC and NOEC (the lowest added amount at which any adverse effect has been observed) was calculated to derive generic risks. Table 7 summarises the ecotoxicity-levels (No Observed Effect Concentrations) for HCH, Nap, BaP, cadmium and zinc, together with the maximum contents of these compounds measured in the Dutch riverbank systems and the limit values set by Netherlands environmental policy.

*Table 7.* NOEC levels (lowest mentioned in referred overviews) of various contaminants: cadmium (Cd), zinc (Zn), Naphtalene (Nap), Benzo-a-Pyrene (BaP), and γ Hexachlorocyclohexane (HCH), for selected groups of organisms at various trophic levels. For aquatic systems, these groups are green algae (*Chlorophyta*), crustacean daphnids (*Daphnia pulex* or *D. magna*) and fish (*Pimephalos promelas*); for terrestrial systems, lettuce plants (*Lactuca sativa*), crustacean isopods (*Oniscus asellus*) and earthworms (*Eisenia fetida* and related species). Maximum contents in the riverbanks and estuarine deposits are listed, as are Maximum Permissible Concentrations, used to set limit values in Netherlands environmental policy.

| | Cadmium | Zinc | Nap | BaP | γ -HCH |
|---|---|---|---|---|---|
| *NOECs for aquatic systems (in µg l⁻¹)* | | | | | |
| Green algae | 2 | 95 | 33,000[1] | 5.7[1] | 80 |
| Daphnids | 0.1 | 37 | 3,879[2] | 5.0 | 90 |
| Fish | 12 | 120 | 450 | 6.3[3] | 250[4] |
| | | | | | |
| *NOECs for terrestrial systems (in mg kg⁻¹)* | | | | | |
| Microbial activities | 36 | 95 | >25 | | |
| Lettuce | 25 | 210 >100 | >1000 | | |
| Isopods | 1 | 510 | 32 | 32 | |
| Earthworms | 5 | 318 | 1.0 | 1.0 | |
| | | | | | |
| *Netherlands Policy Limits (MPCs)* | | | | | |
| Water in µg l⁻¹ | 350 | 6.5 | 1.2 | 0.05 | 2,500 |
| Sediment and soil[6] in mg kg⁻¹ | 2.2 | 477 | 0.14 | 0.26 | 220[5] |
| | | | | | |
| *Contents in riverbanks and estuarine deposits* | 6-30 | 750-1,500 | 1500-2,500 | 1-2.5 | 20-200 |

[1] ECgrowth; [2] LC50; [3] *Brachydanio rerio;* [4] *Lebistus reticulatus;* [5] the β-isomer has MPCs for water of 80, and for soil/sediment of 92, the water/soil/sediment values for γ-HCH are 770, 190, 5; [6] Sediment and Soil MPCs have the same value for almost all compounds.

Comparing the maximum contents with the lowest NOEC, shows that adverse effects may be possible for a number of compounds.

Hendriks *et al.* (1998) extended the PEC or bioavailable fraction to 'availability for food chain transfer' by taking the concentration factor (between consecutive food chain levels) into account (Figure 5) and so calculated a corresponding ecotoxicity effect. For PAHs aquatic invertebrates and fish species are among the sensitive species. For PCBs, it is mainly water birds and mammals which are at risk, whereas for cadmium it is the invertebrates, birds and mammals which are vulnerable. The sensitivity of plants is limited: for instance the waterplant *Elodea nuttalii* did not show any toxic effect at 10-50 µmol l⁻¹ Cd and 100-500 µmol l⁻¹ Zn (Van der Werff 1981).

Van den Brink & Ma (1998) observed that elevated Cd and Zn levels coincide with relatively poor population recovery among badgers, as shown near the rivers Rhine and Meuse.

For highly bioaccumulating compounds in particular the direct ecotoxicity may be less important than the dietary uptake (and further food chain transfer). Elevated PCB contents have been shown for eggs of Antidae like scaup (*Aythya marilla*) and tufted duck (*Aythya fuligula*). Among cormorants (*Phalacrocorax carbo*) elevated PCB levels in eggs have been observed to result in reduced reproduction (Boudewijn *et al.* 1994). Consequently, Van Wezel *et al.* (1999) derived a total (summed) dietary MPC for aquatic birds and mammals of 5 µg kg⁻¹ organic Carbon, for the most toxic, coplanar PCBs which coincides with approximately 50 µg kg⁻¹ soil with 10% organic carbon.

## 4.2 Bioaccumulation and biocentration

Bioaccumulation may pose an extra threat as has already been indicated for PCBs. This also holds for heavy metals. In this context, bioaccumulation is the uptake/accumulation from water, sediment or soil, whereas bioconcentration is uptake through food items in various food chains.

With respect to heavy metals bioaccumulation and bioconcentration through the food chain 'soil>leaf>litter>humus>earthworms' may be environmentally important. This has been studied in what may be called 'artificial riverbanks', *i.e.,* deposits of contaminated harbour sludge which were planted with various tree species (Table 8).

The uptake by the leaves varies with the tree species. In the next steps the composition of the leaves and litter influences the rate and amount of decomposition of the litter and thus the resulting heavy metal contents of litter and humus. The major concentration step is in all cases the uptake by earthworms. Consequently, earthworm feeders run an elevated risk.

Hendriks *et al.* (1998) combined the present contents of the riverbanks and estuarine deposits with the bioaccumulation and bioconcentration potential, and expressed this in a bioconcentration factor. They did this for species at different trophic levels which occur in the river and estuarine area for both cadmium and PCBs (Figure 5).

Like chemical availability, bioaccumulation is governed by a number of soil factors. These were experimentally determined in relation to chemical availability (Table 5) using the earthworm *Eisenia fetida*. The results have been listed as a series of multiple regression equations in table 9. For cadmium and zinc, pH once more is the most important factor. But there are also relevant factors which may influence uptake-processes directly or affect the total functioning of those organisms indirectly.

For biodegradable compounds, bioaccumulation is partly outbalanced by internal breakdown and excretion. Van Brummelen *et al.* (1998) reviewed the bioavailability and ecotoxicity of PAHs. They recommended studying organisms with a low metabolic activity (like invertebrates, molluscs and earthworms, rather than fish).

*Table 8.* Cadmium contents (mg kg⁻¹ dw) in the soil > leaf > litter > humus > earthworms food-chain on harbour sludge deposits planted with poplar, oak or maple trees (according to results of Brils, and of Ma and co-workers).

| Tree species | Soil | Leaf | Litter | Humus | Earthworms |
|---|---|---|---|---|---|
| Poplar | 5.9 | 8.1 | 11.9 | 20.8 | 39.8 |
| Oak | 7.5 | 0.5 | 1.8 | 11.8 | 22.7 |
| Maple | 5.9 | 0.4 | 2.0 | 11.9 | 32.4 |

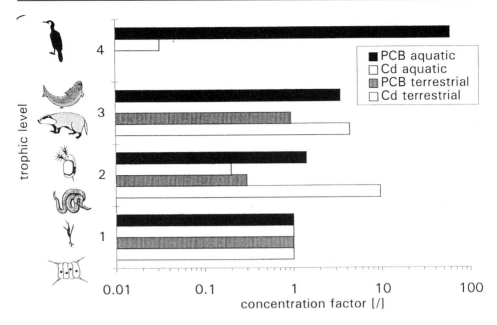

*Fig. 5.* Bioconcentration factor for cadmium and PCBs in representatives of various levels of aquatic and terrestrial food-chains (according to Hendriks *et al.* 1998).

However, for earthworms Posthuma (personal communication) has observed internal degradative metabolism of PAHs.

Conijn (1999) combined the various elements into a risk assessment system for PAHs, which includes uptake in relation to the composition of the diet, internal metabolisation capacity and potential ecotoxicity. Depending on their internal load, it is especially predatory fish species like pike (*Esox esox*), perch (*Perca fluviatilis*), pond loach (*Misgurnus fossilis*) and eel (*Anguilla anguilla*) which are vulnerable. Species with a high internal metabolic capacity like the toad (*Bufo bufo*) and a number of predatory birds are limitedly vulnerable from this perspective. However, the consequence of a high internal metabolic capacity is that metabolisation results in the formation of metabolites which may be mutagenic and carcinogenic, thus increasing the vulnerability of these species.

*Table 9.* Multiple regression equations for BioConcentration Factors (BCFs) in the earthworm *Eisenia fetida* for cadmium, copper, lead and zinc, in relation to various soil factors (arranged in decreasing order of importance), according to the following general equation: Log BCF = a*pH(CaCl$_2$) + b*log OM + c*log clay +d*log Fe$_{ox}$ + e*log Al$_{ox}$ +f* log DOC + g*log I + h (Janssen *et al.* 1998[b]).

**BCF**

| | |
|---|---|
| Cd | $= -0.43*pH + 1.36*\log clay - 1.39*\log OM + 3.19$ |
| Cu | $= -0.65*\log Fe_{ox} - 0.38*\log clay + 1.38$ |
| Pb | $= -0.78*\log clay - 0.45*\log Fe_{ox} + 0.46$ |
| Zn | $= -0.39*pH - 1.06*\log Al_{ox} + 0.73*\log clay + 3.04$ |

A rather specialised dietary route leading to extreme accumulation has been described for the beavers (*Castor castor*) recently introduced into the brackish estuarine Biesbosch area. Salix species showed a remarkable capacity to accumulate cadmium in their bark, with soil contents ranging from 0.4 mg kg$^{-1}$ dw Cd to a maximum of 1.0 mg kg$^{-1}$ dw and bark contents ranging from 8.2 to 13.1 mg kg$^{-1}$ dw (other tree barks had typical contents of 0.3-0.7 mg kg$^{-1}$ dw Cd). Contrary to what had been assumed the introduced beavers fed almost exclusively on this bark which constituted 100% of their diet in the main growth period (April-June) and 92% in the rest of the year. As a consequence, high Cd contents were measured in the target organs (liver and kidneys) of some beavers found dead (Nolet *et al.* 1994).

*4.3 Application for various river (sub)systems*

The above mentioned environmental conditions relevant to mobilisation of inorganic compounds and biodegradation of organic compounds, have the following consequences for the various sub-systems of the river ecosystem (also summarised in Figure 6).
- *Deep streaming water*: turbidity causes a constant mixture, dilution and aeration which promotes biodegradation and mobilisation, but due to the high discharge rate contaminants will also quickly be removed downstream.
- *Stagnant water:* deep waters in particular will have anaerobic deeper water layers and sediments which moreover remain cool, slowing down both biodegradation and mobilisation of heavy metals. Contaminants therefore effectively remain bound.
- *Shallow streaming water:* because of low turbidity, a limited level of erosion, increasing temperatures and direct irradiation impact by the sun, these waters will provide good conditions for slow but steady release of various contaminants. However, photosensitization of PAHs poses a potential threat, especially if these are taken up by aquatic organisms and transferred through the food chain.
- *Sun-exposed short grassy and herbaceous vegetation with aerobic upper soils:* these will provide warm aerobic conditions, which enhance biodegradation and heavy metal mobilisation. For *inundated anaerobic soils* this will not be the case. In swampy conditions, however, pH is low, leading to greater mobilisation of heavy metals.
- *Shaded shrub, reed/willow and tree vegetation with aerobic upper soils:* the soil will be aerobic but does not warm-up, resulting in slow biodegradation. *Inundated anaerobic soils* have very limited biodegradation and mobilisation.

The following contamination situations and episodes are important.
- Most riverbanks have persistent contamination bound to the lower soil layers, resulting in very little biodegradation and mobilisation. For compounds which are persistent and easily bioaccumulate, risks may increase in the course of time.
- Stepwise massive release caused by an accident, large scale digging works or massive erosion during very high tides may lead to sudden mobilisation, resulting in a flush of mobilised contaminants. When this occurs with low river discharges, it causes acute knockdown effects which may be very harmful (compare *e.g.* the Sandoz-accident). Due to the short duration of the flush these acute

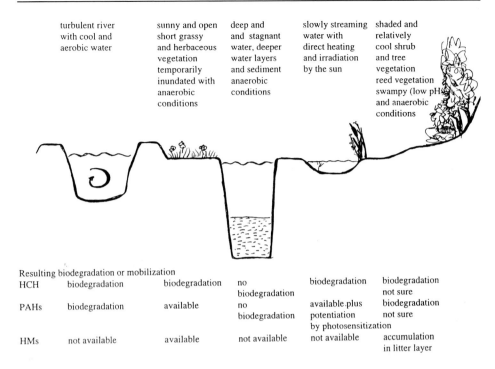

| turbulent river with cool and aerobic water | sunny and open short grassy and herbaceous vegetation temporarily inundated with anaerobic conditions | deep and and stagnant water, deeper water layers and sediment anaerobic conditions | slowly streaming water with direct heating and irradiation by the sun | shaded and relatively cool shrub and tree vegetation reed vegetation swampy (low pH and anaerobic conditions |

Resulting biodegradation or mobilization

| | | | | | |
|---|---|---|---|---|---|
| HCH | biodegradation | biodegradation | no biodegradation | biodegradation | biodegradation not sure |
| PAHs | biodegradation | available | no biodegradation | available plus potentiation by photosensitization | biodegradation not sure |
| HMs | not available | available | not available | not available | accumulation in litter layer |

*Fig. 6.* Environmental conditions relevant to mobilisation of inorganic compounds and biodegradation of organic compounds and consequences for the various sub-systems of the river ecosystem.

effects will not continue long. Given the experiences from the Sandoz accident side streams and river banks provide refugia from which recovery can occur.

– Side streams, rivulets and temporarily inundated areas may experience slow release, which, in combination with the high temperatures in these shallow waters, may pose increased risks.
– In most other situations the biodegradation is so effective (biodegradation rate higher than release rate) that no contaminants will be released, provided the microflora has enough time to adapt to this type of compound.

The consequences of these risk episodes and situations for the various possible management activities are as follows.

– No massive earthwork in the riverbanks or riverbed should be carried out in periods with low discharge levels.
– Care should be taken that discharged or leached water is monitored and cleaned up if contaminated.
– Because of the risk of bioaccumulating contaminants, a constant monitoring programme should be set up for persistent compounds and vulnerable organisms (on the basis of their bioconcentration potential and sensitivity to the specific compounds).
– Deep storage in sandpits with a deeper non-penetrable soil layer, an anaerobic contaminated sediment/soil layer (possibly covered with a non-penetrable clay layer), and a water with anaerobic deeper layers is relatively safe.

- Deep storage in terrestrial soils may be safe if roots cannot penetrate to that depth (>2m), and there is a permanently saturated zone (anaerobic) at the storage level. Large fluctuations in the water table are not acceptable for deep storage.
- Experience gained in the Biesbosch area shows that the total content in sediments does not always reflect risks: the total contaminant contents in sandy/gravely stream gullybeds were low, but availability was high as was the response in bioassays.

## 5. Final remarks

This paper aims to add the issue of contamination and natural attenuation to the agenda of modern, more ecologically based river management. With reference to the questions posed in the introduction, the following conclusions seem reasonable.
1. Most contaminants present will be discharged gradually, providing sufficient time for biodegradation as mostly degradation kinetics normally far exceeds the release kinetics. The resulting amount of released contaminants will be zero or very low; for natural compounds like heavy metals they are more or less in the range of natural releases.
2. In case these contaminants are released in a flush, as may happen at high tides or shortly after excavations, the high discharges connected with such high tides result in sufficient dilution. Potential release situations at low discharge levels have to be monitored as contaminants may pose a risk then, because the release kinetics exceed the degradation kinetics.
3. Because the estuarine section of the river functions as a sink for any released contaminants, persistent contaminants might be bioaccumulated and bioconcentrated by general but sometimes also by very specific food-chain transfer routes. A preventive approach including some form of routine monitoring, in combination with specific ecological interpretation and additional monitoring after a positive signal, might be advisable.

More fundamentally it is important to determine the relevant time and space windows for ecological risk assessment.
4. For incidental flushes, a time window of a few weeks to some months seems relevant, but for persistent contaminants, especially those accumulating slowly, a time window of a few years to decades seems more appropriate. From an ecological perspective, the most relevant time scale is the duration of ecological development or succession. Depending on the various subsystems of the river system, this may vary from a few years to decades.
5. Because of the fluctuating character of the river at high tides, some of the ecosystems coincide with early succession stages and, hence, have short development times. However the shrub and tree subsystems have succession times which allow for gradual bioaccumulation and bioconcentration leading to intoxicating levels.
6. Risk assessment could be confined to a specific location or could be extended to the total river catchment area. All along the river trajectory, environmental conditions could influence the behaviour of contaminants. For instance, the eroded

minerals upstream influence the calcium-content and thus the pH of the water and riverbanks downstream. Contaminants released in the middle part of the river can become sedimented again in the downstream part of the river. It is therefore relevant to consider the total catchment area in an ecological risk assessment.

# References

Baas Becking, L.G.M. 1942. II. Milieu. In: Koningsberger, V.J. (Ed.). Leerboek der Algemeene Plantkunde. Scheltema en Holkema, Amsterdam. pp. 17-38. (in Dutch).

Bal, D., Beije, H.M., Hoogeveen,Y.R., Jansen, S.R.J. & Van der Reest, P.J. 1995. Handboek natuurdoeltypen in Nederland. Rapport IKC Natuurbeheer 11. Informatie- en KennisCentrum Natuurbeheer, Ministerie van Landbouw, Natuurbeheer en Visserij, Wageningen. (in Dutch).

Boudewijn, T., Dirksen, S. & Ohm, M. 1994. Zichtbare effecten van onzichtbare stoffen. Overzicht onderzoek aan vogels in het benedenrivierengbeid 1982-1992. Rijkswaterstaat Zuid-Holland, Rotterdam (in Dutch).

Calmano, W., Hong, J. & Förstner, W. 1993. Binding and mobilization of heavy metals in contaminated sediments affected by pH and redox potential. Wat. Sci. Techn. 28: 223-235.

Conijn, D.M. 1999. Gevolgen van natuurontwikkeling in de uiterwaarden voor de beschikbaarheid, afbraak en toxiciteit van PAK's. Doctoraal scriptie. Vrije Universiteit, Amsterdam (in Dutch with English summary).

De Bruin, D., Hamhuis, D., Van Nieuwenhuijze, L., Overmars, W., Sijmons, D. & Vera, F. 1985. Ooievaar: de toekomst van het rivierengebied. Stichting Geldersche Milieufederatie, Arnhem (in Dutch).

Doelman, P., Haanstra, L., Loonen, H. & Vos, A. 1990. Decomposition of alpha and beta hexachlorocyclohexane in soil under field conditions in a temperate climate. Soil Biol. Biochem. 22: 629-634.

Focht, D.D. 1972. Microbial degradation of DDT metabolites to carbon dioxide, water and chloride. Bull. Environ. Contam. Toxicol. 7: 52-61.

Gerritse, J., Renard, V., Pedro Gomes, M., Lawson, P.A., Collins, M.D. & Gottschal, J.C. 1996. *Desulfitobacterium* sp. PCE1, an anaerobic bacterium that can grow by reductive chlorination of tetrachloroethene or ortho-chlorinated phenols. Archives of Microbiology 165: 132-140.

Grbic-Galic, D. & Vogel, T. 1987. Transformation of toluene and benzene by mixed methanogenid cultures. Applied and Environmental Microbiology 53: 254-260.

Hambrik, G.A.., DeLaune, R.D. & Patrick, W.H. 1980. Effect of estuarine sediment pH and oxidation-reduction potential on microbial hydrocarbon degradation. Applied Environmental Microbiology 40: 365-369.

Health Council of the Netherlands: Committee on Risk measures and risk assessment. 1995. Not all risks are equal. Publication1995/06. Health Council of the Netherlands, The Hague.

Health Council of the Netherlands: Committee on Risk measures and risk assessment. 1996. Risk is more than just a number. Publication 1996/03. Health Council of the Netherlands, The Hague.

Hendriks, A.J. 1995. Concentrations of microcontaminants and response of organisms in laboratory experiments and Rhine delta field surveys. Monitoring and modelling instruments in applied research and management. PhD-thesis. Utrecht University, Utrecht.

Hendriks, A.J., De Jonge, J., Den Besten, P. & Faber, J. 1998. Gifstoffen in het rivierengebied. Een belemmering voor natuurontwikkeling? Landschap 14: 219-233.

Hutchins, S.R., Sewell, G.W., Kovacs, D.A. & Smith, G.A. 1991. Biodegradation of aromatic hydrocarbons by aquifer microorganisms under denitrifying conditions. Environmental Science and Technology 25: 68-76.

Janssen, R.P.T., Peijnenburg, W.J.P.M., Posthuma, L. & Van der Hoop, M.A.G.T. 1997a. Equilibrium partitioning of heavy metals in Dutch field soils. I. Relationships between metal partition coefficients and soil characteristics. Environ. Toxicol. Chem. 16: 2470-2478.

Janssen, R.P.T., Posthuma, L., Baerselman, R., Den Hollander, H.A., Van Veen, R.P.M. & Peijnenburg, W.J.P.M. 1997b. Equilibrium partitioning of heavy metals in Dutch field soils. II. Prediction of metal accumulation in earthworms. Environ. Toxicol. Chem. 16: 2479-2488.

Langenhoff, A.A.M. 1997 Biodegradation of toluene, benzene and naphthalene under anaerobic conditions. PhD Thesis Wageningen University, Wageningen.

Lovley, D.R., Baedecker, M.J., Lonergan, D.J., Cozzarelli, I.M., Philips, E.J.P. & Siegel, D.I. 1989. Oxidation of aromatic contaminants coupled to microbial iron reduction. Nature (London) 339: 297-299.

Lovley, D.R. 1991. Dissimilatory metal reduction. Annual Rev. Microbiology 47: 263-290.

Mulder, H. 1999. Relation between mass-transfer and biodegradation of hydrophobic pollutants in soil. PhD Thesis. Wageningen University, Wageningen.

Nolet, B.A., Dijkstra, V.A.A., & Heidecke, D. 1994. Cadmium in beavers translocated from the Elbe river to the Rhine Meuse estuary and the possible effect on population growth rate. Archives of Environmental Contamination and Toxicology 27: 154-161.

Rijnaarts, H.H.M., Bachmann, A., Jumelet, J.C. & Zehnder, A.J.B. 1990. Effect of desorption and intraparticle mass transfer on the aerobic biomineralization of hexachlorocyclohexane in a contaminated calcareous soil. Env. Sci. Technol. 24: 1349-1354.

Römkens, P.F. & De Vries, W. 1995. Acidification and metal mobilization: effects of land use changes on cadmium mobility. In: Heij, G.J. & Erisman, J.W. (Eds.) Acid rain research: Do we have enough answers? Elsevier, Amsterdam. pp.367-380.

Salomons, W. 1993. Time delayed responses of chemicals in soils. In: Neretnieks, I. & Ågren, T. (Eds.). Workshop on contaminated soils – Risks and remedies. Environmental Protection Agency, Stockholm.

Salomons, W. & Stigliani, W.M. (Eds.). 1995. Biogeodynamics of pollutants in soils and sediments. Springer, Berlin.

Siebel, H.N. 1998. Floodplain forest restoration. Tree seedling establishment and tall herb interference in relation to flooding and shading. IBN Scientific contributions 9. IBN. Wageningen.

US-EPA. 1996. Technical protocol for evaluating natural attenuation of chlorinated solvents in groundwater. Environmental Protection Agency (US-EPA), Air force Centre for Environmental Excellence, Technology transfer division, Brooks Air Force Base, San Antonio.

Van Brummelen, T.C., Van Hattum, B., Crommentuijn, T. & Kalf, D.F. 1998. Bioavailability and Ecotoxicity of PAHs. In: Neilson, A.H. (Ed.). The handbook of environmental chemistry 3, Part J. PAH and related compounds. Springer-Verlag, Berlin. pp. 204-263.

Van den Brink, N.W. & Ma W-C. 1998. Spatial and temporal trends in levels of trace metals and PCBs in the European badger Meles meles L. (1758) in the Netherlands: Implications for reproduction. The Science of the Total Environment 222: 107-118.

Van der Werff, M. 1981. Ecotoxicity of heavy metals in aquatic and terrestrial higher plants. PhD thesis. Vrije Universiteit, Amsterdam.

Van Splunder, I. 1998. Floodplain forest recovery. Softwood forest development in relation to hydrology, riverbank morphology and management. PhD thesis University of Nijmegen, Nijmegen.

Van Straalen, N.M. & Denneman, C.A.J. 1989. Ecotoxicological evaluation of soil quality criteria. Ecotox. Environ. Saf. 18: 241-251.

Van Wezel, A.P., Traas, T., Polder, M., Posthumus, R., Van Vlaardingen, P., Crommentuijn, T. & Van de Plassche, E.J. 1999. Maximal permissible concentrations for polychlorinated biphenyls. Report 601501006. National Institute of Public Health and the Environment, Bilthoven.

Weber, J.H. 1993. Review of possible paths for abiotic methylation of mercury (II) in the aquatic environment. Chemosphere 26: 2063-2077.

Westermann, P. 1994. The effect of incubation temperature on steady-state concentrations of hydrogen and volatile fatty acids during anaerobic degradation in slurries from wetland sediments. FEMS Microbiology Ecology 13: 295-302.

Wijdeveld, A.J., Smits, J.G.C., De Rooy, N.M. & Vink, J.P.M. 1999. Mobiliteit van zware metalen in de uiterwaardbodem. RIZA/WL-rapport 99.021X, RIZA, Lelystad. (in Dutch).

Zehnder, A.J.B. & Stumm, W. 1987. Geochemistry and biogeochemistry of anaerobic habitats. In: Zehnder, A.J.B. (Ed.). Biology of anaerobic micro-organisms. Joh Wiley & sons, New York.

Zobell, C.E. 1950. Bacterial activities and the origin of oil. World Oil 130: 128-138.

# FROM INTEGRATED APPROACHES TO SUSTAINABLE RIVER BASIN MANAGEMENT

R.S.E.W. Leuven[1,3], A.J.M. Smits[2,3] & P.H. Nienhuis[1,3]

[1] Department of Environmental Studies, Faculty of Science, University of Nijmegen, P.O. Box 9010, NL-6500 GL Nijmegen, The Netherlands;
[2] Department of Nature Management of Stream Corridors, University of Nijmegen, P.O. Box 9010, NL-6500 GL Nijmegen, The Netherlands;
[3] Member of the Netherlands Centre for River Studies (NCR), P.O. Box 177, NL-2600 MH Delft, The Netherlands

## Abstract

This paper describes current issues in river management, such as river regulation, flooding, pollution, habitat destruction and fragmentation, water recourse allocation and water-related conflicts. The evolution from integrated approaches to sustainable river basin management is highlighted. Integrated approaches mainly refer to technical, organisational and institutional means of river basin management. Sustainable river basin management focuses on the management goal, *i.e.*, sustainable development. Experiences, innovative viewpoints and new ideas for sustainable management of river basins are summarised. The key to sustainable river basin management is promoting dialogue, encouraging networking and the exchange of data, information and knowledge between decision-makers, scientists, engineers and all stakeholders. Sustainable development requires a carefully considered strategy for the entire river catchment, which includes the following measures: (1) conservation orrestoration of the natural flow regime and the hydromorphological dynamics of rivers,(2) allowing space for rivers and (3) adapting user functions to natural river dynamics. Recommendations for further research focus on integrated modelling and scientific monitoring and the evaluation of river development and rehabilitation programmes, for the sake of improving both science and policy.

## 1. Introduction

River basins are an essential part of the earth's freshwater cycle and have great potential in terms of water related resources and functions, such as navigation, drinking water supply, agriculture, fisheries, biodiversity and outdoor recreation (Smits 2000b, Sparks 2000, Stortenbeker 2000). The history and consequences of river alterations are similar in most of the industrialised nations, where rivers have been increasingly regulated and isolated from their floodplains to increase navigation and commercial activity, but where as a result the flows of natural services from the river-floodplain system have declined (Sparks *et al.* 2000, Smits *et al.* 2000b). Nowadays, there is widespread public support in developed river basins to recover lost or diminished natural functions (Hunt 2000a, Smits *et al.* 2000b, Sparks *et al.* 2000).

*New approaches to river management, pp. 329–347*
*edited by A.J.M. Smits, P.H. Nienhuis and R.S.E.W. Leuven*
*© 2000 Backhuys Publishers, Leiden, The Netherlands*

The rational answer to the drawbacks of single purpose measures has been integrated approaches, *e.g.*, integrated river basin management, where more than one sectoral interest is linked at both strategic and operational levels, and where the entire drainage basin is conceived of as a single ecosystem (Downs *et al.* 1991). Integrated approaches mainly refer to technical, organisational and institutional means, whereas sustainable river basin management has a well defined goal, *i.e.*, sustainable development. In order to prevent further decline of natural services and to recover diminished functions, it is important that international efforts are made to search for ways that lead to sustainable development of river basins (HRH 2000). Sustainable development has become a household word since the "Our common future" report by the World Commission on Environment and Development (Brundtland Commission 1997), and river basin management should also be checked against its "sustainability" standards. An almost classic starting point is to quote the definition this commission gave: "Sustainable development is to ensure that humanity meets the needs of the present, without compromising the ability of future generations to meet their own needs". To "sustain" is to hold, keep up, keep alive, literally "able to last". The concept of sustainable development implies limits imposed by the present state of technology and social organisation on environmental resources, and by the ability of the biosphere to absorb the effects of human activities.

In developing river basins, such as the Elbe, Mekong, Odra, Paraguay and Vistula, loss of natural services does not have be an inevitable consequence of commercial development, if citizens, government officials, planners and engineers learn from previous experience in developed basins (Da Silva 2000, Hunt 2000a, Nienhuis *et al.* 2000, Sparks *et al.* 2000). However, ecological values in developing river basins are often recognised in theory, but in practice 'strong' economic imperatives are still confronted with 'weak' ecological principles. Sound and internationally validated arguments to defend both the environmental quality and the biodiversity of these river basins are often lacking (Da Silva 2000, Nienhuis *et al.* 2000).

A motivating hypothesis for sustainable river basin management is that the total flow of social benefits (broadly defined to include both natural and commercial services) from regulated floodplain-river ecosystems can be increased by selective reconnection of rivers to their floodplains and re-creation of more natural flooding regimes (Sparks *et al.* 2000). A comparable hypothesis for developing basins is that the greatest total flow of benefits will occur from commercial development that retains critical natural processes (Hunt 2000b). However, it is of little use to talk about what could and should be done, if it is more or less clear beforehand that river authorities grant only little space for management alternatives (Hunt 2000a). Therefore, the objective of the book *New approaches to river management* is not to reject or confirm scientific hypotheses, such as those referred to above, but to elucidate expertise and to discuss with all parties concerned (*e.g.*, scientists, non-governmental organisations, policymakers, river managers and authorities) innovative viewpoints and new ideas for sustainable management of river basins (Smits *et al.* 2000a). The available expertise and new approaches may form the basis for future river research, development and rehabilitation programmes.

The goal of this paper is to describe the major results discussed in the present book. Experience, innovative viewpoints and new ideas for sustainable management of river basins will be summarised. The sequence of topics follows the outline given in the general introduction (Smits *et al.* 2000a). Section 2 focuses on developments in river basin management such as current management problems, means and goals, and the lessons learnt. Section 3 deals with the participation of new stakeholders in river basin management. Section 4 presents new methodologies and instruments in sustainable river basin management. Finally, section 5 offers some general conclusions and recommendations for river policy, management and research.

## 2. Developments in river basin management: applications and lessons learnt

### 2.1 Major problems in river basin management

Large river basins of the world show various stages of development and alterations to their streams and floodplains. Western Europe has been modifying its river basins for thousands of years (*cf.* Havinga & Smits 2000), whereas most North American rivers have been seriously altered during the last three centuries (Galloway 2000, Sparks *et al.* 2000). Nowadays, only a few large rivers in the world are more or less pristine. Rare examples are some sections of the Odra and Vistula in Central Europe (Nienhuis *et al.* 2000), the Congo in Africa (Serageldin 1999), and the Amazon and Paraguay in South America (Serageldin 1999, Da Silva 2000). In spite of extensive hydraulic engineering and management efforts, most large river basins are still facing major problems, such as water and sediment pollution, drawbacks of river regulation, water shortage and flooding risks and conflicts related to the allocation of water recourses.

### River regulation

River regulation is a general term describing the physical changes that people impose on watercourses, such as land drainage, flood protection, the building and maintenance of reservoirs, dams and weirs, channelisation and bend cut-offs to serve navigation and water-borne transport, water abstraction for industrial, agricultural and drinking water purposes, and waste-water discharge, leading to the destruction of the original ecosystems. Many of the large rivers in the world have now been regulated, particularly in Western and Southern Europe, where the percentage of rivers that are still in a natural state is very low, *viz.* 0 to 20 per cent. By contrast, many rivers in countries such as Poland, Estonia and Norway still have 70 to 100 per cent of their reaches in a natural state. River regulation often causes major changes in biological river processes, primarily in the flow regime and the transport of dissolved and particulate organic matter, and have led to a river system which has lost its hydrological resilience. The water regime of regulated rivers is subject to unnatural fluctuations during the growing season, which limit native plants and animals on the hydraulically connected floodplains. In the upper Mississippi river basin, unnatural fluctuations appear to be attributable to the operation of the navigation dams (Sparks *et al.* 2000). In addition, leveeing and draining of the floodplains has replaced fish, wildlife and timber production with production of dry land commodity crops (Smits *et al.* 2000b, Sparks *et al.* 2000). The effects of river regulation are seen not just locally, but may be extensive, especially in the downstream reaches of the river (Stanners & Bourdeau 1995). Up to now, river regulation has often been characterised by a dominant technological approach, and certainly not by a sustainable use of environmental resources. Over the last decades, flood risks in many river basins have increased as a result of changes in land use and unintended side effects of river regulation. In spite of extensive civil engineering measures, extreme climatic circumstances still cause dramatic floods in many developed river basins, such as the Meuse, Mississippi and Rhine (Galloway 2000, Smits *et al.* 2000b, Van Leussen *et al.* 2000). In the Rhine river basin, potential damage caused by future flooding is expected to increase and can only be prevented at great efforts and costs (Havinga & Smits 2000).

Past development strategies have focused on the construction of large dams and related infrastructure to achieve the objectives of hydroelectricity generation, expansion of irrigated agriculture, flood control and inland navigation. The idea that dams are the most convenient way to manage rivers and to use water resources is strongly contested by Hunt (2000a). According to Goodland (2000) there still could be a future for dams, but only if they are made to be sustainable. His main message is that while hydropower is far from perfect, its impacts are mitigable, while the impacts of alternatives to hydropower, namely nuclear energy and coal, cannot be mitigated. However, the recent earth quake in Taiwan underlines the break-risks of large dams. Moreover, in October 1999 between 500 and 1,000 inhabitants of floodplains along the Niger were been drowned and more than 300,000 people became homeless after the opening of dams in Shiroro, Kainji and Jebba to prevent extremely high water levels in the upper parts of Niger river basin. In the United States of America nearly five hundred dams have been removed to recover native fish populations, alleviate dam safety concerns or revitalise local communities (Sparks *et al.* 2000).

*River pollution*

River pollution became particularly manifest following the industrial revolution: the river Thames was already extremely polluted in the first half of the 19th century, culminating around the 1950s, while the river Rhine reached its worst pollution level in the late 1960s and early 1970s, and rivers like the Odra, Vistula and Paraguay may not have reached their most polluted state yet (Da Silva 2000, Nienhuis *et al.* 1998, 2000). Water pollution control seems to have been rather successful in several developed river basins. In the past decades, the protection of water quality has mainly focused on the abatement of organic pollution and significant toxic elements, such as heavy metals and non-degradable organic constituents, in order to protect drinking water supplies, fish production and recreation facilities. The result is that the river water quality in Western Europe (*e.g.*, the rivers Thames and Rhine) and the United States of America (*e.g.*, the Mississippi river) has improved significantly over the last decades, mainly due to the drastic clean-up of point-source discharges. Policymakers are eager to illustrate this quality improvement with colourful graphs of decreasing concentrations of pollutants such as cadmium, PCBs, PAHs and phosphate. As a consequence, the priority in river restoration is slowly shifting from classical pollution issues to issues of habitat creation and rehabilitation. Although this shift in priorities is sensible, we should be aware of the fact pollution problems have only partly been solved (Nienhuis *et al.* 1998). The pollution problems that remain to be solved can be typified as persistent, relatively inconspicuous and difficult to master (mainly diffuse sources). The complexity of the remaining pollution problem has been governed by the law of the diminishing returns: the curve of the costs of pollution control versus the results gained shows a downward trend. However, prolonged neglect of the remaining pollution problems may severely endanger the successful implementation of other river rehabilitation measures. An important example highlighted in the present book is the accumulation of pollutants in sediment (Eijsackers & Doelman 2000, Schouten *et al.* 2000). Persistent contaminants are bound to the deeper soil layers of riverbanks, where they are subject to little biodegradation and mobilisation. Within the Netherlands alone, strongly polluted sediments cover more than 100 km$^2$ of the floodplain (Schouten *et al.* 2000). While some of this area is urbanised and most of it is used for agriculture, these polluted sediments represent a direct risk to human health. For persistent compounds which easily bio-accumulate, risks may increase in the course of time. Stepwise massive release caused by accidents, excavations or substantial erosion during high tides results in sudden mobilisation and a flush of released contaminants. At low discharges with limited dilution, this causes acute harmful effects (Eijsackers & Doelman 2000). In addition, erosion of floodplains, riverbanks and riverbeds during major floods release older layers of polluted deposits to be redistributed elsewhere in the basin (Schouten *et al.* 2000). The costs of rehabilitation projects and construction works increase dramatically in areas where the riverbed and the floodplain sediment are highly polluted with heavy metals and organic contaminants. The execution of many projects and public works is stagnating as a result of the high remedial costs of polluted soil.

*Habitat destruction and fragmentation*
Habitat quality has rather recently been recognised as an important aspect of river basin management; it focuses strongly on the ecological integrity of the (mostly physically disturbed) land or water units, based on widely accepted conservation criteria such as naturalness, representativeness, (bio)diversity and rarity (Boon 1993). Habitat quality is exemplified as the environmental quality of a spatial unit, defined at the level of the landscape, ecosystem, ecotope or habitat. Habitat quality is also expressed at the level of the occurrence or absence of populations of specific plants or animals or vegetation units. All over the world, riverine habitats are being destroyed and fragmented due to the utilisation of floodplains for agriculture, housing, industry and transport. Area reduction of 'wild' river habitats, as found in the agriculture-dominated floodplains of most European lowland rivers, increases the risk of local and regional extinction of plant and animal species. Habitat destruction and fragmentation can only be reversed or partly mitigated through extensive ecological infrastructure and high reallocation costs of spatial user functions.

*Water resources allocation*
Rivers are among the most valuable but also the most abused resources on earth. In the course of human history, intensive use has been made of riverine resources, and consequently the quality of the river ecosystems has slowly degraded. During the 21st century, the pressure on freshwater resources will increase dramatically. The world's population has already reached 5.5 billion, and will pass 8 billion within two decades. It is expected that by 2025, two-thirds of the world's population will live under water-stress conditions (United Nations 1997). Demand for water can only increase, but growing pollution is likely to reduce the available quantity of

suitable water. Irrigated agriculture, hydroelectric power generation and maintaining the health of aquatic ecosystems compete with other uses for limited water recources. Due to industrial, domestic and agricultural water demands, water tables are falling fast in many river catchments and an increasing number of rivers have ceased to discharge into the ocean for much of the dry season as so much water is being is abstracted (Goodland 2000). Essentially, no freshwater is released to the sea during a large portion of the dry season by the rivers Ganges, Yellow river, Chao Phraya, Nile and Colorado. For instance, the Yellow river in China's most important agricultural region ran dry in its lower reaches for 226 days out of the year 1997 (Serageldin 1999). Consequently, sea water is penetrating further upstream, hampering yields.

World-wide, there are about 300 river basins which are shared among two or more nations; competition for water among such nations could become a potential source of conflict. Water resource experts around the world have witnessed several examples of conflicts in which control of water resources has played a major role (Bennett 1991, Homer Dixon 1991, Noorduyn & De Groot 1998, Smith 1995). Examples include disagreements between the USA and Mexico over flows and water quality in the Colorado river, disputes between India and Pakistan over the Indus river, disagreements between Iraq and Turkey over apportionment of Tigres and Euphrates flows, discussions in Africa over the water of the Nile and conflicts between India and Bangladesh involving the Farrakah Barrage on the Ganges, between Oezbekistan and Turkmenistan over the water diversion of Amoe river and between Israel, Syria and Jordan over the Jordan river.

## 2.2 Evolution towards sustainable river management

The evolution of river management started with no management at all in the prehistory and basic management in the times of ancient cultures. Since the industrial revolution, we have successively had several stages of sectoral river management (*i.e.,* from single-interest to multi-sectoral approaches), which from the end of the 1970s has subsequently evolved into more integrated approaches. The plethora of terms to define various types of river management makes it difficult to develop a standardised terminology, not least because of the regional nuances attached to each definition (Werritty 1997). This paper generally adopts definitions used by the various authors of the present book.

Sectoral river management is characterised by a static, single-interest, product-oriented engineering approach (Hunt 2000b). Integrated river management (synonymous with comprehensive management) is water system oriented, *i.e.,* focusing on the multifunctional use of the coherent whole of water, sediment, bed, bank, technical infrastructure and biological components (Van de Kamer *et al.* 1998, Smits *et al.* 2000b). It has gradually evolved in integrated river basin management (synonymous with integrated catchment management), which focuses on the entire river catchment. In the Netherlands it has become clear that integrated river basin management should not concentrate only on all the internal factors affecting the water systems, such as water quality, water quantity, sediments and banks, but should also take into account all the external relations which affect water systems. This so-called total river management makes it a part of society, which means that economy, ecology and sociology become directive (Van Rooy & De Jong 1995, Van de Kamer *et al.* 1998). The economy is directive through its awareness of the scarcity of water related resources, ecology through the awareness of the vulnerability and resilience of natural resources, and sociology through its human standards and values. Based on past experiences with extreme floods, present day river management strives to be more in line with the river's natural behaviour. Therefore, river managers are looking for engineering solutions that can both maintain the original objectives and increase the hydrological resilience of river basins (Havinga & Smits 2000). These solutions will have to be more flexible than traditional river management measures. Such aims seem achievable with the help of modern technology and an increasing knowledge of the system. This new form of river management aims to maximise the use of natural dynamics and is therefore referred to as dynamic river management. Both total and dynamic management are regarded as a further elaboration of integrated river basin management. The means whereby integrated river basin management is undertaken typically involve the development and implementation of a catchment management plan whose fundamental aim is to conserve, enhance, and, where appropriate, restore the total river environment through effective land and water resource planning, across the entire catchment area (Gardiner & Cole 1992).

At the end of the 20th century, adaptive management approaches have been evolved in the United States of America. Adaptive river management mainly refers to the planning process. Under a process of adaptive management, river managers are continually adjusting their actions in response to monitoring data which alerts them to changing environmental and economic conditions and social preferences (Galloway 2000, Hunt 2000b, Sparks *et al.* 2000). Adaptive river management is characterised by a more dynamic, multiple-objective management approach. Water resource agencies no longer dominate the decision-making process, but have begun to provide a technical support function to a more democratic process of negotiation among various interests affected by water resource management. Monitoring data and simulation models are used to inform stakeholders and to support decisions (Sparks *et al.* 2000). Water projects are less frequently designed for single purposes, such as flood control or environmental restoration, and more frequently encompass a number of objectives including flood damage reduction, navigation enhancement, water supply, water quality, and development and conservation of natural resources (including biodiversity).

Integrative and adaptive approaches mainly refer to technical, organisational and institutional means and planning processes in river management. Sustainable management of river basins must not be regarded as the means, but refers to the management goal, *i.e.*, sustainable development. This requires a process of change in which the exploitation of resources, the allocation of investments, the orientation of technological developments and institutional arrangements must be in harmony and increase the present, as well as the future, opportunities to accommodate human needs (Brundtland Commission 1987, Leuven *et al.* 1997). This process has socio-economic as well as ecological dimensions, which in practice are closely related (Van Wetten 2000). The strategies needed to solve current problems may differ greatly depending on the economic development and geographical location of individual countries, *e.g.,* developed versus developing river basins or lack of water versus unbalanced use of river systems. Furthermore, strategies for sustainable water management may differ with respect to the perception of risks (*e.g.,* avoidance of ecological versus socio-economic risks) and target images for nature (*e.g.*, conservation versus compensation of ecological values). However, indispensable elements of sustainable management of river basins are (Wójcik *et al.* 1997, Bouma & Saeijs 2000, Goodland 2000, HRH 2000, Hunt 2000a, Matthews & Horner 2000, Quang 2000, Smits *et al.* 2000b, Sparks *et al.* 2000):

- acceptance of the right to safe water resources as one of the basic human rights;
- attention to the long-term impacts of economic development on the river system and future generations;
- mutual dependence of environmental quality (*e.g.*, healthy river and riverine ecosystems) and socio-economic development (*e.g.*, improvement of the livelihoods of the basin's inhabitants);
- inter-basin water diversion and utilisation with special attention to the improvement of in-stream uses of water, including fish production, protection of endangered species and recreational opportunities;
- use of water resources without degrading their quality or reducing their quantity or exceeding the carrying capacity of the river system and inclusion of inevitable environmental damage costs in cost-benefit analysis;
- strategic planning with clear visions, goals and strategies for entire river basins (*i.e.*, integrated or comprehensive catchment management planning);
- transparency and public participation via open planning processes and free access to credible and reliable data, information and knowledge about the quality status and impacts of management alternatives for river systems;
- mutual understanding and respect between riparian nations and international cooperation, in particular to solve transboundary problems concerning water quality and quantity, and to guarantee security or solve conflicts over water resources diversion;
- development and application of sophisticated technical capabilities, *e.g.*, integrated monitoring, modelling, decision support systems, users-friendly knowledge and information systems supporting stakeholder participation and ecologically sound hydraulic infrastructure, navigation and land use concepts.

At present, more and more riparian countries of transboundary rivers are signing agreements for sustainable development of river basins and establishing international river commissions for the joint development and integrated management of the entire catchment area (Nienhuis *et al.* 2000, Quang 2000). In February 1997, the European Commission adopted a proposal for a Water Framework Directive. Its purpose is to establish a framework in order to achieve the following four main objectives of a sustainable water policy: (1) sufficient provision of drinking water; (2) sufficient provision of water for other economic requirements; (3) protection of the environmental quality; (4) alleviation of the adverse impact of floods and droughts. The environmental objective of the directive is to achieve "good status" for all groundwaters and surface waters by 2010 at the latest. To this aim, it will introduce river basin management based on an assessment of the characteristics of each basin; monitoring of the status of its surface and groundwaters; definition of quality objectives; establishment of programmes of measures to achieve the defined objective. However, the administrative structure to achieve this river basin management is left to the discretion of member states of the European Union.

In spite of many positive developments towards sustainable river basin management, integrated management plans for entire river catchments and adaptive management processes are still in their infancy for most of the developed and developing river basins (*cf.* Da Silva 2000, Galloway 2000, Nienhuis *et al.* 2000, Quang 2000, Van Leussen 2000). Hunt (2000b) concludes that, despite the past efforts, the myriad of plans for water resource development in the Mekong river basin have not been assessed from a systematic perspective. Such a perspective would require consideration of the full range of hydrologic, social and economic impacts that implementing all or a subset of these plans would have on the region as a whole. In fact, basic economic, sociological and environmental data regarding the potential impacts of individual water resource development plans is lacking in many cases.

## 3. Participation of new stakeholders in river basin management

Sustainable management of river basins makes high demands on the transparency of the decision process and participation of stakeholders. The key to fair and equitable water resource allocation is the promoting dialogue, encouraging networking and the exchange of data, information and knowledge between decision-makers, scientists, engineers and stakeholders in different countries about river basin management and related issues (Matthews & Horner 2000).

Greater involvement of the public, including local stakeholders who are most directly affected by river development, appears to be a growing, world-wide phenomenon. According to Havinga & Smits (2000) Dutch river authorities have learnt that management measures without public support are almost equivalent to mismanagement. For this reason, public participation is a prerequisite in the decision and implementation stages of river rehabilitation projects. Goodland (2000) describes the historic evolution of transparency and participation in the USA over the period 1945 – 2000, broadening, for instance, the constituency of a dam design team from engineers to economists, environmentalists, sociologists, affected people and NGOs. The treatment of stakeholders has evolved from warning, through information, consultation and participation, to partnerships.

Goodland (2000) states that stakeholder participation is essential for democracy, and greatly improves project selection and design. External scrutiny and participation in the whole process is essential to reduce any possible conflict of interest. Most importantly, participation and transparency foster early agreement and builds consensus, thus reducing controversy and opposition later on. This expedites project implementation. Transparency and participation mean that civil society exercises a role in the selection of criteria to be subsequently used for decision-making and in identifying stakeholders. These normally include affected people (ultimately all tax payers) or their advocates, government, academia, syndicates, consumer and safety organisations, as well as project proponents. Civil society assists in the selection and design of studies needed before decisions can be made, in the interpretation of the findings of such studies, in the burden sharing or relative weights given to criteria for multi-criteria analyses (MCA) or integrated evaluation methods. Proponents receive many useful proposals from non-traditional stakeholders. With the objective of developing a consensus approach to solving water problems, those responsible have learned that more available information produces better results than less (Galloway 2000).

Partnerships with other stakeholders and actors play a dominant role in initiatives aimed at river rehabilitation, whereas scaling up of results and approaches (*e.g.*, transcending to other political levels, sectors or regions) can be regarded as an even higher goal than the immediate project results. Van Wetten (2000) describes a new approach to wetland management interventions by partnerships. Instead of focusing solely on 'problems', more attention is given to 'opportunity identification' as a basis for modifying programmes and projects for wetland management. Assessing the basic causes of opportunities as well as constraints creates new options for innovative partnerships and coalitions. The concepts of scaling up and strategic communication are used to improve the outreach, outputs and sustainability of the interventions.

The World Hydrological Cycle Observing System (WHYCOS) is one of the networks providing communication services between stakeholders (Matthews & Horner 2000). It provides a scientific basis for monitoring and assessing water resources for sustainable river basin management. In addition, WHYCOS aspires to contribute to an improved understanding of the interaction of hydrological processes with the climate, the environment, natural resource capital, investment and national, regional and global markets through managed open discussion. Through WHYCOS and appropriate decision aiding tools and skills, it would be possible to bring together all the social, technological, ecological and scientific aspects of river basin development. By observing the interaction between the hydrological cycle and all social, economic and environmental activities, WHYCOS can provide data and information to generate knowledge. In turn, this knowledge can be managed by the communities within the river basin for decision-making with the objective of discovering the "truth" about the sustainable development potential of the river basin.

At present, many river rehabilitation projects and hydro dam projects are being undertaken by a variety of partnerships among private landowners, non-governmental conservationists and environmental organisations, and governmental agencies (Sparks *et al.* 2000, Goodland 2000 Van Wetten 2000). In the USA, a rising tide of public interest in protecting and restoring rivers and floodplains has stimulated the expansion of governmental conservation programmes to encourage farmers to convert erodible and flood-prone land near streams from crop production into permanent vegetation (Sparks *et al.* 2000). The new generations of these programmes concentrate on riparian zones and on specific problem watersheds that deliver excessive amounts of sediment and water. Corporaal (2000) proposes a new tax bonus for rural entrepreneurs (so-called "fisquality") to improve water retention by watersheds. These entrepreneurs can play an important role in the establishment of a hydro-ecological network in river catchments, aiming at flood as well as drought prevention.

Economic arguments play an important role in societal discussions on justifying interventions in river systems. Bouma & Saeijs (2000) discuss the need for an ecocentric cost-benefit analysis and illustrate their plea with a case study of hydraulic engineering projects in lake Grevelingen, situated in the delta of the rivers Rhine and Meuse.

## 4. New methodologies and instruments in sustainable river basin management

*4.1 Natural resilience and flow regime as driving forces*

There is increasing awareness that the structure and function of natural and restored rivers vary across space and time. This variation (disturbance regime) is required to maintain many riverine ecosystems (Poff *et al.*1997). Planning and engineering to incorporate this variability requires changes on the part of the development agencies, whose historic missions have generally involved reducing variability in water flow, shoreline configurations, channel positions of rivers, etc. (Havinga & Smits 2000, Hunt 2000b, Smits *et al.* 2000b, Sparks *et al.* 2000).

The starting point of sustainable river basin management must be to accommodate user functions (*e.g.*, navigation, agriculture and urbanisation) to the dynamics of the natural river system and not the other way round (Hunt 2000b, Smits *et al.* 2000a,b). Rehabilitation of the natural resilience of rivers, by allowing them more space, is the best strategy to prepare for uncertain future developments such as climate change, rising surface levels of the floodplains by sedimentation and lowering surface levels on the landside of the dikes in the downstream parts of the river basin, due to subsidence of the soils (Smits et al. 2000b, Van Leussen 2000). However, there are clear indications that this is not sufficient in the long term. Therefore, more efforts will also have to be made to reallocate non-river based activities and to adapt present day riverine user functions to natural water systems. Moreover, the potential to naturalise rivers and their floodplains systemically cannot be fully realised just by restoration actions in the mainstem river and its floodplain. Rivers are products of their watersheds, so actions are also needed in tributaries and uplands, *i.e.*, the entire catchment (Smits *et al.* 2000a,b, Sparks *et al.* 2000, Van Leussen 2000). From this point of view, the tasks and responsibilities of future river managers are no longer confined to water quantity and water quality, but a more pro-active role in the spatial planning process of the entire river catchment is required (Smits *et al.* 2000b).

The water regime of regulated rivers is subject to unnatural fluctuations during the growing season, which limit native plants and animals on the hydraulically connected floodplains. It is encouraging that unnatural fluctuations appear to be attributable to the operation of the navigation dams. At several locations in the USA, the operating rules for dams, reservoirs, and other river facilities now take into account the natural life cycles of fish and wildlife affected by the contained rivers (Galloway 2000). Early results of experiments with a more natural flow regime indicate that the condition and production of wetland vegetation can be improved without adversely affecting commercial navigation (Sparks *et al.* 2000).

In addition, dike and revetment designs for the Mississippi river have been modified to increase the usefulness of dikes and revetments in developing habitat, while at the same time preserving their channel stabilisation functions. A specially submerged bendway weir has been designed to mitigate environmental impact (Galloway 2000).

disposal sites and the high costs involved. In the Netherlands, a new policy of dynamic soil management has been developed in order to control the high costs of river rehabilitation projects resulting from polluted sediments, while maintaining the original management goals and reducing the risk to human health and ecosystems (Schouten *et al.* 2000). As long as polluted soils do not increase the overall risk, they may be reused as much as possible within the floodplain area. This approach opens up opportunities for re-using polluted sediments in local civil engineering works where pollution already exists, reducing costs and risks at the same time. Removal or isolation of strongly contaminated sediments should reduce the total emission of contaminants resulting from erosion and solution or dispersion after the work has been carried out. Accurate soil quality probability maps are being generated for the purpose of developing and applying dynamic soil management (Section 4.5).

*4.5 New scientific tools*

This book present several new tools for the scientific underpinning of sustainable river basin management, such as environmental least-cost ranking, stakeholder and policy analysis, new monitoring techniques and decision support systems.

According to Goodland (2000), the main means to approach sustainability is to integrate environmental and social criteria into traditional economic least-cost sequencing, which makes it environmental least-cost ranking (ELCR). When the best mode and the best site for a project (*e.g.*, a hydro dam) have been selected, the normal project-level environmental assessment (EA) should be used to mitigate residual impacts, such as by lowering the dam or moving it upstream. While project-level EA is essential and needs to be strengthened, ELCR to select the best projects is far more powerful.

Policy analysis provides a framework for sustainability assessment of large infrastructural projects by generating possible and feasible alternatives and comparing their socio-economic, ecological and institutional impacts. Leentvaar & Glas (2000) present results of a policy analysis for the Gabcikovo-Nagymaros hydropower project in the Danube, which aims to clarify and rationalise the various options for management actions and provides information on the 'pros' and 'cons' of the range of choices that can be made.

Stakeholder analysis has become a useful tool in promoting participation (Goodland 2000). Strategic environmental analysis (SEAN) is a new planning framework for opportunity identification and the designing of sustainable development policies (Van Wetten 2000). This methodological framework includes practical tools and guidelines for analysing the environmental potentials for, and constraints on, human development. It is designed for use at the earliest possible stage of policymaking, to allow the relevant environmental issues to be fully integrated into policy design. The methodology is based on experiences with environmental impact assessment (EIA), environmental profiles, and environmental planning, monitoring and evaluation.

Geographic information systems (GIS) and remote sensing (RS) are important tools for analysis and visualisation of geographical entities of river systems and for decision support for management measures (Leuven *et al.* 2000). Schouten *et al.* (2000) describe the development and application of new GIS-based soil quality probability maps for dynamic soil management. These maps are prepared using the various statistical relations in combination with geomorphologic and soil information. These soil quality probability maps allow an estimate to be made of the amount of polluted sediments to be removed as well as a cost calculation. Smits *et al.* (2000b) discuss a new promising RS method involving laser-altimetry for monitoring of the vegetation dynamics in floodplains. Recently, some experiments have been carried out with the objective to convert data on the vegetation structure directly into hydraulic roughness data for a floodplain.

## 4.6 Further research and monitoring

According to Sparks *et al.* (2000) a key question for the public and for policymakers in developed river basins of the world is whether the total flow from natural and commercial benefits from a regulated river-floodplain system can be increased by selective re-connection of the rivers with their floodplains and re-establishment of more natural flooding regimes. The communities along the rivers are particularly concerned about the quality of the naturalised environment that is achieved and the impact it will have on the local economy and quality of life. Attractive natural environments could attract outdoor recreationists and offer an alternative to the agriculture-dependent economy that may be increasingly subject to boom-or-bust cycles governed by world market prices.

A comparative historical approach is especially useful in identifying impacts of alterations to river systems (Havinga & Smits 2000, Sparks *et al.* 2000). However, such insights need to be incorporated into models to predict effects of alternative development or recovery plans. Therefore, Sparks *et al.* (2000) make a plea for scientific monitoring and evaluation of both river recovery and river development programmes, for the sake of improving both science and policy. Management cannot be adaptive without information about the current status and trends in the key physical driving variables (*e.g.*, the sediment and water regimes), biological interactions and indicators of interest (*e.g.*, population status of key species). A management experiment is worthless without data to show whether the hypotheses can be rejected or accepted. Failure is instructive, as long as sufficient information is gathered to understand why the failure occurred. Similarly, little is gained by success if the reasons for success are not known; it may be impossible to extend the results to another site, or even to repeat them at the same site. According to Havinga & Smits (2000), sustainable river basin management means the application of measures that are able to cope with dynamic river reactions and that are flexible in view of future demands. These measures do not provoke large-scale effects, thus maintaining hydromorphological resilience. Instead of large rigid constructions, small sized measures to correct river responses will be used. To restore riverine habitats, more vegetation will be allowed in the floodplains. In practice, the river will show more dynamic changes, in water levels as well as in bed geometry, complicating river management. Readiness for action requires information regarding these changes. For this purpose an extensive monitoring and impact assessment programme (including forecasting) has to be available.

To support stakeholder participation in river rehabilitation projects, inter-related hydrological, ecological, and economic models must be developed to predict what will happen to total social benefits (from both commercial and natural sources) if selected portions of the floodplain and of the annual flood cycle are restored, or to evaluate effects of development alternatives in river basins (Sparks *et al.* 2000). Assessing the sustainability of large dams and other hydraulic infrastructure necessitates the development of systemic models that have the ability to simulate the complex hydrodynamic processes that characterise water and sediment movement through an entire catchment (Hunt 2000b).

A comprehensive set of indicators for the sustainable development of river basins is often lacking (Nienhuis *et al.* 1998, 2000). There is a need to develop such indicators of interest. Examples of the areas in which indicators need to be developed include the above-mentioned key physically driven processes, efficiency of water resource use, the health of river and riverine ecosystems, and stakeholder participation.

## 5. General conclusions and recommendations

– Sustainable river basin management requires full understanding of rivers as dynamic and open systems, which should be considered as ecological continua from the source to the sea. Integrated river basin management, catchment management planning and adaptive management approaches are the means to achieve sustainability.
– Historical developments in river basin management along various large rivers in the USA and Europe have shown that prevention is better than cure. Neglecting water pollution control means roll-off problems to future generations in countries or areas located downstream in a river basin. Generally, it results in high risks and sanitation costs, due to deposits of polluted sediment. Rash habitat destruction always means high rehabilitation costs in future. An unbalanced inter-basin diversion of water recourses is a potential source of conflicts between nations or communities. Ill-considered and single-purpose river regulations always have drawbacks, which must be compensated for by other interventions. This action-reaction spiral decreases the resilience of river systems and ultimately results in higher risks of flooding, higher management costs and severe deterioration of riverine ecosystems. Therefore, sustainable river basin management requires the well-considered application of the precautionary principle.
– Restoration of resilience is the only solution to break the action-reaction spiral in unsustainably developed river basins. It requires a carefully considered strategy for the entire river catchment, which includes allowing more space to rivers and restoring of the natural flow regime and hydromorphological dynamics of rivers. These measures also fit in with the prerequisites for ecological rehabilitation of river basins.
– Sustainable management of developing river basins means that user functions of the catchment (*e.g.*, navigation, agriculture and urbanisation) must be accommodated to the dynamics of the natural river system and not the other way round; the damage experienced by several industrialised basins can be avoided.
– Stakeholder participation is a prerequisite for sustainable river basin management. River managers have learnt that management measures without public

support are almost equivalent to mismanagement, because much time and money is spent on the implementation and maintenance of undesirable measures. Stakeholder participation is not only essential for democracy, but may also greatly improve project selection and design. Most importantly, participation and transparency foster early agreement and build consensus, thus reducing controversy and opposition later on and expediting project implementation.

– Important issues for further research are integrated modelling, retrospective studies and scientific monitoring and evaluation of both river recovery and river development programmes, for the sake of improving both science and policy. First of all, this requires the development of a comprehensive set of indicators for the various dimensions of sustainable river basin management. Modelling of river basins must facilitate catchment management planning and adaptive management, and should be focussed on the development of inter-related hydrological, ecological, and economic models. The models must have the ability to simulate the complex hydrodynamic processes that characterise water and sediment movement through an entire catchment and to predict what will happen to total social benefits (from both commercial and natural sources) for various development alternatives in river basins (*e.g.*, changes in climate, water and land use and navigation). Retrospective research should not be focussed only on impacts of river alterations and rehabilitation, but must also include cost-benefit analysis, stakeholder participation and institutional arrangements.

– In spite of river-specific expertise and great differences in the development of river basins, the new approaches to sustainable river basin management are basically applicable to other river systems and are particularly important for those river basins which have not yet been developed.

## References

Bennett, O. (Ed.). 1991. Greenwar; environment and conflict. Panos Publisher Ltd, London.

Boon, P.J. 1993. Essential elements in the case for river conservation. In: Boon, P.J., Calow, P. & Petts, G.E. (Eds.). River conservation and management. Wiley, Chichester. pp. 11-33.

Bouma, J.J. & H.L.F. Saeijs, H.L.F. 2000. Eco-centric cost-benefit analysis for hydraulic engineering in river basins. In: Smits, A.J.M., Nienhuis, P.H. & Leuven, R.S.E.W. (Eds.). New approaches to river management. Backhuys Publishers, Leiden. pp. 167-178.

Brundtland Commission. 1987. Our common future. World Commission on Environment and Development of the United Nations. Oxford University Press, Oxford.

Corporaal, A. 2000. "Fisquality", a proposal for a tax bonus to improve hydro-ecological resilience of river catchments. In: Smits, A.J.M., Nienhuis, P.H. & Leuven, R.S.E.W. (Eds.). New approaches to river management. Backhuys Publishers, Leiden. pp. 179-186.

Da Silva, C.J. 2000. Ecological basis for the management of the Pantanal – Upper Paraguay basin. In: Smits, A.J.M., Nienhuis, P.H. & Leuven, R.S.E.W. (Eds.). New approaches to river management. Backhuys Publishers, Leiden. pp. 97-118.

Downs, P.W., Gregory, K.J., & Brookes, A. 1991. How integrated is river basin management? Environmental Management 15: 299-309.

Eijsackers, H.J.P. & Doelman, P. 2000. Using natural cleaning processes in the river ecosystem: a new approach to environmental river management. In: Smits, A.J.M., Nienhuis, P.H. & Leuven, R.S.E.W. (Eds.). New approaches to river management. Backhuys Publishers, Leiden. pp. 307-328.

Galloway, G.E. 2000. Three ages of river management along the Mississippi: engineering and hydrological aspects. In: Smits, A.J.M., Nienhuis, P.H. & Leuven, R.S.E.W. (Eds.). New approaches to river management. Backhuys Publishers, Leiden. pp. 51-64.

Gardiner, J.L. & Cole, L. 1992. Catchment planning: the way forward for river protection in the UK. In: Boon, P.J. Calow, P. & Petts, G.E. (Eds.). River conservation and management. John Wiley, Chichester. pp. 397-406.

Goodland, R.J.A. 2000. Is there future for big dams? In: Smits, A.J.M., Nienhuis, P.H. & Leuven, R.S.E.W. (Eds.). New approaches to river management. Backhuys Publishers, Leiden. pp. 187-207.

Havinga, H. & Smits, A.J.M. 2000. River management along the Rhine: a retrospective view. In: Smits, A.J.M., Nienhuis, P.H. & Leuven, R.S.E.W. (Eds.). New approaches to river management. Backhuys Publishers, Leiden. pp. 15-32.

HRH. 2000 The value of sustainable river management: Opening address by His Royal Highness Prince Willem-Alexander of Orange (HRH). In: Smits, A.J.M., Nienhuis, P.H. & Leuven, R.S.E.W. (Eds.). New approaches to river management. Backhuys Publishers, Leiden. pp. 3-6.

Homer-Dixon, T.F. 1991. On the threshold: environmental changes as causes of acute conflict. International Security 16/2: 76-116.

Hunt, C.E. 2000a. New approaches to river management in the United States. In: Smits, A.J.M., Nienhuis, P.H. & Leuven, R.S.E.W. (Eds.). New approaches to river management. Backhuys Publishers, Leiden. pp. 119-139.

Hunt, C.E. 2000b. Following a diversified strategy to achieve the sustainable use of the Mekong river basin. In: Smits, A.J.M., Nienhuis, P.H. & Leuven, R.S.E.W. (Eds.). New approaches to river management. Backhuys Publishers, Leiden. pp. 209-223.

Leentvaar, J. & Glas, P.C.G. 2000. A policy analysis for the upper Danube river section in Hungary. In: Smits, A.J.M., Nienhuis, P.H. & Leuven, R.S.E.W. (Eds.). New approaches to river management. Backhuys Publishers, Leiden. pp. 249-266.

Leuven, R.S.E.W., Thörig, M.W.H., Nienhuis, P.H. & Van de Laar, B.J. 1997. Environmental utilisation space: a useful concept underpinning sustainable management of river catchments? In: Smith, P. & Tenner, A. (Eds.). Dimensions of sustainability. Nomos Verlagsgesellschaft, Baden-Baden. pp. 361-362.

Leuven, R.S.E.W., Poudevigne, I. & Teeuw, R.M. (Eds.). 2000. Application of GIS and RS in river studies. Backhuys Publishers, Leiden.

Matthews, G.J. & Horner, M. 2000. Bridging the communication gap in river management. In: Smits, A.J.M., Nienhuis, P.H. & Leuven, R.S.E.W. (Eds.). New approaches to river management. Backhuys Publishers, Leiden. pp. 155-165.

Nienhuis, P.H., Leuven, R.S.E.W. & Ragas, A.M.J. (Eds.). 1998. New concepts for sustainable management of river basins. Backhuys Publishers, Leiden.

Nienhuis, P.H., Chojnacki, J.C., Harms,, O., Majewski, W., Parzonka, W. & Prus, T. 2000. Elbe, Odra, and Vistula: reference rivers for the restoration of biodiversity and habitat quality. In: Smits, A.J.M., Nienhuis, P.H. & Leuven, R.S.E.W. (Eds.). New approaches to river management. Backhuys Publishers, Leiden. pp. 65-84.

Noorduyn, R.E. & De Groot, W.T. 1998. Milieu en veiligheid. Een overzicht met nadruk op de ontwikkelingslanden en de rol van de milieukunde. Milieu – Tijschrift voor Milieukunde 13/2: 71-84. (in Dutch with English summary)

Poff, N.L., Allan, J.D., Bain, M.B., Karr, J.R., Prestegaard, K.L., Richter, B.D., Sparks, R.E.& Stromberg, J.C. 1997. The natural flow regime. Bioscience 47/11:769-784.

Quang, N.N. 2000. Management of the Mekong river basin. In: Smits, A.J.M., Nienhuis, P.H. & Leuven, R.S.E.W. (Eds.). New approaches to river management. Backhuys Publishers, Leiden. pp. 85-96.

Schouten C.J.J., Rang, M.C., De Hamer, B.A. & Van Hout, H.R.A., 2000. Strongly polluted deposits in the Meuse river catchment and their effects on river management. In: Smits, A.J.M., Nienhuis, P.H. & Leuven, R.S.E.W. (Eds.). New approaches to river management. Backhuys Publishers, Leiden. pp. 33-50.

Serageldin, I. 1999. World's rivers in crisis. World Water Vision, Press Release. World Commission on Water for the 21st Century, Washington, D.C.

Smith, D.R. 1995. Environmental security and shared water resources in Post-Soviet Central Asia. Post-Soviet Geography 6: 351-370.

Smits, A.J.M., Havinga, H. & Marteijn, E.C.L. 2000a. New concepts in river and water management in the Rhine river basin: how to live with the unexpected? In: Smits, A.J.M., Nienhuis, P.H. & Leuven, R.S.E.W. (Eds.). New approaches to river management. Backhuys Publishers, Leiden. pp. 267-286.

Smits, A.J.M., Nienhuis, P.H. & Leuven, R.S.E.W. 2000b. New approaches to river management: general introduction. In: Smits, A.J.M., Nienhuis, P.H. & Leuven, R.S.E.W. (Eds.). New approaches to river management. Backhuys Publishers, Leiden. pp. 7-14.

Sparks, R.E., Braden, J., Demissie, M., Mitral, P., Schneider, D., White, D. & Xia, R. 2000. Technical support of public decisions to restore floodplain ecosystems: a status report on the Illinois river project (USA). In: Smits, A.J.M., Nienhuis, P.H. & Leuven, R.S.E.W. (Eds.). New approaches to river management. Backhuys Publishers, Leiden. pp. 225-247.

Stanners, D. & Bourdeau, P. (Eds.). 1995. Europe's Environment. The Dobris Assessment. European Environment Agency Copenhagen, Earthscan Publications, London.

Stortenbeker, C. 2000. New approaches to river management: integration of knowledge and ideas. In: Smits, A.J.M., Nienhuis, P.H. & Leuven, R.S.E.W. (Eds.). New approaches to river management. Backhuys Publishers, Leiden. pp. 1-2.

United Nations. 1997. Comprehensive assessment of the freshwater resources of the world. United Nations, New York.

Van de Kamer, S.P.G., Postma, R., Marteijn, E.C.L. & Bakker, C. 1998. On the way to total water management for large rivers in the Netherlands. In: Nienhuis, P.H., Leuven, R.S.E.W. & Ragas, A.M.J. (Eds.). New concepts for sustainable management of river basins. Backhuys Publishers, Leiden. pp. 291-307.

Van Leussen, W., Kater, G. & Van Meel, P. 2000. Multi-level approach to flood control in the Dutch part of the river Meuse. In: Smits, A.J.M., Nienhuis, P.H. & Leuven, R.S.E.W. (Eds.). New approaches to river management. Backhuys Publishers, Leiden. pp. 287-305.

Van Rooy, P.T.J.C. & De Jong, J. 1995. Op weg naar totaal waterbeheer 1: ontwikkelingen. H$_2$0 28/3: 62-66. (in Dutch).

Van Wetten, J.C.J. 2000. Partners in wetland conservation and development: strategic environmental analysis for the Ukrainian Danube delta. In: Smits, A.J.M., Nienhuis, P.H. & Leuven, R.S.E.W. (Eds.). New approaches to river management. Backhuys Publishers, Leiden. pp. 141-153.

Weritty, A. 1997. Enhancing the quality of freshwater recources: the role of integrated catchment management. In: Boon, P.J. & Howell, D.L. (Eds.). Freshwater quality: defining the indefinable? The Stationery Office, Edinburgh. pp. 489-505.

Wójcik, W., Leuven, R.S.E.W. & Foxon, T. 1997. Challenges of sustainable water management of river catchments? In: Smith, P. & Tenner, A. (Eds.). Dimensions of sustainability. Nomos Verlagsgesellschaft, Baden-Baden. pp. 353-360.

# INDEX OF AUTHORS

# SUBJECT INDEX